THE GREAT ADVENTURE
A Journey Through the Bible

THE BIBLE TIMELINE

The Story of Salvation

STUDY SET

JEFF CAVINS, TIM GRAY
& SARAH CHRISTMYER

ASCENSION PRESS

West Chester, Pennsylvania

Nihil obstat: Rev. Robert A. Pesarchick, S.T.D.
                 Censor Librorum
                 November 12, 2010

Imprimatur: +Justin Cardinal Rigali
               Archbishop of Philadelphia
               November 18, 2010

The Bible Timeline is a resource of *The Great Adventure* Catholic Bible Study Program.

Jeff Cavins, General Editor, *The Great Adventure* Catholic Bible Study Program, and Presenter, *The Bible Timeline*
Sarah Christmyer, Editor, *The Great Adventure* Catholic Bible Study Program, and Author, *The Bible Timeline* Study Set
Tim Gray, Ph.D., Contributing Editor, *The Bible Timeline*

Ascension Press
Post Office Box 1990
Chester, PA 19380
0520
.com
tholics.com

United States of America

940-76-0

THE BIBLE TIMELINE

The Story of Salvation

THE GREAT ADVENTURE
A Journey Through the Bible

Contents

Questions

Responses

Maps and Charts

Welcome to *The Great Adventure*

*"To fall in love with God is the greatest of all romances;
to seek him, the greatest adventure."*

– St. Augustine

The Bible is at the heart of our Catholic Faith—and our relationship with God. It is the living Word of God, where our Father meets with us and lovingly speaks to us. Reading the Bible should bring us closer to Christ, but understanding it is not always easy. Many people tell us they have tried time and again to prayerfully read Scripture, but they get frustrated because they "just don't get it."

The Great Adventure is designed so that anyone can make sense of the Bible and experience the life-changing power of God's Word. At the core of *The Great Adventure* is the concept that there is a story running through the seventy-three books of the Bible that ties all of Scripture together and makes sense not just of the Bible, but of our lives as well.

That story is God's plan as it has unfolded throughout salvation history and continues to unfold today. Once we grasp this "big picture," the readings at Mass begin to make more sense, our Scripture reading and study come to life, and we see how our lives fit into God's loving plan.

Hundreds of thousands of participants have discovered the riches of Scripture by experiencing one or more *Great Adventure* Bible studies. It is our prayer that you will gain a newfound understanding of God's Word that will transform your life and bring you closer to Christ.

Jeff Cavins, Creator & President, *The Great Adventure*
Sarah Christmyer, Co-developer & Author, *The Great Adventure*

About *The Great Adventure* Catholic Bible Study Program

At the core of *The Great Adventure* is *The Bible Timeline* Learning System: a simple way to get the "big picture" of the Bible by focusing on the story that runs throughout Sacred Scripture. *Great Adventure* Bible studies explore the biblical narrative in light of Catholic teaching and the historical, cultural, and literary context of the Scriptures to discover what Scripture reveals about God's plan and our place within it. Studies of individual books of the Bible are supplemented by thematic and "life application" studies.

Every *Great Adventure* study is designed to foster:

- Familiarity with the Bible and ease of reading it

- Bible study habits consistent with the guidelines of the Catholic Church

- Personal engagement in the Word of God

- Faith-sharing based on the Word of God

- Growth in knowledge about Scripture and the Catholic Faith

About *The Bible Timeline: The Story of Salvation*

The Bible Timeline is a fascinating study that takes you on a journey through the entire Bible. You will go deep into each period of salvation history and discover the amazing story woven throughout all of Scripture. Using the a unique color-coded *Bible Timeline* system, you will learn the major people, places, and events of the Bible and see how they all come together to reveal the remarkable story of our faith.

Materials

Materials for *The Bible Timeline: The Story of Salvation* include:

- **Study Set.** Contains engaging study questions (with session summaries, home reading assignments, charts, and diagrams), Talk Notes, responses to the questions, *The Bible Timeline* Chart and Bookmark. *(You will need one Study Set for every participant, study leader, and small-group facilitator.)*

- **Video Presentations** (one 15-minute introduction and twenty-three, 50-minute sessions). Presented by Jeff Cavins, these twenty-four video presentations provide comprehensive teaching and commentary on salvation history. *(You will need one DVD Set.)*

In addition, every participant, leader, and small-group facilitator should have a Catholic Bible and the *Catechism of the Catholic Church*. We recommend the Revised Standard Version–Catholic Edition (RSV-CE) or the New American Bible (NAB).

How the Study Works

Every *Great Adventure* study includes four essential steps, which are designed to fit together and build upon each other. Following these steps in order will help you to get the most out of each session.

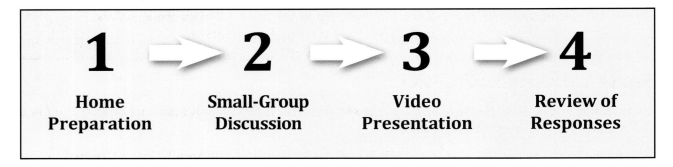

1	2	3	4
Home Preparation	Small-Group Discussion	Video Presentation	Review of Responses

Step 1: Home Preparation

Note: There is no home preparation required for the first week, Introduction.

Each session begins with personal study that involves reading Scripture and answering a series of questions that will help you understand and think more deeply about what you have read. Some questions will include additional reading from other parts of the Bible or from the *Catechism of the Catholic Church* to help you consider the passage in light of the bigger picture of salvation history and Catholic teaching.

We recommend that you allow at least 90 minutes to complete the reading and answer the questions for each session. We also suggest that home preparation be done in several sittings over the course of a week. This will help you create a habit of daily Bible reading and prayerful meditation.

Step 2: Small-Group Discussion

The small-group discussion is one of the most effective components of a *Great Adventure* Bible study. During this discussion, members of your small group will have an opportunity to share their insights into the Scripture reading. The goal of the small-group discussion is to help participants obtain a richer understanding of the readings and apply them to their lives. Trained facilitators guide the small-group discussion and keep it on track. To learn how to facilitate a small-group discussion, visit BibleStudyForCatholics.com/Facilitators. Be sure to follow the "Ten Commandments of Small-Group Discussion" on page xi.

Step 3: Video Presentation

Jeff Cavins wraps up each session with a video presentation that offers unique insights and profound connections to help you gain a deeper understanding of the Bible and its relationship to the Catholic Faith, with a special emphasis on ways to apply what you have learned to your life.

Step 4: Review of Responses

Note: There are no responses for the Introduction or Session 1.

The final step—reviewing the responses at the back of this Study Set—is done at home prior to beginning the reading for the next session. These responses will help you read the Scripture passages for the next session in the proper context.

For the most effective study experience, complete these steps in the following order: (1) Read and answer the questions; (2) discuss them in your small group; (3) view the video presentation; and (4) review the responses. During the discussion, your small-group facilitator will incorporate points found in the responses, but the richness that comes from individual insights can be lost when participants view the responses prior to the discussion.

> For more information about how to plan and promote a Bible study and how to facilitate a small-group discussion, visit **BibleStudyForCatholics.com/Leaders,** or call our Study Consultants at 1-800-376-0520.

Session Outline and Reading Guide

Each session in this Study Set has the following sections. (Note: The Introduction and Session 1 follow a different format and do not have responses.)

1. Session Questions (used during **Step 1: Home Preparation** and **Step 2: Small-Group Discussion**)

    A. Establish (or review) the Context

    B. Read the Story

    C. Take a Deeper Look

    D. Application

    E. Wrap-Up (only in sessions that conclude a biblical period)

2. Session Talk Notes (used during **Step 3: Video Presentation**)

3. Session Responses (used during **Step 4: Review of Responses**)

The following chart offers an overview of the **home preparation** readings assigned in each session of the study. The main reading is provided in section **B. Read the Story** and should be read before you answer the session questions. Additional Bible readings and *Catechism* readings are provided in section **C. Take a Deeper Look** and should be read as you answer the study questions for each session.

Session (Video Time) & Narrative Book	Main Reading	Additional Bible Readings	*Catechism* Readings (CCC)
Introduction (12:13)	—	—	—
1. Finding the Story in Scripture (49:06)	CCC 50–141	—	—
2. Early World – Part 1 (51:28) *Genesis 1–11*	Genesis 1–3 **Going Deeper** (optional): CCC 279–421	John 1:1-14	345–349, 356–357, 364, 369–373
3. Early World – Part 2 (47:22) *Genesis 1–11*	Genesis 4–11	Acts 2:1-13; 1 Peter 3:18-22	845, 1213, 1219–1220
4. Patriarchs – Part 1 (50:27) *Genesis 12–50*	Genesis 12; 15–18; 22 **Going Deeper** (optional): Genesis 12–24	Jeremiah 2:11-23; Colossians 2:11-12; James 2:14-23	143–147, 154–155
5. Patriarchs – Part 2 (51:48) *Genesis 12–50*	Genesis 25; 28–29; 32; 37–50 **Going Deeper** (optional): Genesis 25–50	Romans 9:10-13	218
6. Egypt and Exodus – Part 1 (51:17) *Exodus*	Exodus 3–5; 7; 11–12; 14; 16–17 **Going Deeper** (optional): Exodus 1–18	Matthew 26:17; John 1:29; 6; 1 Corinthians 5:7-8; 1 Peter 1:17-19; 1 Corinthians 10:1-4	206
7. Egypt and Exodus – Part 2 (50:11) *Exodus*	Exodus 19–20; 23–25; 32–34; 40 **Going Deeper** (optional): Exodus 19–40	Luke 12:16-31; Hebrews 9:4; Revelation 11:19–12:6	696–697
8. Desert Wanderings (51:14) *Numbers*	Numbers 1–2; 10–12; 13–14; 16–17; 20; 22–24 **Going Deeper** (optional): Numbers	Deuteronomy 8; Matthew 4:1-4	1897–1900
9. Conquest and Judges – Part 1 (49:44) *Joshua; Judges*	Joshua 1–4; 6–8; 23–24 **Going Deeper** (optional): Joshua	2 Corinthians 10:3-4; Ephesians 6:11-18; 1 Timothy 6:11-12; Hebrews 11:31; James 2:24-26; 1 Peter 2:11	—
10. Conquest and Judges – Part 2 (51:36) *Joshua; Judges*	Judges 1:1–3:6; 6–7; 17–21; Ruth **Going Deeper** (optional): Judges	Psalm 115:1-9; John 20:23	1210–1213, 1325, 1426, 1446, 1730–1748, 2085–2086, 2112
11. Royal Kingdom – Part 1 (49:56) *1 Samuel; 2 Samuel; 1 Kings 1–11*	1 Samuel 1–4; 7–12; 15–16; 26 **Going Deeper** (optional): 1 Samuel	Genesis 21:1-3; 25:21; 30:22-24; Judges 13:2, 24; Psalm 47, Psalm 2; Luke 1	—

Session (Video Time) & Narrative Book	Main Reading	Additional Bible Readings	*Catechism* Readings (CCC)
12. Royal Kingdom – Part 2 (51:00) *1 Samuel; 2 Samuel; 1 Kings 1–11*	2 Samuel 5–7; 11:1–12:25; 1 Kings 2:1-12; 3; 6:1–7:19; 10:23-29; 11 **Going Deeper** (optional): 2 Samuel; 1 Kings 1–11	Deuteronomy 17:16-17; Psalm 110:4; 51; Proverbs 1:1-7; 2:1-11; Matthew 12:6; 26:61; 1 Corinthians 3:16; Hebrews 7:1-4, 14-17; 6:19	1847, 1850, 2580–2581
13. Divided Kingdom – Part 1 (50:44) *1 Kings 12–22, 2 Kings 1–17*	**Going Deeper** (optional): 1 Kings 12–22; 2 Kings	Hosea 1–3; Jonah	2582–2584
14. Divided Kingdom – Part 2 (50:38) *1 Kings 12–22, 2 Kings 1–16*	**Going Deeper** (optional): 1 Kings 12–22; 2 Kings	Deuteronomy 30:15-20; 2 Chronicles 11:5–12:1; Isaiah 5–6; 22:15-24; Micah 6:1-8	552–553
15. Exile (50:07) *2 Kings 17–25*	2 Kings 17; 18:9-12; 24–25	Jeremiah 31; 33–34; Ezekiel 34; Daniel 1–7; Matthew 18:21-35; Mark 14:60-65	2838–2845
16. Return (50:03) *Ezra; Nehemiah*	Ezra 1; 3–7; 9:1–10:17; Nehemiah 2; 4:1–5:13; 9:32–10:29 **Going Deeper** (optional): Ezra; Nehemiah; Esther	Isaiah 44:24-28; 45:1-6, 13; Jeremiah 29:10-14;	—
17. Maccabean Revolt (50:09) *1 Maccabees*	1 Maccabees 1–6 **Going Deeper** (optional): 1 Maccabees	Wisdom 3:1-8; Sirach 2; 2 Maccabees 7; 12:38-46	Catechism 957–958, 988–996, 1030–1032
18. Messianic Fulfillment – Part 1 (50:35) *Luke*	Luke 1:1–9:50 **Going Deeper** (optional): Luke	Genesis 3; Exodus 17:1-7; 20; Deuteronomy 6; 8; John 6	1384, 1716–1729, 2052
19. Messianic Fulfillment – Part 2 (51:40) *Luke*	Luke 9:51–19:27 **Going Deeper** (optional): Luke	Matthew 16:13-20; 18:18-20; 25:31-46; John 20:21-23; Galatians 3:26–4:7	553, 588–589, 2762–2766, 2803–2806
20. Messianic Fulfillment – Part 3 (49:28) *Luke*	Luke 19:28–24:53 **Going Deeper** (optional): Luke	Genesis 3; Exodus 12; Isaiah 52-53; John 21:2-19; Romans 6:1-14; Romans 6:5; 1 Corinthians 5:7; Galatians 3:13; Hebrews 2:14-18; 1 Peter 1:18-20; Revelation 5:6-14	613–614, 1213–1216, 1227–1228, 1340
21. The Church – Part 1 (50:55) *Acts*	Acts 1:1–8:4 **Going Deeper** (optional): Acts	Matthew 28:16-20; Mark 16:14-18; Luke 24:13-49; John 20:19-23; 21:15-19; 1 Timothy 3:8-13	761, 767–768
22. The Church – Part 2 (49:48) *Acts*	Acts 8:5–15:35 **Going Deeper** (optional): CCC 683	Genesis 12:1-3; Matthew 15:11, 19-20; 1 Timothy 1:12-17	880–892
23. The Church – Part 3 (51:30) *Acts*	Acts 15:36–28:31 **Going Deeper** (optional): CCC 748	Ezekiel 37; 1 Corinthians 1:10-17; 5:1-2; 6:12-20; 8; 11:17-34; 13; Philippians 1:12-18; 1 Thessalonians 2–4	817–819

What to Do for Each Session

1. Welcome and Introduction (10 minutes)

2. Small-Group Discussion (40 minutes)

3. ***Note to Study Leaders:*** There is no small-group discussion for the first session. Instead, use this time to divide participants into small groups of eight to twelve people, ensure that everyone has the study materials, and explain how the study works. Each small group should be led by a trained facilitator.

4. Video Presentation (50 minutes)

5. Closing and Prayer (5 minutes)

Getting the Most Out of This Study

This study will help you understand the Bible in a new way. The "head knowledge" you gain will help you grow in "heart knowledge" as you follow up on what you have learned. The Bible will always remain a mystery, though, and that is part of the beauty of it: We can never exhaust the treasures of Scripture. Fortunately for us, the Bible is not a subject to master; it is a place to encounter the living Word of God.

Whenever you open your Bible to read, *start with prayer,* and place yourself in God's presence. You might take Samuel's prayer as your own: "Speak, Lord, for your servant is listening" (1 Samuel 3:10). When you read, adopt an attitude of listening. Try not to treat Scripture as a text, but as a personal message from God. What is he saying? What does it mean? What does it mean for my life? If you come to the Word focused on having an encounter with the Lord, he will speak to your heart, and you will be transformed.

An Important Note About the Responses to the Study Questions

Responses to the study questions are provided in the back of this Study Set. These responses do not exhaust the meaning that can be found in the Scripture reading. People will have unique insights. The responses have two important functions:

1. The first purpose of the responses is to provide participants with a review of each session, which will help establish a context for the reading and questions in the following session. The best time to read the responses is just before starting on the next session.

2. The second purpose of the responses is to provide guidelines for the small-group facilitators. **Facilitators:** Complete the Scripture reading and answer the questions on your own before reading the responses in preparation for facilitating the small-group discussion.

Participants should not review the responses for each session until after the session is completed. Although it might be tempting to look at these responses in advance, it is important to wait for the following reasons.

1. Bible study is not about simply watching a video presentation or reading a Bible commentary. It is just as important to immerse yourself in the Word of God itself and engage it with your heart and mind. The questions in *The Great Adventure* studies are designed to draw you into the Scriptures so that the Word of God will be planted and grow in your heart. Reading a response written by someone else may satisfy your mind for a moment, but it will not result in the kind of growth that will occur if you attempt to answer the question on your own first.

2. The success of a small group depends on a good discussion. A group of participants who have spent time pondering the Scripture passages on their own will have more varied insights to discuss.

For these reasons, please wait to read the responses until after the session. When you follow the steps of this study as intended, you will explore the Word of God in different ways—in the reading, the small-group discussion, the video presentation, and, finally, in the responses. Follow these steps over time, and you will be more than fed—you will learn to feed yourself.

Ten Commandments of Small-Group Discussion

1. **Enjoy yourself!**

2. **Speak with respect and charity.**

3. **Do not ridicule or dismiss what others say. Keep comments positive.**

4. **Come prepared.**

5. **If you were not able to prepare, let others speak first.**

6. **Stick to the topic and questions at hand.**

7. **Start and end on time.**

8. **Allow silence. Give people a chance to think.**

9. **Listen to others without interrupting.**

10. **Keep personal matters within the group.**

THE BIBLE
TIMELINE
The Story of Salvation

Study Leaders: *The* Introduction *is much shorter than the other sessions in* The Bible Timeline *study. This gives you the time you need for everyone to get to know each other. Your goals for this first week are to ensure that everyone feels welcome, has the study materials, and knows how the study works. Consider offering refreshments and other community building activities.*

Facilitators: *There is no small-group discussion for this first week. Instead, use this time to explain how the study works (page vi) and to review the "Ten Commandments of Small-Group Discussion" (page xi). Then, consider offering an icebreaker so the people in your group can get to know each other. For icebreaker ideas, visit BibleStudyForCatholics.com/Facilitators.*

Preparing to Read the Bible and Answer the Questions in the Study Set

Reading

The Bible Timeline: The Story of Salvation covers fourteen books of the Bible over approximately six months of study. (Those books are Genesis, Exodus, Numbers, Joshua, Judges, 1 and 2 Samuel, 1 and 2 Kings, Ezra, Nehemiah, 1 Maccabees, Luke, and the Acts of the Apostles.) Because these books are not spread evenly among the biblical time periods, the amount of reading required for each session varies greatly. (For example: The first time period, Early World, is told in only eleven chapters of Genesis, while the Royal Kingdom time period covers 1 and 2 Samuel and part of 1 Kings.) Tips for managing the reading are on page 10.

Questions

Preparation for each session should be done over several days rather than all at once. Allow a total of 90 to 120 minutes to complete each session. Each set of questions is divided into the following parts:

A. Establish (or Review) the Context

This section prepares you by reviewing what has gone before and by putting the new session into the context of the entire story.

B. Read the Story

The second step is to read from the narrative book that tells the story of the particular time period being studied. Sometimes, an entire period is addressed in a single session. More often, though, periods are divided between two or three sessions. Ideally, you will read through the entire Scripture narrative for each period (see the explanation under "Reading" above). Because some study participants may lack the time to do all the readings, sessions that cover long stretches of Scripture will provide a summary or will propose a shorter reading assignment.

The focus here is on reading and absorbing the general tone and idea (i.e., the outline of events). If you are reading an entire book, *do not try to understand everything.* Many things will become clearer as you proceed through the study. Pretend you are looking at a map before driving through an unfamiliar country. You just want to get the lay of the land so you know where you are going.

Always pray before you read, asking God to help you take his Word into your heart.

C. Take a Deeper Look

The first time you visit a foreign country, you will likely visit just a few important landmarks in each major city rather than trying to see everything of interest. Similarly, on this visit to the "foreign country" of the Bible, you will focus on just a few important people and events in each time period.

Approach the questions, then, not expecting to learn all there is to know about the reading you have just completed, but rather to understand its place in the overall story. Some questions will establish the main themes and events of the time period, while others will refer you to the *Catechism* or will bring in another book of the Bible to give you a fuller understanding.

Do not worry if you do not understand a question or if other questions come to mind while you are completing the questions. Write these questions somewhere so you can come back to them later. Remember—it is impossible to know everything about the Bible. If this study answers *all* your questions, we will have failed in our efforts! Instead, we hope to give you the basics and then make you thirsty to learn more, starting you off on a lifetime of seeking God in his Word.

D. Application

At least one question at the end of every session asks you to think about how what you have read applies to the present day—either to our society or to you personally. After meditating on the question, respond to God with a brief written prayer if you choose.

E. Wrap-Up

The final session for each biblical time period concludes with a "Wrap-Up" section to help you fix in your mind what the time period is about and to help you remember it. Do not skip this brief but important step.

For More Information About the Bible and Scripture Study

The Bible Timeline: The Story of Salvation focuses on reading and getting a basic understanding of the narrative thread that runs through Scripture and makes sense of it and of our Faith. A more detailed presentation of the biblical narrative that follows the time periods presented in the *Bible Timeline* can be found in:

- *Walking With God: A Journey Through the Bible* by Tim Gray and Jeff Cavins

Those desiring more information about such issues as biblical authorship, inspiration, principles of interpretation, differences between Protestant and Catholic versions of the Bible, or biblical terms and practices may find the following resources helpful:

- *The Bible Compass: A Catholic's Guide to Navigating the Scriptures,* Edward Sri

- *Catholic Bible Dictionary,* Scott Hahn

- *Making Senses Out of Scripture: Reading the Bible as the First Christians Did,* Mark P. Shea

- Church documents on Scripture:

  - *Verbum Domini* (The Word of God), Pope Benedict XVI (2010)

  - *The Interpretation of the Bible in the Church,* Pontifical Biblical Commission (1994)

  - *Dei Verbum* (Dogmatic Constitution on Divine Revelation), Second Vatican Council (1965)

  - *Divino Afflante Spiritu* (On Promoting Biblical Studies), Pope Pius XII (1943)

  - *Providentissimus Deus* (On the Study of Holy Scripture), Pope Leo XIII (1893)

Introduction Talk Notes

I.   Introduction to *The Bible Timeline: The Story of Salvation*

A.   God has a "plan of sheer goodness" (CCC 1)

B.   "The desire for God is written in the human heart" (CCC 27)

II.   What *The Bible Timeline* Is and What It Is Not

A.   Pastoral, not academic

B.   Introduces the Bible narrative

C.   Faithful to the Church

III. Goals of *The Bible Timeline*

A.   Transformation

B.   Comprehend God's plan

C.   Find your story in "his-story"

D.   Provide a sound platform for further devotion, reading, and study

IV. Materials

A.   Catholic Bible, *Catechism of the Catholic Church*

B.   *Bible Timeline* Chart

C.   *Bible Timeline* Bookmark

D.   Study Set

V.   Guidelines for Fruitful Study

A.   Allow time for home preparation: fifteen minutes a day[1]

B.   Small-group discussion

C.   Video presentation

D.   Review responses

VI.   Home Preparation for the Next Session

A.   Getting to know your Bible

B.   The Bible in the Catholic Church

C.   Finding the story in Scripture

D.   Discussion questions

E.   Praying with *The Bible Timeline*

VII.   You Can Understand the Bible

---

[1]   This is recommended for answering questions; additional time is needed for reading, which can be heavy in *The Bible Timeline* study. Suggestions for reading are provided on page 10.

Note: Please read the Introduction before continuing if you did not go through it in your small group.

In next session's video presentation, Jeff Cavins will review the role of Scripture in the Catholic Church, discuss the importance of reading the Bible and some obstacles people face, and present the Church's solution for making sense of what we read and what we believe. Finding the "story," or grand narrative, that ties it all together is the key, and *The Bible Timeline* offers a way to do that.

A. Review: Getting to Know Your Bible

If you are not familiar with your Bible, spend some time getting acquainted with it.

1. This study uses the Revised Standard Version–Catholic Edition (RSV-CE). Other Catholic translations include the New American Bible and the New Jerusalem Bible. It is important for this study that you have a Catholic Bible or one that includes the seven deuterocanonical books (referred to as the "Apocrypha" by Protestants). You may notice a few minor differences in verse numbering between some Catholic translations. While it is not necessary that you use the RSV-CE, please be aware that if you use another translation, differences in wording may make some of the questions difficult to understand.

2. Look through the information provided in the front and back of your Bible. It may contain helpful articles, charts, and maps. Next, check to see if an introduction is provided to each of the Bible books and whether there are notes or references to related Scripture passages in the margins or at the bottom of each page. Take a closer look at any features that interest you, and note them for future reference.

3. Locate the listing of Old Testament books and page numbers in your Bible. Sometimes the list of New Testament books is at the beginning of the Bible; sometimes it comes after the Old Testament. Familiarize yourself with the names of the books in both Testaments.

Why Are Catholic and Protestant Bibles Different?

In the early days, the Church used a Greek translation of the Old Testament called the Septuagint. This included the thirty-nine books of the modern Jewish canon plus seven books Jews consider sacred but did not later retain in their canon (the "deuterocanonical" books). Catholic Bibles follow the Septuagint and include all forty-six books in their Old Testament, while the Protestant reformers chose to follow the shorter Hebrew canon. The Catholic canon also includes additional text in the books of Esther and Daniel.

The forty-six Old Testament books can be classified as follows:

- The Law (also called the *Torah,* the "Pentateuch," or the "Books of Moses"): Genesis, Exodus, Leviticus, Numbers, Deuteronomy

- The Prophets: Joshua, Judges, 1 and 2 Samuel, 1 and 2 Kings, Isaiah, Jeremiah, Ezekiel, Hosea, Joel, Amos, Obadiah, Jonah, Micah, Nahum, Habakkuk, Zephaniah, Haggai, Zechariah, Malachi

- The Writings: Psalms, Proverbs, Job, Song of Songs, Ruth, Lamentations, Ecclesiastes, Esther, Daniel, Ezra, Nehemiah, 1 and 2 Chronicles

- Deuterocanonical books: Tobit, Judith, 1 and 2 Maccabees, Wisdom, Sirach, Baruch (plus some additional passages in Daniel and Esther)

Catholic and Protestant versions of the Bible contain the same twenty-seven New Testament books:

- The four Gospels: Matthew, Mark, Luke, John

- Acts of the Apostles

- The Pauline epistles (or letters): Romans, 1 and 2 Corinthians, Galatians, Ephesians, Philippians, Colossians, 1 and 2 Thessalonians

- The pastoral epistles (or letters): 1 and 2 Timothy, Titus, Philemon, Hebrews

- The Catholic epistles (or letters): James; 1 and 2 Peter; 1, 2 and 3 John; Jude (Note: The term "Catholic" here means that these letters were written to all Christians rather than to a particular community.)

- The Revelation to John (the Apocalypse)

4. Make sure you know how to look up a passage of Scripture using its "Scripture reference": a location reference made up of the name of the book followed by the chapter and verse numbers.

- 1 Samuel 7 refers to the entire seventh chapter of the book of 1 Samuel (pronounced "first Samuel" because there also is a 2 Samuel, or "second Samuel").

- Genesis 1:1 refers to the book of Genesis, Chapter 1, verse 1.

- Numbers 5:2-6 refers to the book of Numbers, Chapter 5, verses 2, 3, 4, 5, and 6.

B. The Bible in the Catholic Church

Catholics read Scripture "from within the heart of the Church," recognizing that God's revelation, both written and oral, comes to us through the Church and is authentically interpreted by the Church's teaching office, the Magisterium. This study series follows Catholic principles of interpretation and often makes reference to passages in the *Catechism of the Catholic Church* (CCC) and various Church documents on Sacred Scripture.

Every paragraph in the *Catechism* is assigned a number, which appears at the start of the paragraph in bold type (the italic numbers in the margins refer to related paragraphs). This study uses the bold paragraph numbers to identify assigned *Catechism* readings.

Read **CCC 50–141** to begin getting familiar with the role of Scripture in the Catholic Church. Jeff Cavins' video presentation will cover crucial points to remember, but you may want to note any sections you would like to return to in the future.

C. Finding the Story in Scripture: *The Bible Timeline* Chart

In the video presentation for this session, Jeff Cavins will introduce *The Bible Timeline* Chart, which is the central feature of *The Bible Timeline* learning system. If you are not familiar with the Chart, look at yours now and jot down the features you notice so you will be acquainted with it when it is explained. Particularly notice the way the books of the Bible appear on the Chart and how the flow of events and people named in the central section relates to those books. A diagram of the main features of the Chart is on page 8.

D. For Discussion

1. What has been your experience with Scripture in the Catholic Church? When have you heard it? Read it? Learned about it?

   Early in life (grade school) at St. Rita's. & first Communion there. Sad to admit it now, but I mostly went to church because I had to. I wish I would have been able to appreciate it then. I really had not started to read scripture until I started to get involved in men's group. I am just actually starting to learn about it.

2. Have you ever tried reading through the Bible? If so, explain your experience. Did you make it all the way through, and if not, why not?

   I only tried to read certain passages when they were presented to me during my time here.

3. What do you hope to get out of this Bible study?

   I hope to understand the bible better, to become closer to God & his teachings & to become a better man to all those that I encounter.

Praying with *The Bible Timeline*

Responsive Prayers based on the twelve periods of Bible history are on the inside front cover of this Study Set Workbook. You will use them in your group discussions. At each session, you will pray up to and including the period you are studying that week to help you learn the periods and take them to heart. Later, you can pray the Responsive Prayer on your own.

Understanding *The Bible Timeline* Chart

The cornerstone of *The Great Adventure Bible* Study Program is *The Bible Timeline* Learning System, which is built upon a chart that arranges the key people, places, and events of the Bible in chronological order. This revolutionary study aid shows how all the books of the Bible fit together to tell the story of salvation history. People who experience *The Bible Timeline* studies or live seminars learn the "big picture" of salvation history. They learn general principles that enable them to approach the Bible with confidence and purpose because they have the tools needed to understand the story.

Each period of *The Bible Timeline* is assigned a unique color to help you remember the narrative. For example, in the Early World, during which the world was created, turquoise is used to represent the color of the earth as seen from space.

The growth of God's family is traced through history from "One Holy Couple" (Adam and Eve) in Genesis through "One, Holy, Catholic Church."

Fourteen of the Bible's "narrative" books tell the biblical story from beginning to end.

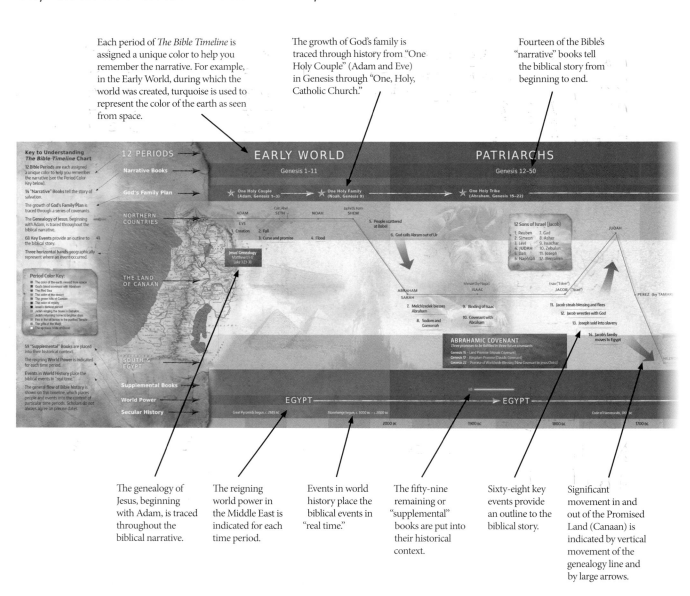

The genealogy of Jesus, beginning with Adam, is traced throughout the biblical narrative.

The reigning world power in the Middle East is indicated for each time period.

Events in world history place the biblical events in "real time."

The fifty-nine remaining or "supplemental" books are put into their historical context.

Sixty-eight key events provide an outline to the biblical story.

Significant movement in and out of the Promised Land (Canaan) is indicated by vertical movement of the genealogy line and by large arrows.

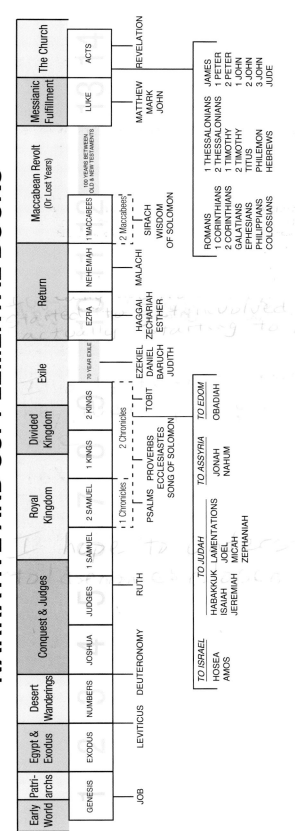

NARRATIVE AND SUPPLEMENTAL BOOKS *

Early World	Patri-archs	Egypt & Exodus	Desert Wanderings	Conquest & Judges	Royal Kingdom	Divided Kingdom	Exile	Return	Maccabean Revolt (Or Lost Years)	Messianic Fulfillment	The Church
		EXODUS	NUMBERS	JOSHUA	1 SAMUEL	2 SAMUEL	1 KINGS	2 KINGS		NEHEMIAH	1 MACCABEES		LUKE	ACTS

GENESIS

JOB

LEVITICUS   DEUTERONOMY

JUDGES

RUTH

70 YEAR EXILE

100 YEARS BETWEEN OLD & NEW TESTAMENTS

EZRA

REVELATION

1 Chronicles   2 Chronicles

PSALMS   PROVERBS
ECCLESIASTES
SONG OF SOLOMON

HAGGAI
ZECHARIAH
ESTHER

MALACHI

2 Maccabees
SIRACH
WISDOM
OF SOLOMON

EZEKIEL
DANIEL
BARUCH
JUDITH

TOBIT

TO ISRAEL
HOSEA
AMOS

TO JUDAH
HABAKKUK   LAMENTATIONS
ISAIAH   JOEL
JEREMIAH   MICAH
           ZEPHANIAH

TO ASSYRIA
JONAH
NAHUM

TO EDOM
OBADIAH

MATTHEW
MARK
JOHN

1 THESSALONIANS   JAMES
2 THESSALONIANS   1 PETER
1 TIMOTHY   2 PETER
2 TIMOTHY   1 JOHN
TITUS   2 JOHN
PHILEMON   3 JOHN
HEBREWS   JUDE

ROMANS
1 CORINTHIANS
2 CORINTHIANS
GALATIANS
EPHESIANS
PHILIPPIANS
COLOSSIANS

Key to Period Colors

Turquoise	The color of the earth viewed from space
Burgundy	God's blood covenant with Abraham
Red	The Red Sea
Tan	The color of the desert
Green	The green hills of Canaan
Purple	Royalty
Black	Israel's darkest period
Baby blue	Judah "singing the blues" in Babylon
Yellow	Judah returning home to brighter days
Orange	Fire in the oil lamps in the purified Temple
Gold	Gifts of the Magi
White	The spotless bride of Christ

Early World	
Patriarchs	
Egypt and Exodus	
Desert Wanderings	
Conquest and Judges	
Royal Kingdom	
Divided Kingdom	
Exile	
Return	
Maccabean Revolt	
Messianic Fulfillment	
The Church	

* To read Scripture in the context of the underlying narrative of God's plan, fourteen of the Bible's narrative books have been arranged chronologically so that they tell the entire story from the beginning to the end. The remaining books, called "supplemental" on *The Bible Timeline* Chart, are no less important than the narrative books but are arranged on the Chart and in this diagram in such a way that their relationship to particular time periods can be seen easily.

Preparing to Read Through the Biblical Story

The remaining twenty-two sessions will take you on a journey through the twelve time periods of Bible history, focusing primarily on the fourteen "narrative books" of *The Bible Timeline*. In the process, you will be asked to read at least the highlights of the story in each period. At times, that can mean a lot of reading—even if you opt not to do the "Going Deeper" reading, which involves reading the entire narrative book(s) for each period. Keep the following tips in mind as you read the chapters assigned in Section B – "Read the Story" of each session.

1. **Keep your eye on the goal,** which is simply to get the gist of the story. Speed-read if you have to. Try to get "the big picture" of the time period. The study questions will take you back to important sections, and you can always return later for a closer look.

2. **Establish a "parking lot,"** a small notebook or a few pieces of extra paper, where you can jot down questions to return to at another time. This will help you move on if you find yourself slowed down by intriguing or difficult passages.

3. **Use a simple translation for reading.** We recommend the RSV-CE for answering the questions, but there is no reason you cannot use a simpler version the first time you read when your goal is simply to get the flow of the story. Some people have found it helpful to use the New Jerusalem Bible or a paraphrase version like "The Way" Catholic Living Bible, for their first read-through. Another option is to listen to the story using a Catholic audio Bible and then use a print Bible for the questions.

4. **Plan to save a thorough reading for later.** When you have finished this study, and while it is fresh in your mind, plan to take the next few months and read at your own pace through the whole story. If you are new to the Bible, this will be much easier to do after you have the background provided in this study. Use the "Ninety-Day Reading Plan" on page 167 to guide you through the story, or read it with the help of *The Bible Timeline Guided Journal*.

Facilitators: There are no specific Responses for Session 1. Use the group-discussion time to discuss the questions on page 7.

- Group members may want to look at other Bibles and compare the features they offer. Make sure everyone has a Catholic Bible and that they can find their way around in it.
- Did everyone read CCC 50–141? What, in particular, stood out to them?
- Make sure everyone has a *Bible Timeline* Chart, and direct their attention to the Talk Notes on page 11. The Talk Notes are a good place for participants to take notes during the video presentation. Also point out the "Narrative and Supplemental Books" and "Key to Period Colors" guides on page 9.
- Review the reading guidelines in the box at the top of this page. You may need to return to this in the weeks ahead.
- Spend most of your time on the three discussion questions on page 7.
- Point out the Responsive Prayers (one for each time period) that are on the inside front cover of this Study Set Workbook. Starting with the next session, pray the Responsive Prayer to close each small-group discussion. This will help participants to fix the significance of each time period in their minds and to take its message to heart. Have one person read the intercessions (with the group responding), or have group members take turns reading the intercessions.

Watch Jeff Cavins' video presentation for *Session 1 – Finding the Story in Scripture*.

Session 1 Talk Notes

Finding the Story in Scripture

I.   The Approach this Study Takes to Scripture: Find the Story First

A.   God has a plan (see CCC 1)

1.   The plan is revealed in the Bible

2.   A "pastoral narrative approach" – Learn the plan; walk in it

II.   Where the Bible Fits into Our Catholic Faith

A.   The "problem of the heap" (Frank Sheed)

B.   A tool for understanding our Faith: the *Catechism of the Catholic Church*

1.   Four divisions or "pillars"

   a.   Creed – the plan (the story of salvation) in tightly wound form (St. Augustine)

   b.   Sacraments and liturgy – how we get into the story

   c.   Life in Christ – how we live in the story (Galatians 2:20)

   d.   Prayer – the living relationship between God and the Church

III.   Everybody Is Looking for a Story

A.   Example: *Titanic*

B.   St Augustine – have to become "like a little one" to gain riches of Scripture (*Confessions* 3-5, p. 70)

IV.   How Do We Read the Bible and Understand God's "Plan of Sheer Goodness"?

A.   The problem with reading the Bible like a book

1.   Note: St. Jerome – "Ignorance of the Scriptures is ignorance of Christ" (CCC 133)[1]

2.   Not chronological

3.   A library of seventy-three books arranged by literary genre, tied together by God's plan

B.   *The Bible Timeline* Learning System: making the complex simple

1.   Twelve Bible time periods, color-coded (a mnemonic device)

2.   Fourteen "narrative books" that keep the plot moving

3.   The fifty-nine remaining, or "supplemental," books

4.   Understanding *The Bible Timeline* Chart

---

[1]   *Dei Verbum*; Philippians 3:8; St. Jerome, *Commentariorum in Isaiam libri xviii* prol.: PL 24, 17b.

V.   The Place of the Bible in the Catholic Church

A.   The relationship between Sacred Tradition and Sacred Scripture

1.   We are people of the Word (see CCC 108)

2.   One common source, two modes of transmission (CCC 80–82)

B.   Divine inspiration

1.   "God is the author of Sacred Scripture" (CCC 105)

2.   "God inspired the human authors" (CCC 106)

3.   "The inspired books teach the truth … without error" (CCC 107)

C.   Criteria for interpreting Scripture (CCC 109–114)

1.   Be attentive to the content and unity of the whole Scripture

2.   Read the Scripture within the living Tradition of the whole Church

3.   Be attentive to the analogy of faith (the truths all fit together)

D.   The senses of Scripture (CCC 115–119)

1.   The literal sense – the intended meaning

2.   The spiritual sense (three aspects)

a.   Allegorical – how does it relate to Christ?

b.   Moral – how does it relate to my conduct and life?

c.   Anagogical – how does it relate to eternity?

VI.   Getting Started

A.   How to choose a Bible (*Great Adventure* study questions use the RSV-CE)

B.   Get a Bible you can "live in"

1.   Highlight meaningful texts for later reference

2.   Highlight texts for teaching, explaining to others

3.   Make it a personal journal of your walk with God

C.   How to mark your Bible (keep it simple)

A. Establish the Context

The first eleven chapters of Genesis, which describe the Early World period in our study, contain some of the best-known stories in the Bible—Creation, Adam and Eve, Cain and Abel, Noah, and the Tower of Babel. It is here that the story we are studying starts and where it finds its roots: "in the beginning," with God creating the heavens and the earth. Too often, discussion of these stories involves whether they, in fact, happened, whether they are "true" in the way we think of scientific truth. The Bible is not a science book, however, and the first chapters of Genesis were not written so we would know the scientific beginnings of the universe. To find the intended sense of these passages, we need to take into account the type of literature they are and understand the ways the ancient Hebrews viewed history and wrote it. They were not "all about the facts" the way we are. They wove in story and poetic language to get across far deeper meaning. And God inspired the first part of Genesis to be told through story to help us understand the meaning of our existence, not "the facts" of our beginning—the "who" and "why," not the "when" and "how." Why are we here? Are we ruled by fate or chance, or is God in control? Why is there evil, and why would a good God allow it? And so on.

The *Catechism* tells us that the first three chapters of Genesis, which this session will cover, were placed at the start of the Bible "to express in their solemn language the truths of creation—its origin and its end in God, its order and goodness, the vocation of man, and, finally, the drama of sin and the hope of salvation. Read in the light of Christ within the unity of Sacred Scripture and in the living Tradition of the Church, these texts remain the principal source for catechesis on the mysteries of the 'beginning': creation, fall, and promise of salvation" (CCC 289).

The story of Adam and Eve in the Garden is not a children's tale or something to be taught in religious education class and then forgotten. It is not the literal kind of history we are familiar with today, but neither is it myth; it is a kind of history that focuses on truth and meaning.[1] The biblical Creation narrative is loaded with truths that help us know God and ourselves, truths that help us understand why we are here and how to make choices and trust God even when this is difficult. Read on, and let the story take root in your heart and mind. It is not just the story of Adam and Eve; it is *our* story.

B. Read the Story (Genesis 1–3)

Read **Genesis 1–3** to become familiar with the main characters and events of the first part of the Early World, the part pertaining to Creation and the fall of man. After reading, trace the action in the center section of your *Bible Timeline* Chart. This session takes you only partway into the Early World period. Identify the main characters, and notice the flow of key events and where they take place. Any questions? Jot them down.

Going Deeper (optional): You can gain insight into the Church's understanding of **Genesis 1–3** by reading **CCC 279–421.**

As always, pray before you read.

---

[1] As Pope Pius XII wrote in *Humani Generis* (HG), "The first eleven chapters of Genesis, although properly speaking not conforming to the historical method used by the best Greek and Latin writers or by competent authors of our time, do nevertheless pertain to history in a true sense, which however must be further studied and determined by exegetes; the same chapters, … in simple and metaphorical language adapted to the mentality of a people but little cultured, both state the principal truths which are fundamental for our salvation, and also give a popular description of the origin of the human race and the chosen people" (HG 38).

C. Take a Deeper Look

Answering these questions will draw you into the heart of the story. If you do not understand something, make a note of it to bring up in the discussion.

The Creation of Heaven and Earth

1. There are two accounts of Creation in Genesis 1 and 2, told from different viewpoints. Read **Genesis 1** carefully several times.

    a. What does this account tell you about God? Think about the way God creates; the order in which he forms and fills the earth; the way he blesses; even the simple fact that he creates the earth and people at all. *That he loves us & made all things wonderful & good for us to enjoy.*

    b. What does Genesis 1 tell you about the nature and purpose of the world and the things around us? *Everything God created is good & provided for us.*

The Creation of Mankind

2. The creation of mankind is told twice, in **Genesis 1:26-31 and 2:4-25.** Read both accounts, paying close attention to **Genesis 1:27.**

    a. What does it mean to be created in God's image? Read also **CCC 356–357 and 364.** *To share God's love & communion w/other persons.*

    b. What does "male and female he created them" add to your understanding of the image in which we are created? For help with this question, read **CCC 369–373.** *Man & woman are equal & compliment one another.*

3. **Think About It:** Genesis 2:1-3 tells us that after completing his work of Creation, God rested on the seventh day, blessed it, and made it holy. Years later, the children of Israel will be commanded to refrain from work on the seventh day in imitation of God. If we are created in his image, is there any sense in which we stifle the image of God in ourselves when we ignore this command? Or, to put it another way: In what way does this command enable us to more fully live in God's image? For further reading about the Sabbath, see **CCC 345–349.**

How to Read the Account of the Fall

"The account of the Fall in Genesis 3 uses figurative language, but affirms a primeval event, a deed that took place *at the beginning of the history of man*.[2] Revelation gives us the certainty of faith that the whole of human history is marked by the original fault freely committed by our first parents."[3]

CCC 390 (emphasis in original)

Fall and Promise

Note: *Though the Genesis accounts of the Creation and Fall are written in figurative language, it does not, therefore, follow that Adam and Eve do not represent a single set of original people. The Church teaches us that "because of its common origin the human race forms a unity, for 'from one ancestor [God] made all nations to inhabit the whole earth.'"[4] To believe that Adam and Eve represent a larger number of ancient people is not consistent with the truth conveyed by the Scripture and taught by the Church that our state of original sin "proceeds from a sin actually committed by an individual (Adam) and which, through generation, is passed on to all and is in everyone as his own."[5] As the Catechism goes on to explain, "The whole human race is in Adam 'as one body of one man.' By this 'unity of the human race' all men are implicated in Adam's sin, as all are implicated in Christ's justice."[6]*

4. "Behind the disobedient choice of our first parents lurks a seductive voice, opposed to God" (CCC 391). That is the voice of Satan, the devil, who is pictured in Genesis 3 as a serpent. Review the command God gives to Adam in **Genesis 2:16-17;** then read the exchange between the Serpent and the woman in **Genesis 3:1-4.**

   a. What is the Serpent trying to accomplish?

   To trick Eve to disobey & to sin.

   b. What strategy does he use? *Lies & cunning*

5. In **Genesis 3:4,** the Serpent calls God a liar—"You will not die," he says—and proceeds to tell the woman why it will be to her benefit to disobey God.

   a. What are these "benefits"? *God will understand what will happen to you. You will know the difference between right & wrong.*

---

2   Cf. *Gaudium et Spes* 13.
3   Cf. Council of Trent: DS 1513; Pius XII: DS 3897; Paul VI: AAS 58 [1966], 653.
4   CCC 360; Acts 17:26; cf Tobit 8:6.
5   cf. Romans 5:12-19; Council of Trent, Session V, canon 1-4; *Humani Generis* 37.
6   CCC 404.

b.   Do these benefits offer Eve anything she does not already have? What *do* they offer?

6.   What immediate effects do Adam and Eve's disobedience have on their behavior, which show the consequences of their sin? *They realize they are naked. They were frightend & hid from God.*

7.   Read God's curse on the Serpent and on Adam and Eve in **Genesis 3:14-19.**

a.   Does God abandon his disobedient children? What ray of hope do you see? *No. ~~You sti~~ They still have their lives. They will survive but will have struggles*

b.   Is there anything about their punishment that might help mankind learn the lesson Adam and Eve so sadly failed? *To trust & listen to God.*

8.   **New Testament Connection:** The apostle John borrows language and imagery from the Creation story to begin his Gospel. Read **John 1:1-14.** What new creation is he describing? *Jesus Christ.*

D. Application

These questions will help you apply one of the key themes of the session to your life. After meditating on them, respond to God with a brief written prayer if you choose.

What are some ways we hide from the presence of God? How does sin drive us further from his presence?

Dear Lord …

Session 2 Talk Notes

Early World – Part 1

I. Introduction to the Early World – Part 1: How to Read Genesis 1–11

   A. A unique type of literature: poetry, not science; "why," not "how"

      1. CCC 390: "Genesis 3 uses figurative language, but affirms … a deed that took place at the beginning of the history of man."

   B. Genesis 1–11 as "anti-myth"; in contrast to *Enuma Elish,* Babylonian creation myth

      1. God alone is king

      2. Mankind created in his image as sons and daughters

II. Creation

   A. Creation of the earth: God builds a dwelling place for us and him

      1. "The earth was without form and void" (Genesis 1:1)

God brings form	God fills the void
Day 1: light and darkness	Day 4: sun, moon, stars
Day 2: water and sky	Day 5: fish and birds
Day 3: land	Day 6: land animals, mankind

   B. Creation of humanity (Genesis 1–2): How are we different from the animals?

      1. Created in God's image and likeness (1:26-31)

         a. Intellect (reason)

         b. Free will (ability to act; governed by the intellect)

         c. Capacity to love (St. John Paul II, the Trinity is a family)

         d. Dominion over animals and earth (name; till and keep)

      2. Created male and female (creation of woman – 2:18-25)

   C. Two complementary stories (Brichto: "synoptic-resumptive" technique)

   D. The seventh day (Genesis 2:1-3)

      1. Seventh day breaks from pattern of repetition: It has no end

      2. The Sabbath day is holy, represents divine rest (Mark 2:27 – created for man)

      3. Man created *on* the sixth day but *for* the seventh day

      4. Meaning of "six" in the Bible

5. "Seven" = *sheva, shava* = to swear an oath (therefore related to covenant, Heb., *berit*)

    a.   CCC 51 – We were created to share in God's divine life

III. Test and Temptation (Genesis 3)

A.   The nature of the test

    1.   The prohibition

    2.   Who was the Serpent *(nahash)?* (See Revelation 12:9; CCC 390–395)

    3.   How he lures them (3:1-5; CCC 398)

B.   The key: Do you trust God? (CCC 397) – Sin is lack of trust in his goodness

IV. Fall and Promise (Genesis 3)

A.   Results of the Fall (3:7-13)

    1.   Immediate consequences: ruptured relationships (CCC 400; Romans 7:15)

    2.   Intellect darkened; will weakened

    3.   Result: concupiscence (CCC 405)

B.   Why do we sin?

    1.   St. Augustine: Out of an inordinate desire for things, we prefer a lesser good

    2.   The pursuit of natural goods can lead us to live as though God does not exist

    3.   Threefold temptation to sensual lust, worldly greed, pride (1 John 2:16)

    4.   St. John Paul II – Sin is "a suicidal act," and one's "internal balance is destroyed"; "its first and most important consequences … are in his relationship with God"

C.   What to do when sin stalks us

    1.   Resist temptation (2 Timothy 2:22)

    2.   If you sin, repent, go to confession, do penance

    3.   The result if you do not repent

    4.   Romans 2:4 – God's kindness is meant to lead us to repentance

V. God Has a Plan: "First Good News," *Protoevangelium* (Genesis 3:15)

A. Review the Context

God's story, as it concerns us and our salvation, opens "in the beginning." At the very start of Genesis, we were introduced to God: the powerful Creator and loving Father who infused the world with goodness and beauty. He created mankind in his image and to share his life. Wanting us to share his life and love of our own free will, he gave our first parents a test: Would they trust in his love and goodness and submit to his Word, or would they abuse their freedom and follow their own wills? Tempted by the Serpent, they chose a counterfeit. They preferred themselves to God, wanting to be like him but on their own terms, apart from him. The results were immediate: a radical disruption in their relationship with God and with each other. Pain, death, and decay entered the world.

The Church tells us that the personal sin that Adam and Eve committed was transmitted to the rest of the human race in the form of a fallen nature, "a human nature deprived of original holiness and justice" (CCC 404). This is the same thing as saying we are born without sanctifying grace, that principle of spiritual life in the soul that causes one to turn toward God. Original sin is thus not something we do; it is something we are: It is a state of being. From the moment we are born, we lack the original holiness and justice that Adam and Eve cast aside. Our souls are wounded in a sense. We are turned away from God. Our wills are weakened. We are subject to pain and death, and we are inclined to sin (sometimes called "concupiscence"). Fortunately, God was not willing to abandon his children to the fate they chose. In Genesis 3, we read that he left Adam and Eve with a flicker of hope: One day, a "seed of the woman" will crush the head of the "seed of the serpent."

We are all ears.

B. Read the Story (Genesis 4–11)

Read **Genesis 4–11** to become familiar with the main characters and events of the second part of the Early World, in which God's family grows and spreads to fill the earth. Next, trace the action in the center section of the Early World on your *Bible Timeline* Chart. Identify the main characters, and notice the flow of key events and where they take place. Any questions? Jot them down.

If you have trouble understanding some of what's going on in the reading, do not let it bother you. In fact, expect to find things you do not understand (what are those "Nephilim" referred to in Chapter 6, and did people really live to be nine hundred years old?). Write things down if they bother you, so you can return to them later in a deeper study of Genesis. There is enough in this one book to keep you studying for a lifetime should you choose to do so. Remember—this study is an overview intended to give you the big picture. Treat it like a preliminary walk-through. Your goal is to get the lay of the land, not to explore every crevice.

As always, pray before you read.

C. Take a Deeper Look

Answering these questions will draw you into the heart of the story. If you do not understand something, make a note of it to bring up in the discussion.

Cain and Abel (Genesis 4:1-16)

1. With the births of Cain and Abel, we see the first offspring of the woman, Eve. Is there any chance one of these might be the promised "seed" who will defeat Satan? Do they look like it to you? Explain.

    Cain — Because he was given a second chance to have offspring & live a fruitful life.

2. What is wrong with Cain's offering as compared with Abel's?

    I do not know — Please explain.

The Family Grows (Genesis 4:17–5:32)

Genesis 4 and 5 give us two genealogies: One draws a quick sketch of the descendants of Cain; the other gives a detailed, written account of Adam's line (literally, "This is the book of the generations of Adam") through a third son, Seth. These are not comprehensive family trees listing every descendant. The author is using a literary device called a toledot—*"the generations of"—which serves to focus the reader on the story line.*

3. Compare and contrast the two family lines. Why do you think the author focuses on Seth's descendants rather than on those of Cain in Adam's "official" genealogy?

The Flood and God's Covenant with Noah (Genesis 6–10)

4. Lamech names his son "Noah," which means "rest," saying, "Out of the ground which the Lᴏʀᴅ has cursed this one shall bring us relief from our work and from the toil of our hands" (Genesis 5:29). Taking this together with **Genesis 6,** what other relief is needed on the earth?

5. What is God's solution to the problem?

6. **New Testament Connection:** The Church has long seen that God's actions in the Old Testament prefigure what he will do one day through his Son, Jesus Christ. The Old Testament figures are called "types" of the New Testament. Think for a moment about the Ark: A great vessel rides above the deathly waves of a flood and carries the righteous to safety. Can you think of a New Testament parallel of which the Ark is a type? Read **1 Peter 3:18-22** along with **CCC 845 and 1219–1220.** What do the Ark and the Flood signify? Explain.

7. Read **Genesis 8:20–9:17.**

    a. What solemn promise does God make to Noah, and with what sign does he seal that covenant?

    That there will never be a flood that destroys the earth.

    A rainbow

    b. As is typical with covenants, this covenant makes demands on Noah and his sons as well. What are they?

The Tower of Babel (Genesis 11)

8. a. Review the events following the Flood and God's covenant with Noah (see **Genesis 9:18–11:9**). Do you see any change in man's behavior? What is the new civilization like? Did the "Flood solution" to evil work?

b. **Think About It:** Have you ever wondered why God does not just reach down and "wipe out the bad guys"? He did this once and promised never to do it again. Why not? Why was that not the solution? What is it about baptism and the Church that is more effective than the Flood that prefigured them? For help with this question, read **CCC 1213ff.**

9. In **Genesis 11,** men build "a tower with its top in the heavens." What might this tower express about their relationship with God?

10. **New Testament Connection:** God's response to mankind's self-exaltation and determination to rely on themselves instead of on God is to confuse their languages and to divide and scatter the people across the earth. In the New Testament, something happens that is, in effect, a reversal of the Babel event. Read **Acts 2:1-13.** What happens?

D. Application

These questions will help you apply one of the key themes of the session to your life. After meditating on them, respond to God with a brief written prayer if you choose.

What enables Enoch and Noah to stand alone and remain righteous amid great wickedness? Are you the same kind of light, or is it too easy to succumb to the influence of others? How can you keep your own light bright against the darkness?

Dear Lord …

E. Wrap-Up

Conclude your study of the Early World period, and fix it in your mind by doing the following:

1. Recall the color of this time period, turquoise, and think of it in terms of your reading to help you remember it.

2. Quickly review Sessions 2 and 3. Write a brief summary of what the Early World period is about or its significance as part of the "big picture."

Session 3 Talk Notes

Early World – Part 2

I. Introduction to the Early World – Part 2

St. John Paul II, *Crossing the Threshold of Hope* – "At the root of the Fall is a failure to grasp the nature of God's fatherhood"

A. Adam and Eve after the Fall

    1. Harmony in relationships destroyed (with selves, God, creation)

    2. Expelled from Garden; exiled

    3. Struggle with concupiscence (inclination to selfishness)

    4. Lack of trust in God

B. Early World Part 2 shows what happens as the earth is populated

    1. The line of promise traced by genealogies (*toledot* = "the generations of")

II. Adam and Eve Are Fruitful and Multiply (Genesis 4–5)

A. Cain and Abel (4:1-24)

    1. Cain: the promised "seed"? (4:1)

    2. Cain's sin and punishment (verses 2-16)

        a. Romans 6:16-18; 1 John 3:11-12

        b. God puts a mark on Cain

            i. Who are the other people?

    3. Cain's descendants (verses 17-24)

        a. Industrious

        b. Musical

        c. Violent (see especially Lamech, verse 23)

        d. Polygamous

B. Seth and his descendants (4:25–5:32)

    1. Contrast to Cain's line

        a. Enoch (5:24)

        b. Noah (5:29) – shall bring relief

    2. Significance of ages (lifespan): literal or figurative?

        a. Emphasis on death and drop in lifespan due to sin

C. Wickedness increases on the earth (6:1-8)

   1. *Nephilim* (6:4: Heb., "fallen ones") – "Mighty men" or warriors, "men of renown"

   2. The "sons of God" and "daughters of men" (see RSV-CE footnote)

   3. One man finds favor: Noah

III. Re-Creation and Another Fall: The Flood and Its Aftermath (Genesis 6:11–9:28)

A. God's plan to deal with wickedness: Build an ark

   1. Take your family (Shem, Ham, Japheth, and wives)

   2. Take two of every unclean species, seven of every clean species

B. Typological meaning of the Ark and the Flood: the Church and baptism

   1. A family affair (CCC 701)

   2. "Forty" – the number of trial and testing

C. Re-creation (Genesis 9:1-17)

   1. Signs of new creation: seven days; winds blowing over the earth

   2. God's covenant with Noah (One Holy Family)

      a. Terms and sign of the covenant (rainbow)

D. Another "fall": Noah's sons (Genesis 9:18-28)

   1. "Uncovering nakedness": an idiom? (see Leviticus 18:18-22, 20:17)

   2. The curse and a blessing

IV. The Earth Is Again Populated (Genesis 10)

A. Shem (Middle East, Mesopotamia)

B. Japheth (north of that, spreading east and west)

C. Ham (Canaan and North Africa)

V. The Tower of Babel (Genesis 11)

A. "Let us make a name for ourselves" (verse 4)

B. God confuses their language; they scatter

C. Tower most likely a *ziggurat*

D. The significance of Shem's line (*Shem* is Hebrew for "name"; *Baruch HaShem* = "blessed be the name")

VI. Conclusion

A. Establish the Context

As the world became populated, the descendants of Adam and Eve continued to make choices similar to the one that precipitated their fall from grace. Over time, two types of civilizations grew up: Some people, like Enoch and Noah, called on God's name and worshiped him; others were more like Cain—violent and wicked, choosing themselves over God.

God set apart the righteous Noah and his family and destroyed the rest with a flood, but nothing changed in the hearts of mankind. By Genesis 11, they had banded together to provide strength and security. They sought self-sufficiency, power, and a name for themselves through building a tower to heaven. True to his promise, God reacted not by destroying but by confusing their language. The Early World closed with God's children scattered in confusion.

We pick up the story in Genesis 12 many generations later, around 2000 BC in Mesopotamia—the territory in and around the Tigris and Euphrates Rivers and their tributaries. It is the Middle Bronze Age. Rival city-states have been united under the kings of Ur. The culture is polytheistic. *Ziggurats* similar to the Tower of Babel are being built in many cities, while in far-away Britain, Stonehenge is under construction. The *Epic of Gilgamesh*[1] was written during this time period and so was the Code of Hammurabi, an ancient law code that gives us insight into the Mesopotamian culture. This part of the world is represented by the "Northern Countries" section of *The Bible Timeline* Chart.

It is from this ancient civilization that God will take one of the descendants of Noah's son Shem, a man named Abram, calling him to leave everything and travel to a new place where God will make of him a nation, a new kind of civilization, that will call on God's name. This is the beginning of the period of the Patriarchs: the fathers of God's Chosen People, the nation of Israel. What will this people be like? Pay attention: The answer foreshadows the kingdom of God.

B. Read the Story

The rest of the book of Genesis tells the story of the Patriarchs and the beginnings of the people of Israel. Patriarchs – Part 1 focuses on the life of Abraham and God's promise to him and his descendants. Part 2 will look at the growth of his family and the passing down of that promise. Read **Genesis 12, 15–18, and 22** to get familiar with the incidents that will be covered in this session. They are (1) the covenant promise God forges with Abraham, which provides an outline for God's plan and the rest of the story and (2) the faith that grows in Abraham from the time he is called, through his struggle with childlessness, to the ultimate test when God asks him to give up the son on whom all God's promises rest. Trace the action in the center section of your *Bible Timeline* Chart. Identify the main characters, and notice the flow of key events and where they take place. Any questions? Jot them down.

Going Deeper (optional): To get the entire story of this time period, read **Genesis 12–24.**

As always, pray before you read.

---

[1]   This great epic poem from ancient Sumeria is one of the earliest-known literary works.

C. Take a Deeper Look

Answering these questions will draw you into the heart of the story. If you do not understand something, make a note of it to bring up in the discussion.

God's Promise to Abram (Genesis 12:1-9)

The genealogy at the close of Genesis 11 narrows the focus down through Shem's line to a seventy-five-year-old man named Abram. God calls Abram to leave his country and people and go to a land he will show him. Look at the map below and trace Abram's journey from Ur (at the mouth of the Tigris and Euphrates Rivers) as far as Haran in the North. This is where Abram is at the start of Genesis 12.

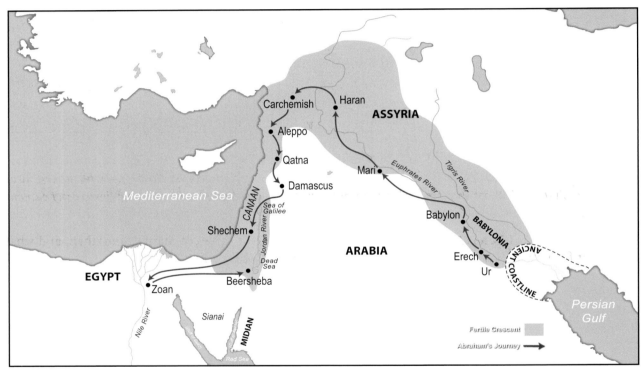

Abraham's Journey

1. Read **Genesis 12:1-3.** What three-part promise does God make to Abram? (Hint: The promise is simplified in the "Abrahamic Covenant" box in the Patriarchs section of your *Bible Timeline* Chart.)

Melchizedek's Blessing

In Genesis 14, Abram returns from a victory and meets Melchizedek, king of Salem, who brings out bread and wine and blesses Abram. Some ancient Jewish and Christian sources have proposed that Melchizedek was none other than Noah's son, Shem, whom we last saw receiving a blessing from his father at the end of Genesis 9. While we do not know whether the ages recorded in Genesis refer to literal numbers of years, those given in Chapter 11 would have Shem living beyond the time of Abram. From the time of Adam until after the Exodus, the firstborn son functioned as both a sort of king and priest of the extended family. If this is indeed Shem, he may, in this scene, be "officially" passing on God's blessing from his authority as firstborn, king, and priest.

The primary importance of Melchizedek, though, is that he is a "type" of Christ. His name means "king of righteousness," and he is king of Salem (which means "peace")—a city that will later become Jerusalem. As a king and priest who receives Abram's tithes and who blesses and gives bread and wine, he prefigures Jesus Christ, the High Priest, enthroned in the heavenly Jerusalem, who blesses us and offers himself in bread and wine. St. Paul draws some parallels between Christ and Melchizedek in Hebrews 7.

From Promise to Covenant (Genesis 15 and 17)

Over the course of several chapters, God makes a series of progressive covenants with Abram to fulfill the promises he made in Chapter 12. A covenant is a solemn, unbreakable, sworn oath that unites two parties in a permanent family bond.

2. Review **Genesis 15 and 17.** Which of the original promises do these covenants strengthen, and what new information does each one add? (See the chart on page 30 for help.)

3. a. Read **Genesis 15:2-6,** in which Abram's faith is counted as righteousness. How might trying to count the stars in the sky help Abram to trust in God's promise, and how is this a profound example of what faith requires? (Hint: What seems to be the time of day, and why does that matter?)

   b. In **Genesis 15:8-21,** why is it significant that God (represented by smoke and fire) passes between the pieces of animal, and how would that reassure Abram? (Read also **Jeremiah 34:17-20.**)

4. Read **Genesis 17:1-23.**

    a. What is to be the significance of circumcision to Abram's family? To what does it bind them?

    b. **New Testament Connection:** Under the New Covenant, the Old Covenant sign of circumcision is replaced by a sacrament, which is a tangible sign that brings into reality (i.e., it "effects") what it signifies. Read **Colossians 2:11-12.** What is that sacrament, and how does it relate to circumcision?

An Impossible Child (Genesis 16–18)

5. Frustrated and probably bewildered at their childlessness in the face of God's promise, Abram and Sarai (newly named Abraham and Sarah) take things into their own hands. In **Genesis 16,** they produce an heir (Ishmael) for Abraham through his servant Hagar. What astonishing promise does God give them in **Genesis 17:15-22 and 18:1-15,** and what will be the role of the promised child (Isaac) in relationship to God's covenant promises?

Sodom and Gomorrah

The infamous account of the destruction of Sodom and Gomorrah and of Lot's wife turning into a pillar of salt is related in Genesis 19. The verses leading up to it in Chapter 18 show Abraham pleading with God to spare the city for the sake of the righteous inside it. These verses are a beautiful example of the mercy of God and the effectiveness of prayer, and they also give us insight into the character of Abraham.

The Ultimate Sacrifice (Genesis 22)

6. By Genesis 22, the promised son has been born and has become a young man. All the hopes of God's covenant rest on Isaac. Read this chapter carefully.

   a. At the beginning of this chapter, the author says that God tests Abraham. What kind of test is it? Is there any way in which this test is similar to the test of Adam and Eve?

   b. Does Abraham pass the test? What is the result?

   c. **Living Tradition:** In Genesis 15, Abraham's faith in God's promise to give him descendants as numerous as the stars was exhibited in his belief. Now, he is being asked to prove that belief by acting on it. Read **CCC 143–147 and 154–155** as well as **James 2:14-23.** What is the relationship between obedience and faith?

7. *Catechism* **Connection:** It is in giving up his son that Abraham becomes the father of the nation that will bless the world. In doing so, he is able to "share in the power of God's love that saves the multitude" (CCC 2572). What does Abraham's act foreshadow, which God will ultimately do? Give as many parallels as you can between the two events.

D. Application

These questions will help you apply one of the key themes of the session to your life. After meditating on them, respond to God with a brief written prayer if you choose.

God proclaims to Abraham and Sarah that he will give them a son. When they hear this, Sarah laughs with unbelief (Genesis 18:12). Are there issues in your life at which you laugh in response to God's promises? What from Abraham's life can you take on your faith journey?

Dear Lord …

The Covenantal Structure of Salvation History

The charts below diagram the way salvation history can be viewed as unfolding through a series of covenants God makes with his people. Adam and Eve were created in a close relationship with God that was shattered at the Fall, a relationship that is later most closely imaged by families and by bonds of kinship created through covenantal promises. God moves to restore humanity to relationship with himself by means of a series of covenants.

The first diagram shows how God later expands on aspects of the initial promise he made to Abraham in Genesis 12. Each of these covenantal promises to Abraham and his descendants (of land, kingdom, and worldwide blessing) is fulfilled in a future covenant: the Mosaic Covenant, the Davidic Covenant, and the New Covenant in Jesus Christ.

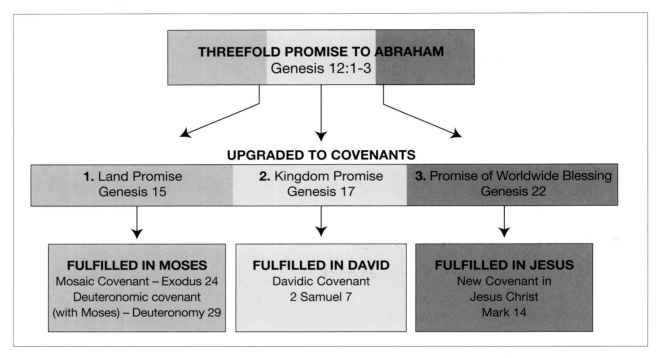

This diagram shows the progressive growth of God's family from One Holy Couple to One, Holy, Catholic, and Apostolic Church, illustrated by means of these same covenants:

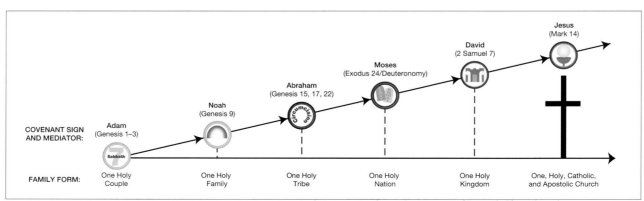

Session 4 Talk Notes

Patriarchs – Part 1

I. Introduction to Patriarchs – Part 1

II. Test and Promise

A. God calls Abram from Ur of the Chaldees (Genesis 12:1)

    1. Abram's background (see also Joshua 24:2-3)

        a. The centrality of blessing

    2. Abram's problem: Sarai is barren

    3. Abram's "insurance policy": Lot

    4. Abram's destination: the strategic land of Canaan

        a. Roughly the size of New Jersey

        b. Connects North to South

        c. Flowing with milk and honey

B. God's promises to Abram (Genesis 12:2-3)

    1. Three promises to his seed (descendants)

        a. Land

        b. Kingdom ("I will make your name great" – implies dynasty)

        c. Worldwide blessing

    2. The problem: Abram has no seed or land; Sarai is barren

C. Testing and blessing

    1. Famine and trip to Egypt (Genesis 12:10-20)

        a. Return to Bethel

    2. Abram and Lot separate (Genesis 13)

    3. Melchizedek ("my kingdom is righteous") blesses Abram (Genesis 14)

        a. King of Salem (later *Jeru-salem*)

        b. A priest of God Most High who blesses Abram

        c. "A priest forever according to the order of Melchizedek" – Hebrews 7:1-3

III. God's Covenant with Abraham: A Blueprint for the Rest of the Story

   A. The Land Promise deepened (Genesis 15)

      1. "Count the stars, if you are able" (belief reckoned as righteousness)

      2. "Bring me a heifer" – the meaning of covenant

         a. All covenants extend kinship bonds (Frank Moore Cross, Jr.)

         b. God's covenants bind his family to himself

      3. The covenant ritual and the meaning of blood sacrifice

      4. What is implicit in Genesis 12 becomes explicit in Genesis 15, 17, 22

   B. Another "insurance policy": Hagar (Genesis 16)

      1. Ishmael, father of the Arab nations (God as master)

      2. Similarities in language to the Fall narrative

   C. The Kingdom Promise deepened (Genesis 17)

      1. Abram ("exalted father") and Sarai – renamed Abraham ("father of many nations") and Sarah

      2. Circumcision: the sign of the covenant

      3. Kings shall come forth from you

      4. A son promised: Isaac = "laughter" (Genesis 18)

   D. Abraham intercedes for Sodom and Gomorrah (Genesis 19)

   E. The ultimate test and a covenant of worldwide blessing (Genesis 22)

      1. God tests Abraham: "Take your son, your only begotten son Isaac"

      2. Looking for the Lamb

      3. YHWH *jireh* – God will provide

IV. The Family Grows: A Wife for Isaac (Genesis 24)

A. Review the Context

At the start of the Patriarchs period, God took the descendants of Shem—one of Noah's sons in the Holy Family with which God made a covenant after the Flood—and formed them into One Holy Tribe through Abraham and sealed their relationship with the sign of circumcision. In this covenant, God promised three things to Abraham and his descendants: land, a kingdom, and that they would be the source of worldwide blessing. From this point on, we will be looking for those promises to be fulfilled.

Due to Abraham's obedience, a giant step was taken toward the solution to the problem—toward fixing the broken relationship with God—that occurred at the Fall. Adam and Eve said "no" to God, but Abraham said "yes." His repeated, "Here am I," in Genesis 22 underlines his willingness to do God's will whatever the cost, as does the fact that he offered up his only son. In Eden, Adam and Eve lost God's friendship. But the New Testament author James writes that Abraham, who acted on what he believed, was called the *friend* of God (2:23). This patriarch is a model of faith. As such, he can truly be called the father of not just those who descend from him by blood but of all who believe. This is our story, not just the story of Israel. God's plan to restore his family is not built on a blood relationship but on the ties of faith.

There is a lot of movement on the geographical "stage" during this time period. If you have not done so already, familiarize yourself with the way movement is shown on the *Bible Timeline* Chart. In general, major movement from one location to another is demonstrated by the movements of the red genealogy line (and sometimes by the colored arrows). For example, between the Early World and Patriarchs periods, the line shows Abram obeying God's call to leave Ur and move south to the land of Canaan. Later in the Patriarchs period, we see Jacob fleeing from Canaan northward to Haran and then back to Canaan before traveling south into Egypt at the close of the period. The horizontal band at the center of the Chart represents Canaan; from this point on, whenever God's people are there, they are in the land promised to Abraham and his descendants.

B. Read the Story

Patriarchs – Part 2, which covers the rest of Genesis, shows how God's covenant promise passes down through the generations. This session is best done in more than one sitting. **Read Genesis 25, 28, 29, and 32** before you answer questions 1 to 4 about Jacob, who becomes father of the twelve tribes of Israel. Then read **Chapters 37–50** before answering the remaining questions about Jacob's son Joseph, who is sold into slavery and is raised to a position from which he can save the surrounding world from famine. Trace the action in the center section of your *Bible Timeline* Chart. Identify the main characters, and notice the flow of key events and where they take place. Any questions? Jot them down.

Going Deeper (optional): To get the entire story of this period, read **Genesis 25–50.**

As always, pray before you read.

C. Take a Deeper Look

Answering these questions will draw you into the heart of the story. If you do not understand something, make a note of it to bring up in the discussion.

Birthright and Blessing

Ancient inheritance laws gave special rights to the firstborn son. On a man's death, his firstborn son received a double portion of the inheritance and took over as head of the family, acting as both "priest" and "king" for the extended family circle. As head, he had authority over other family members and also took responsibility for younger brothers and unmarried sisters. These rights and responsibilities were sacrosanct. They could be sold or shifted to another only by the son's consent or at the father's direction. This "birthright" (*bekhorah* in Hebrew) generally came also with a "blessing" (*berakhah*). In our story, this blessing carries with it the covenant promises of the LORD.

Jacob (Genesis 25–36)

1. Read **Genesis 25.**

   a. The lives of these early people often exhibit what will be true of the nations that come from them. In Genesis 25, God tells Rebekah that the twins jostling in her womb will become two struggling nations, and that the nation that springs from the elder will be weaker and will serve the nation that comes from the younger. How is this demonstrated in the lives of Jacob and Esau far before they give rise to nations?

   Esau seemed to give up his birthright rather easily to replace his hunger. This showed weakness in my eyes.

   b. In choosing which son of Isaac to bless, God goes against ancient laws that give the eldest son leadership in the family. Does God choose Jacob because of his own merit? How do you know?

   He chose Jacob before he was born – before he could do good or bad

   c. Why do you think God does this? (Read also **Romans 9:10-13** and **CCC 218.**)

2. **Think About It:** The "ladder" in Jacob's dream (Genesis 28) is likely the stepped sides of a tall, sloping tower known as a *ziggurat*. Think back to the last time you saw such a tower, in Genesis 11. Compare and contrast this event with the previous one. What does the comparison tell you about what God desires for and from his people?

   God desires greatness not only for themselves but to serve him.

3. Read **Genesis 29.** Fleeing Esau's wrath, Jacob goes north to Haran to live with his mother's family. (This movement out of Canaan is represented by the names of Jacob's sons in the "12 Sons of Israel" box in the Patriarchs section of your *Bible Timeline* Chart.) How does Jacob get back what he dished out to his brother?

By having to serve Laban another Seven years - It is not the custom to give the younger daughter before the firstborn.

4. Jacob's years in Haran are arduous, and Jacob continues to wrestle with Laban and a contentious home life. Nevertheless, God blesses him with twelve sons and a daughter and increases his flocks and herds. After a time, and in obedience to God's call, he sets out for home.

   a. Read **Genesis 32.** What does Jacob learn about God in his midnight wrestling match?

   b. To name something in ancient times meant you had dominion over that thing. When God renames Abraham, the new name marks him as God's servant and also indicates the role he will play as patriarch. What is the significance of Jacob's new, God-given name?

   Jacob is now known as The face of God! or Israel (depending on translation)

Joseph (Genesis 37–50)

5. Jacob (Israel) is now the father of twelve sons from whom will come the twelve tribes of Israel. Read **Genesis 37–50.** This "account of Jacob" focuses on Joseph, who is his eleventh son and the firstborn son of his beloved wife, Rachel. As were those before him, Joseph is tested. In spite of dreams indicating that he will rule over his brothers, circumstances are against him for years. The question is still, "Will you trust God?" How does he fare?

6. Taken together, Genesis 38 and 39 present a curious juxtaposition of events in the lives of Joseph and his older brother, Judah. How would you compare and contrast the two men based on these chapters?

7. Follow Jesus' genealogy line (the red line) on your *Bible Timeline* Chart through the Patriarchs period. Which son of Jacob does it go through, and which grandson? Do you notice anything unusual?

Judah and Joseph: A Study in Contrast?

Does it surprise you to learn that from these two very different men, Judah and Joseph, will come the two leading tribes of Israel (Judah in the South, and Ephraim—Joseph's son—in the North)? A review of Genesis 48 and 49, in which Jacob blesses his sons and predicts their future, tells of the prominence of Ephraim and the rich blessing on Joseph, and assigns sovereignty to the tribe of Judah (Genesis 49:8-12): "Your father's sons shall bow down before you," Jacob says. "The scepter shall not depart from Judah, nor the ruler's staff from between his feet, until he comes to whom it belongs; and to him shall be the obedience of the peoples." The "scepter" points to the universal kingship that will belong one day to the "lion of the tribe of Judah," Jesus Christ.

8. After Jacob's death, his brothers ask forgiveness and offer themselves to Joseph as slaves. Read Joseph's reply in **Genesis 50:19-20.** What can Joseph see that his brothers do not? What gives him this perspective? *That Joseph is in the place of God (Heaven)*

9. **Think About It:** Genesis closes with the reconciliation of a father and his sons, even as it began with a shattered relationship. Thinking back over Joseph's life, can you see how he is a "forerunner" of Jesus? List as many parallels as you can find between the two. *Forgave all who trespassed upon him.*

10. By the end of Genesis, what progress has been made toward the fulfillment of God's promises to Abraham? *By allowing him many descendants & the land of Canaan.*

D. Application

These questions will help you apply one of the key themes of the session to your life. After meditating on them, respond to God with a brief written prayer if you choose.

Do circumstances in your life threaten to pull your eyes off God and away from his promises? Do you feel helpless or abandoned by God? Is guilt enslaving you? What can you learn from the story of Joseph that will help you?

Dear Lord …

E. Wrap-Up

Conclude your study of the Patriarchs period, and fix it in your mind by doing the following:

1. Recall the color of this time period, burgundy, and think of it in terms of your reading to help you remember it.

2. Quickly review Sessions 4 and 5. Write a brief summary of what the Patriarchs period is about or its significance as part of the "big picture."

*many wives
Slaves / children by se—
servants were the
father of produce a son
Through Hagar*

Session 5 Talk Notes

Patriarchs – Part 2

I. Introduction to Patriarchs – Part 2

II. Jacob and Esau (Genesis 25:29-34)

    A. Birthright = leadership, responsibility, and double inheritance

        1. Esau sells his birthright for a bowl of stew

            a. Hebrews 12:16-17 (NAB): Esau was "a profane man" (treated the holy as common)

    B. Blessing = prosperity, vitality, fertility

        1. Rebekah and Jacob cheat Esau out of the blessing

    C. Consequences of Jacob's deception: What you sow is what you will reap

III. Jacob in Exile (Genesis 28–30)

    A. The ladder and the blessing (28:10-22)

    B. Jacob is "Jacobed" (29:1-30)

    C. Jacob's twelve sons (listed in birth order, by mother)

        1. Leah: Reuben, Simeon, Levi, Judah
        2. Bilhah: Dan, Naphtali
        3. Zilpah: Gad, Asher
        4. Leah: Issachar, Zebulun
        5. Rachel: Joseph, Benjamin

IV. Jacob Returns to Canaan (Genesis 31–34)

    A. Jacob wrestles with God at Peniel ("the face of God")

        1. Jacob renamed "Israel": "He who strives with God"

    B. Jacob encounters Esau (Edom)

    C. Rape and revenge at Shechem (Chapter 34)

V. Joseph (Genesis 35–50)

    A. Joseph's coat

    B. Joseph's dreams

    C. Joseph sold into slavery (Chapter 37)

    D. Judah and Joseph: two brothers contrasted (Genesis 38–39)

        1. Judah and daughter-in-law Tamar

        2. Joseph and Potiphar's wife

        3. Parallels and contrasts

    E. Joseph in prison (Genesis 39–41)

        1. More dreams: the butler (cupbearer) and the baker

        2. Pharaoh's dream

    F. Joseph set over the land of Egypt (Genesis 41ff)

        1. *Al ha-bayit* = "over the household"

VI. Joseph and His Brothers (Genesis 42–45)

    A. Famine and testing

    B. Judah steps up

    C. Resolution

VII. Jacob's Family Moves to Egypt: The Blessing Passed Down (Genesis 47–50)

VIII. Conclusion

A. Establish the Context

During the period of the Patriarchs, God raised up fathers for the new family he was calling to himself: Abraham, Isaac, Jacob (later named "Israel"), and Joseph. We remember this period, which is described in Genesis 12–50, by the color burgundy, which represents the blood of the covenant God made with Abraham. This covenant provided a blueprint of God's plan of salvation: God would make of Abraham a great nation, giving him many descendants and a land to live in. One day, they would become an everlasting kingdom that would bring blessing to all nations on earth.

We learn this through stories that convey deep truths about the nature of God's family. Consider that God called Abraham "out of the blue" to leave his comfortable home and travel to a strange place, where he made him a great promise. This was not Abraham's doing but God's. God continued to demonstrate his sovereign choice and initiative by fulfilling his promise through Isaac, the impossible child of his choice, rather than through Ishmael, the child of Abraham and Sarah's planning. God then chose Jacob over his older twin, Esau—right from the womb—before Jacob had done anything to deserve it. And to this unlikely man, God gave twelve sons and began building a nation that would call on his name, not exalt its own. The fact that Israel was chosen from among all the nations to bring them blessing had nothing to do with Israel's merit; it had everything to do with the love of the Father. It is the same today with the Church.

The last patriarch, Joseph, gives us a picture of the way Israel would one day bless the world through Jesus. Just as Joseph was raised quite literally from a pit to power at the right hand of Pharaoh, a position from which he reunited his brothers with their father and provided food to the world, so Jesus is later raised from the pit of death to sit at God's right hand, a position from which he reunites his brethren with the Father and provides spiritual food to the world.

With the Israelites back in Egypt after Joseph's death, God's promises hang in the air. Israel is growing, but the family has left the Promised Land and—to our knowledge, for nothing is recorded in Scripture—hears nothing from God for four hundred years. Has God forgotten them? It must feel that way when a new pharaoh rises to power and makes them his slaves. The people cry out to God. Can they trust him? Will he remember his promises? The next historical period is called Egypt and Exodus. For the bulk of it, nothing happens except that the family of Israel grows. What happens at the end is the greatest, most important event in Jewish (Old Testament) history. We will read about it in the book of Exodus.

B. Read the Story

Exodus 1–18 acquaints us with the main characters and events of Part 1 of Egypt and Exodus, which deals with Israel's redemption from slavery. Read **Exodus 3–5, 7, 11–12, 14, 16, and 17** before you answer the questions. These chapters will give you the highlights of this period: God revealing himself to Moses and calling him to deliver his children from Egyptian slavery; some of the ten plagues; the Passover and the Red Sea crossing; and God's provision in the desert. Trace the action in the center section of your *Bible Timeline* Chart. Identify the main characters, and notice the flow of key events and where they take place. Any questions? Jot them down.

Going Deeper (optional): To get the entire story of this period, read **Exodus 1–18.**

As always, pray before you read.

C. Take a Deeper Look

Answering these questions will draw you into the heart of the story. If you do not understand something, make a note of it to bring up in the discussion.

God Reveals Himself (Exodus 1–4)

Exodus 1–2 tells of Israel's plight in Egypt and the birth of Moses, the man God will call on to deliver them. Moses is saved from the Pharaoh's edict that all Hebrew boys be killed in childbirth and is then raised by Pharaoh's daughter in the royal court. As a grown man, he flees the country after killing an Egyptian he sees beating a Hebrew. He lives forty years as a shepherd in Midian (in the desert of southeastern Sinai and west central Arabia), where he is at the start of Chapter 3.

Back in the time of the Patriarchs, God declined to reveal his name to Jacob. Some four hundred years later, as God prepares to wrest Israel from the hand of Pharaoh, he tells Moses the name by which he wants his people to know him: in Hebrew, YHWH (pronounced Yahweh) from the Hebrew verb "to be." It means, "I AM," or "I am he who is," or "I am who I am." It has no tense and encompasses all tenses. It can mean equally "I AM WHO I AM" or "I WILL BE WHAT I WILL BE."

1. a. Read **Exodus 3.** What might Moses have learned about God in this encounter, particularly in the revelation of God's name? List as many things as you can think of. (To read what the *Catechism* says about God's name, see CCC 206.)

    Perform miracles to moses
    God will be with him when going to Egypt? Will give
    power to moses to perform miracles.
    The name is mysterious – as God is a mystery & above all.

    b. When Pharaoh responds to Moses by increasing the people's work, and they blame Moses, he crawls back to God in despair. God repeats his name and expands on his earlier revelation. Read **Exodus 6:1-8.** What extension of his name does God proclaim in using the words "I AM" and "I WILL"? List them. What effect should knowing these have on Moses and the people?

    God states; "I" Punish Egypt & Free you
    "I AM THE LORD" Bring you into the promised land
    WILL BE YOUR GOD

2. Read **Exodus 3:18 and 4:21-23.** What message does God send to Pharaoh, and what does it say about Israel's relationship to God and to the other nations?

    To let his people go to worship God
    ISRAEL is First Born – Let my first born
    go to serve me.
    First Born – Heirarchy Importance

3. "Let my son go *(halak)* that he may serve *(obed)* me," says God in Exodus 4:23. "Go *(halak)* now, and work *(obed)*," replies Pharaoh (Exodus 5:18). Who is this battle between, and what are the stakes?

    God & Pharaoh
    Pharaoh puts himself above GOD

God Delivers Israel (Exodus 5–15)

4. a. God sends Egypt signs and plagues to display his power and to convince Pharaoh to let his children go. Read **Exodus 7:8-13.** What should be clear to Pharaoh in this initial sign from God? (Note: The snake was the emblem of divine majesty in Egypt and could be seen in the image of a cobra on Pharaoh's crown. Wadjet, the cobra goddess, was protector of the pharaoh.) The Hebrew used here, *tannin,* can also be translated "crocodile" or "dragon," and the pharaohs identified themselves with the strength and power of the crocodile god, *Sobek.*

That God is all powerful & will win out in the end.

b. Ancient Egyptians worshiped many gods. Hapi, representing the spirit and essence of the Nile, was one of several associated with the river considered to be the sacred lifeline of Egypt, its source and sustainer. The frog-headed goddess, Heqt, goddess of fertility, was believed to assist women in childbirth and control the frog population. The greatest of gods was the sun, called Aton or Amon-Ra, who ruled and protected by day, but was thought to sleep when he disappeared at night. What message do you think God sends with the plagues?

There is only one God & he controls all life, not ~~God's~~ the God's created by the Egyptians.

Who Hardens Pharaoh's Heart?

Exodus tells us ten times that Pharaoh hardens his own heart and then ten more times that God hardens the heart of Pharaoh. Which is it? Ultimately, the answer lies somewhere within the mystery of God's providence and mankind's free will. A metaphor that can help us understand this is the effect of the sun upon different materials. Exposed to the sun's warmth, wax becomes pliable and can be molded and shaped into something of use or beauty. If you leave clay in the sun, however, it soon becomes too hard to use. In one sense, the sun is responsible for the clay's hardened state. But to say Pharaoh's heart hardens when exposed to God's commands says more about the nature of his heart than it does about God.

The Egyptian Book of the Dead tells us that the Egyptians believed that at death, one's heart was weighed in a balance against a feather representing truth and righteousness. Any heart weighed down by sin was too "heavy" (the literal translation of one of the words used here for "hardened") to remain on the scale and be admitted to the afterlife. Ultimately, this story is not about whether God or man is responsible for heavy hearts; it is about the way different hearts respond to his will and the result.

5.   a.   The tenth plague, the death of the firstborn, brings about the Passover. It calls for extensive preparation, each element signifying some aspect of the people's redemption (bitter herbs for the bitterness of slavery, for example). Read **Exodus 12.** Israel is to obey God's instructions and "keep this service" (observe this rite) as a lasting ordinance. This word, "service," is the same word used in Chapter 1 for slavery. Explain how this new "service" to God will differ from service to Pharaoh.

Passover will be to honor God & give service to him.

   b.   **New Testament Connection:** Today, we show our "service" to God through the liturgy, which literally is "the work of the people." We eat bread and drink wine (in reality, the Body and Blood of Christ) as a memorial of Christ's sacrifice, similar to the way Israel, at Passover, ate lamb as a memorial of the Passover sacrifice. Read **John 1:29; Matthew 26:27-28; 1 Peter 1:17-19;** and **1 Corinthians 5:7-8.** Describe the correlation between the Passover lamb and Jesus.

It is the Body & Blood of Christ.

6.   **Think About It:** The story of Israel's deliverance from Egypt, including the Passover and the crossing of the Red Sea, was used in the early Church for catechesis in preparing adults to be baptized. How does it help you understand what it means to be saved from sin and born again as God's child?

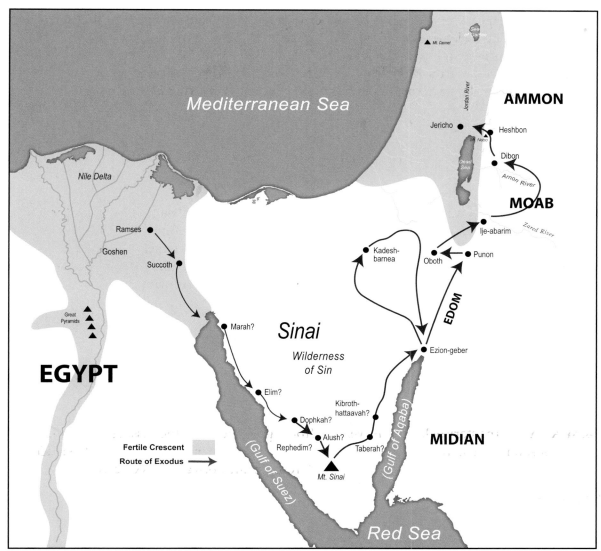

Proposed Routes of the Exodus and Desert Wanderings
(The exact route across the Red Sea is not known for certain)

The Journey to Sinai (Exodus 16–18)

The people's glorious song of deliverance in Exodus 15 shows that they know God is their strong deliverer and that he will establish them according to his promise. But there is a difference between knowing and doing. They have been slaves for hundreds of years. They do not know how to live as God's people. In many ways, they are like little children who must learn to rely on him for all their needs.

7. a. Read **Exodus 16.** When God tells Moses he will send bread from heaven (manna) every day, he says he will do it to prove or test the people, to see whether they will follow his Law. What are the rules governing the gathering of manna, and what are they meant to teach?

b.   Read **John 6,** and describe the relationship between the manna of Exodus and the "bread from heaven" in John.

8.   Read **1 Corinthians 10:1-4.** How does St. Paul understand the water from the rock described in Exodus 17?

D. Application

These questions will help you apply one of the key themes of the session to your life. After meditating on them, respond to God with a brief written prayer if you choose.

Do you know God by name? Meditate on "yhwh" and what it means. Jesus also is "I am." In John 8:58, he says, "Before Abraham was born, I am!" At other times he says, "I am": the good shepherd; the bread of life; the light of the world; the Way, the Truth, and the Life. He *is* all of these things. What difference does that make to you?

Dear Lord …

Session 6 Talk Notes

Egypt and Exodus – Part 1

I. Introduction to Egypt and Exodus – Part 1

II. God Calls Moses (Exodus 1–4)

A. Egyptian oppression of God's firstborn, Israel

B. The birth of Moses (*Moshe,* "to draw out")

C. Moses flees to the wilderness

D. The burning bush (Exodus 3)

    1. *Theophany* (Gk., "appearance of God")

        a. The God of Abraham, Isaac, and Jacob

        b. I have seen their affliction

        c. I will send you; I will be with you

        d. Sign – You will worship God on this mountain

    2. God reveals his name: YHWH *(yod he vav he),* "I AM WHO I AM"

        a. Name gives access

        b. The alpha and omega, the *aleph* and the *tav*

        c. The *Tetragrammaton,* the unpronounceable name

E. The request – a three-days' journey to worship God

III. The Battle for Israel: "Let My Son Go that He May Serve Me" (Exodus 5–6)

A. Will they "work" *(avad)* for Pharaoh or "serve" *(avad)* God?

B. Pharaoh's heart is "hardened"

C. Pharaoh: "I do not know the LORD" (5:2)

    1. Pharaoh increases the load, denies rest and worship

IV. The Ten Plagues (Exodus 7–12)

A. A strike against the false gods of Egypt

B. The tenth plague – death of Egypt's firstborn (Chapter 12; see Numbers 33:4)

    1. Preparations for the Passover

    a. "Take a lamb"

    b. Inspect it from the tenth to the fourteenth days of Nissan

    c. At twilight (3 PM), sacrifice the lamb

    d. Roast the lamb and eat it

    e. Take the blood, put it on lintels of house

    f. Prepare unleavened bread

    g. Gird loins, put on sandals

  2. Death of the Egyptian firstborn

  C. Consecration of the Hebrew firstborn (Exodus 13)

V. Crossing the Red Sea (Exodus 14–15)

  A. The single most important redemptive event in Israel's history

  B. Importance to Christians: Jesus is the Paschal Lamb

  1. Crossing through water prefigures baptism (CCC 1094, 1221)

  2. Passover meal prefigures Eucharist

VI. God's Provision in the Desert (Exodus 16–17)

  A. Manna

  1. Deuteronomy 8:16: God's purpose for the manna (see also 2 Corinthians 2:9)

  2. (Heb., *man hu,* "what is it?"; *man,* "what?")

  3. John 6: more bread in the wilderness. What is it?

  4. Teaching them to trust

  B. Victory over enemies (battle against the Amalekites – Chapter 17)

  1. "Faith" = *emunah*

VII. Conclusion: Freedom from Slavery and to Free Life as God's Children

A. Review the Context

In Part 1 of Egypt and Exodus, God called Moses to deliver his firstborn son, Israel, from Egyptian slavery to serve him. In the process, he revealed his name to Israel—YHWH, "I AM"—and freed them in such a way that the full impact of that name was displayed before Egypt as well. In a series of plagues, he exposed the gods of Egypt to be the imitations they were and showed himself to be both the source and the sustenance of all life and power. God brought his people safely through the Red Sea and drowned the enemy behind them—a picture of our baptism, by which we are freed from the power of sin and reborn through water to a new life in Christ.

The "red" of the Red Sea gives us a color by which to remember this period. If Part 1 showed us how God redeemed Israel, Part 2 shows us how God establishes it as a nation so his people can live as the free children of God. This is vital knowledge for us, because Christians are the successors of Israel, members of the kingdom that God promised would be a source of his blessing to the world. Freedom from Egypt did not mean Israel automatically started to live like God's children should. In the same way, being freed from the power of sin through baptism into God's family is a big step, but it is not everything. The travels and trials Israel faces en route to the Promised Land—and the way God prepares them to face these—are an image of our journey to heaven and give us guidance on the way.

As you read through the rest of Exodus, notice that God does not free Israel from slavery and then send them off as individuals to make their way to Canaan as best as they can. He forms them into a people, gives them laws to guide their behavior and worship, and provides them with a leadership structure. They are to march forth together, not under their own power but with the power of God. That is why we have the Church. We are all in this together.

B. Read the Story

In the second half of Exodus, God's people become a nation and are given the Law, the Tabernacle, and the Levitical priesthood. Read **Exodus 19, 20, 23–25, 32–34, and 40** for the highlights of this time period. Trace the action in the center section of your *Bible Timeline* Chart. Identify the main characters, and notice the flow of key events and where they take place. Any questions? Jot them down.

Going Deeper (optional): To get the entire story of this period, read **Exodus 19–40.**

As always, pray before you read.

C. Take a Deeper Look

Answering these questions will draw you into the heart of the story. If you do not understand something, make a note of it to bring up in the discussion.

Rules to Live By (Exodus 19–24)

If the question, "Who will you serve?" defined Egypt and Exodus – Part 1, then the question in Part 2 might be, "How will you serve?" The children of Israel spend an entire year at the base of Mount Sinai after leaving Egypt. During that time, they meet God, hear his voice, and become his people.

1. Previously, God promised to make of Israel a nation and a kingdom. In Exodus 19:1-6, what kind of nation and kingdom does he say they will be if they obey him and keep his covenant? What impact does he plan for his "firstborn son," Israel, to have on the world?

   That they will be priests of the Lord, to serve him & spread his word.

   Mount Sinai is thought to be the same mountain on which Moses met God in the burning bush. This time, the whole top of the mountain is burning with God's holy fire. Moses meets God there and receives what we know as the Ten Commandments, written by the finger of God on two tablets of stone. These are commands that liberate. They tell the newly freed slaves how to live as redeemed people in order to keep from falling back into bondage.

The Ten Commandments

The following list of the Ten Commandments is from Deuteronomy 5:6-21, from which the traditional Catholic numbering is derived. The commandments also appear in a slightly different form in Exodus 20:2-17.

1. I am the LORD your God, who brought you out of the land of Egypt, out of the house of bondage. You shall have no other gods before me. You shall not make for yourself a graven image, or any likeness of anything that is in heaven above, or that is on the earth beneath, or that is in the water under the earth; you shall not bow down to them or serve them; for I the LORD your God am a jealous God, visiting the iniquity of the fathers upon the children to the third and fourth generation of those who hate me, but showing steadfast love to thousands of those who love me and keep my commandments.

2. You shall not take the name of the LORD your God in vain: for the LORD will not hold him guiltless who takes his name in vain.

3. Observe the sabbath day, to keep it holy, as the LORD your God commanded you. Six days you shall labor, and do all your work; but the seventh day is a sabbath to the LORD your God; in it you shall not do any work, you, or your son, or your daughter, or your manservant, or your maidservant, or your ox, or your ass, or any of your cattle, or the sojourner who is within your gates, that your manservant and your maidservant may rest as well as you. You shall remember that you were a servant in the land of Egypt, and the LORD your God brought you out thence with a mighty hand and an outstretched arm; therefore the LORD your God commanded you to keep the sabbath day.

4. Honor your father and your mother, as the LORD your God commanded you; that your days may be prolonged, and that it may go well with you, in the land which the LORD your God gives you.

5. You shall not kill.

6. Neither shall you commit adultery.

7. Neither shall you steal.

8. Neither shall you bear false witness against your neighbor.

9. Neither shall you covet your neighbor's wife.

10. You shall not desire your neighbor's house, his field, or his manservant, or his maidservant, his ox, or his ass, or anything that is your neighbor's.

---

2. a. How do the commandments in **Exodus 20:2-11** summarize the lessons of Israel's delivery from Egypt?

That God alone is the one that saved them from slavery.

b. How do the rest of the commandments follow on or relate to the first set?

That God gave everything to us & we need to live according to his rules & teachings.

Exodus 21–23 are called "the Book of the Covenant"—a list of ordinances that apply the basic laws found in the Ten Commandments to everyday situations that Israel will face as a nation. In Chapter 24, Israel enters a covenant with God; the Law they receive is, in effect, the terms Israel agrees to.

3. Read **Exodus 23,** which emphasizes the importance of worshiping God alone, keeping the prescribed feasts, and obeying and serving God. What does it say will be the benefit to Israel of doing this?

They will have plenty of food & drink, healthy children, long lives. They will be protected from their enemies

4. **New Testament Connection:** The Israelites tend to be anxious about what they will eat and drink and how they will fare against their enemies. After years of slavery, they look first for human solutions to their needs. But now, as God's people, they must learn that if they put God first in their lives, he will watch over them.

Read **Luke 12:16-31.** How is this concept of giving priority to God preserved in the New Covenant?

If we seek God's kingdom & live according to Gods will, All things we need will be provided to us.

Rules for Worship (Exodus 25–31)

5. At the top of Mount Sinai, God gives Moses explicit directions for building a portable tent of meeting called a "tabernacle" (literally, "dwelling place") and its furnishings.

a. Read **Exodus 29:42-46.** What is the purpose of the Tabernacle, which will distinguish Israel from all nations on earth? (See also **Exodus 33:14-16.**)

The place where sacrifices are made to God ~~at the entrance of meeting place~~ where God will will meet the Israelites. God will be with them & by being with them it will show other nations that Israel is special

The Tabernacle in the Wilderness

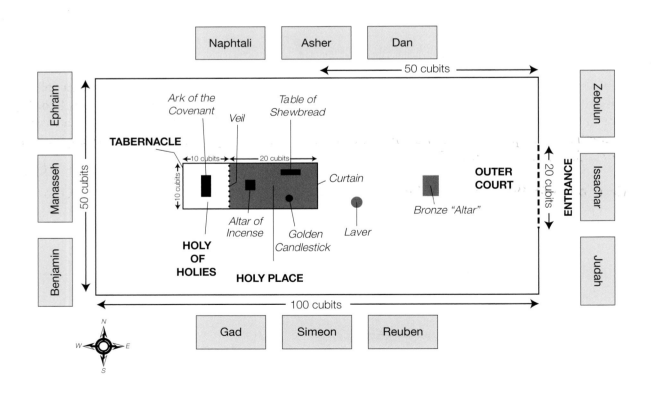

Plan of the Tabernacle (Exodus 40:16-34) and Arrangement of Tribal Camps (Numbers 2)

b. Exodus 25 describes the most important piece of furniture in the Tabernacle, the Ark of the Covenant, which is given pride of place in the Holy of Holies. This symbolizes the throne of God; it is the place where God will come down and speak. Read **Exodus 16:33-34 and 25:10-22** and **Hebrews 9:4.** What items are to be placed in the Ark?

Manna in a jar
Sacred chest for the commandments
An Acacia Table
Lampstand

6. **New Testament Connection:** Read **Revelation 11:19–12:6.**

a. Describe the woman in this passage. Who does she represent, and how do you know?

Mary . Because it states she bore a male child that would rule all nations

b. **Think About It:** Revelation 11:19 seems to indicate that this woman can also be seen as the New Testament fulfillment of the Ark of the Covenant. Is there any way in which the contents of the Ark support that idea?

A New Priesthood (Exodus 32–40)

7. Forty days after pledging to be God's people forever, the people get impatient and construct a golden calf to worship. God intends to consume them **(Exodus 32).** Read this chapter, and then review **Exodus 5:22–6:8,** about a time when Moses believed God had "done evil" to the people (when Moses had asked Pharaoh to let the people go and worship, and instead, he earned impossible work for the people and a no-confidence vote for himself).

Think About It: What does the golden calf incident draw out from Moses that he lacked in Exodus 5, and on what basis does he appeal for God's mercy?

By appealing to God by saying that if he destroys them, The Egyptians will think that they were freed just so God could get rid of them.

8. Up until this time, the firstborn of each family unit acted as a priest for the family. As a result of the golden calf incident, the tribes are, in a sense, "laicized." No longer will each family have its own priest, but the priests will come from the tribe of Levi. What attributes do you see in the Levites that qualify them to be priests?

9. **New Testament Connection:** The end of Exodus describes what happens when work is completed on the Tabernacle: "The cloud covered the tent of meeting, and the glory of the LORD filled the tabernacle" (Exodus 40:34). From that time on, the cloud and fire lead them on their journeys, a visible affirmation of the presence of God. This is not the first time God's presence has been shown by fire or cloud (remember the burning bush in Exodus 3; the cloud and fire on Mount Sinai in Exodus 24; and the cloud that descended to Moses' tent when God spoke with Moses in Exodus 33). Keeping these in mind, read **CCC 696–697.** Who later fulfills these Old Testament figures, and how?

Jesus; by showing himself to his disciples.

D. Application

These questions will help you apply one of the key themes of the session to your life. After meditating on them, respond to God with a brief written prayer if you choose.

The incident of the golden calf shows that it is one thing to bring Israel out of Egypt, but it is another to get Egypt out of Israel. God's children will continue to struggle with an attraction to other gods. You might not be tempted to erect a golden calf in your living room, but are there other things, ideas, or people you give credit for God's work in your life? Are there other things you put before him? How can the lessons Israel learned in these early years help you today?

Dear Lord …

E. Wrap-Up

Conclude your study of Egypt and Exodus, and fix it in your mind by doing the following:

1. Recall the color of this time period, red, and think of it in terms of your reading to help you remember it.
2. Quickly review Sessions 6 and 7. Write a brief summary of what the Egypt and Exodus period is about or its significance as part of the "big picture."

Session 7 Talk Notes

Egypt and Exodus – Part 2

I. Introduction to Egypt and Exodus – Part 2

A. God will give Israel its identity (Exodus 19:6 – "a kingdom of priests and a holy nation")

   1. "Priest" = *kohen,* plural, *kohanim*

B. God will give Israel the Law, the Tabernacle, the Sabbath

II. God Enters into a Covenant with Israel: One Holy Nation (Exodus 19–24)

A. God offers to make Israel his own (Exodus 19:6)

B. The terms of the covenant

   1. Law

      a. *Torah:* from Hebrew root *yarah,* "to throw or to cast"; "to shoot at a target"

      b. Understand Law in the context of the covenant and relationship

      c. To sin: *chet,* "to miss the mark"

   2. Ten Commandments (Exodus 20)

      a. The First Commandment: "Have no other gods before me"

         i. Our vocation is to manifest God to the world (CCC 2085)

         ii. Prohibition against divination (CCC 2116)

         iii. Prohibition against graven images: changes with the incarnation of Christ (CCC 2130–2131)

   3. The Book of the Covenant (Exodus 21–23) – treatment of sojourners

C. The covenant sealed (Exodus 24)

III. God Gives Them a Pattern for Worship and the Tabernacle (Exodus 25–31)

IV. The Covenant Broken and the Consequences (Exodus 32)

A. The golden calf

   1. Moses intercedes for the people

      a. On the basis of God's reputation

      b. On the basis of God's covenant promise

    2. God repents: *shuv* (Heb., "to turn or return") or *metanoia* (Gk., "to change one's mind, repent")

    3. Why does nothing happen to Aaron?

  B. Institution of the Levitical priesthood (verses 26-29)

    1. Levites like deacons, responsible for furnishings, serving in the Tabernacle

    2. Priests from family of Aaron (also tribe of Levi)

  C. A system of sacrifice ushered in

    1. Guidelines for worship and service: Leviticus

      a. The priestly code (Leviticus 1–16)

      b. The holiness code (Leviticus 17–27)

    2. Liturgical calendar

      a. Special days and years

      b. Special feasts

V. Covenant Renewal (Exodus 33–34)

  A. The importance of God's presence among them

    1. It makes Israel distinct

    2. True also of Christians (John 1: "The Word became flesh and dwelt among us")

    3. What makes Catholics different: his real presence in the Eucharist

  B. New tablets, Aaron's rod, manna placed before the Ark of the Covenant

    1. In Revelation 11:19–12:1, the new Ark of the Covenant

VI. Building and Blessing the Tabernacle (Exodus 35–40)

  A. A microcosm of Creation

  B. The glory of the LORD filled it (his presence)

VII. Conclusion

A. Establish the Context

The book of Exodus chronicles the most significant event in the formation of the people of Israel: their dramatic deliverance by God from Egyptian slavery. In their early days of freedom, God provided his new family with all they needed: protection, food from heaven, and water from a rock. He gave them strong leaders and established them with a new covenant as a nation. He gave them the Law, which was essentially instructions for how to live as free children of God. He gave them the Levitical priesthood to help them approach him and worship him. And he gave them the Tabernacle: a place where he could meet with them and a tangible sign of his dwelling in their midst.

Getting Israel out of Egypt and setting them up as his people was one thing. It soon became evident that the real trick would be purging Egypt from their hearts. Spiritually, they were still children, and they needed to learn to trust their Father and walk in faith before they would be ready to possess the land promised them. The book of Numbers picks up the story here and tells how the people fare in the period of Desert Wanderings.

B. Read the Story

This session's reading, which will help you become familiar with the forty years Israel spends wandering in the desert between leaving Egypt and entering the Promised Land, is best done in more than one sitting and may require extra time to complete. First read **Numbers 1–2 and 10–12** and answer questions 1 to 4. Then read **Numbers 13–14, 16–17, 20, and 22–24** and answer the rest of the questions. You may find it helpful to read through the questions first so you will know what to focus on and what you can skim through. To place the desert wanderings on a map, see the map of the Exodus on page 43.

After reading, trace the action in the center section of your *Bible Timeline* Chart. Remember to read the events in chronological order. In this time period, the events start at the bottom in the South and progress up toward Canaan. Identify the main characters, and notice the flow of key events and where they take place. Any questions? Jot them down.

Going Deeper (optional): To get the entire story of this period, read the whole book of **Numbers.**

As always, pray before you read.

C. Take a Deeper Look

Answering these questions will draw you into the heart of the story. If you do not understand something, make a note of it to bring up in the discussion. Some questions will bring in the supplemental book of Deuteronomy to show how it weaves together with the narrative book (Numbers) and enriches the story. Consult your *Bible Timeline* Bookmark or Chart to see how it fits in.

Preparing to Leave Sinai (Numbers 1–10)

1. Israel has been at Mount Sinai for a year. The people have received the Law and the assurance of the presence of God in their midst, enthroned on the Ark of the Covenant. Now, they are preparing to depart for Canaan.

a. Read **Numbers 1–2.** What does God have Moses do before setting out, and for what purpose?

Count all ~~men~~ the people in the tribes, particularly men over 20. These men would be used to fight in Israels army.

b. One tribe is exempt from this process. Why?

Levites. To care for the tabernacle

2. In Chapter 10, the blasts from the silver trumpets lend a decidedly military air to Israel's proceeding. Notice the order of the procession, particularly the way in which the Ark of the Covenant and the Tabernacle are situated in relation to the tribes. Who or what is at the very front, and what does this show? (See verses 33-36.)

The Sacred Chest. This is God leading Them.

Israel Rebels (Numbers 11–25)

3. After the people leave Egypt, God tells Moses that he will send manna to "test" the people. Read **Deuteronomy 8.** (Deuteronomy, which is the supplemental book for this period, records Moses' final address to the people before they enter Canaan.)

a. Elaborate on God's purpose in giving them manna and on what they are meant to learn from it.

That they need more than food to live, they need every word spoken by God.

b. Read **Numbers 11.** At the start of their journey, what does Israel's failure to pass God's test say about its relationship with him?

God became angry but did not abandon them.

c. **New Testament Connection:** Read **Matthew 4:1-4,** in which Jesus rebuffs Satan using Moses' words from Deuteronomy 8:3. What parallels do you see between these stories?

4. In **Numbers 12,** an attack on Moses' authority comes from those closest to him, his siblings Miriam and Aaron. What is the true nature of their complaint and their attitude toward God-given authority?

They feel betrayed because God spoke NOT ONLY to moses but also to them.

5. a. It looks as though Israel is at last ready to possess the land promised to Abraham. Read **Numbers 13–14.** What happens?

    b. Compare and contrast the test Israel faces in spying out the land with the test Adam and Eve faced.

    c. Despite what they know of God and what they have been promised, the people of Israel fail to trust in God. As a consequence, they will wander a year in the desert for each day they have spent spying out the land. What does this setback in Israel's story tell you about the nature of sin and its punishment? Is there a correlation?

6. a. In **Numbers 16–17,** a second attack on Moses' authority comes, this time from the people. What is the charge this time, and to whom is the challenge really made?

    b. How is God's response different this time from his response to Miriam's challenge? What lasting proof does he give that Aaron's authority comes from him?

7. By **Numbers 20,** forty years have passed, and the children of Israel are back at Kadesh. They complain about the lack of water. Moses is instructed to speak to the rock in front of them, but he takes his staff and strikes the rock twice. Consequently, he and Aaron are prohibited from leading the children of Israel into the Promised Land. Does this seem like a harsh punishment? Why do you think they receive such discipline?

8. In Numbers 22, Israel has amassed on the Plains of Moab, just east of the Jordan River across from Jericho. God has led them in a number of military victories. The local kings are nervous and hire the powerful prophet, Balaam, to curse Israel. Able to say nothing other than the words God puts in his mouth, however, Balaam blesses them instead. Review the things Balaam says about Israel in **Numbers 22–24.** How do you explain the magnitude of God's blessing following their continual grumbling and lack of faith?

The Covenant in Moab (Numbers 26–36)

In the final chapters of Numbers, Moses takes a military census of the next generation. He gives the people final instructions and commissions Joshua to succeed him. He gives guidelines for dividing the land among the tribes and tells them to give the Levites six towns as cities of refuge to save innocent people from being killed before standing trial. His farewell address is detailed in the book of Deuteronomy. It is a long book, but it will be worth your time to look through it if you can. Take note especially of Chapters 10–11 and 27–30, which tell what God has promised to Israel and what will be required of them as God's people. God's love pervades the message, which is really a renewal of his covenant. As Moses says: "You stand this day all of you before the LORD your God ... that you may enter into the sworn covenant of the LORD your God, which the LORD your God makes with you this day; that he may establish you this day as his people, and that he may be your God, as he promised you, and as he swore to your fathers, to Abraham, to Isaac, and to Jacob" (Deuteronomy 29:10-13). "This day you have become the people of the LORD your God" (Deuteronomy 27:9).

God's family has become a nation.

D. Application

These questions will help you apply one of the key themes of the session to your life. After meditating on them, respond to God with a brief written prayer if you choose.

The Church's teaching on authority is founded on Scripture—on this and other passages where God appoints leaders to represent him and teaches his people what attitude they should have toward authority. These are timeless principles that do not change. Read **CCC 1897–1900,** focusing particularly on **CCC 1899.** Have you or anyone you know ever questioned the Church's authority over faith and morals? What problems do you see in today's society that echo the challenges Moses faced from Miriam and Aaron or from Korah, Dathan, and Abiram?

Dear Lord ...

E. Wrap-Up

Conclude your study of the Desert Wanderings period, and fix it in your mind by doing the following:

1. Recall the color of this time period, tan, and think of it in terms of your reading to help you remember it.

2. Quickly review this session. Write a brief summary of what the Desert Wanderings period is about or its significance as part of the "big picture."

Session 8 Talk Notes

Desert Wanderings

I. Introduction to Desert Wanderings

    A. Book of Numbers – Hebrew, *B'midbar:* "in the wilderness"

II. Starting for Canaan from Sinai

    A. Census, order of encampment (Numbers 1–2)

        1. The Tabernacle and Ark at the center

            a. Importance of God's presence

                i. CCC 1183: the tabernacle in Catholic churches

        2. Forty stages listed in their journey: a time of testing

    B. Priestly duties and dedication (Numbers 3–8)

        1. The Aaronic blessing (6:22-26)

            a. Letter *shin* begins the word *Shaddai* (*El Shaddai* = "all-sufficient one")

        2. New Covenant: priesthood of believers

        3. Role of the Levites (see Numbers 7; also 1–4, 8:5, 8:14)

    C. Passover and departure (Numbers 9–10)

III. Learning to Trust God (Numbers 11–13)

    A. To provide for their needs (complaints about food, Chapter 11)

        1. Wisdom 11:15-16

        2. Israel at an "adolescent" stage

    B. And those he appoints to authority (Miriam, Aaron challenge Moses, Chapter 12)

        1. Verse 7 – Moses entrusted with all of God's house (*bayit,* "household"; *al ha-bayit,* "over the

household")

C. To bring them into the Promised Land (Chapter 13)

1. *Kadesh Barnea,* "place of separation" (*kadosh* = "holy," separate, distinct), related to word for marriage *(kiddushin),* prayer for dead *(kaddish)*

a. Twelve tribes sent out

b. Report of the spies

IV. Rebellion and Punishment (Numbers 14–19)

A. The people rebel (Chapter 14)

1. God's response: for lack of trust, forty years of wandering

2. Penitential discipline (Chapter 15)

a. Offerings

i. Example: drink offering (verse 5) – the firstfruits

b. Distinctive clothing – tassels on garments (15:38)

i. *Tallit* (prayer shawl); *tzittziot* ("tassels" or "fringes")

- David cuts off Saul's garment

- Woman with issue of blood: healing virtue (cf. Malachi 4:2 "healing in his wings" *(kanaph)*

B. Korah's Rebellion (Chapter 16:25-32)

1. Aaron's Rod (17:1-2, 8): his God-given authority demonstrated

2. Earthquake swallows rebels

C. Principle to remember: Obedience is better than sacrifice

V. Moses Strikes the Rock (Numbers 20)

A. God's instruction: Speak to the rock

B. Moses' punishment (James 3:1)

C. The rock "followed them" through the wilderness

    1. Allegorically, the rock was Christ (1 Corinthians 10:4-5)

VI. Moving North to Moab (Numbers 21–25)

A. Defeat of Sihon and Og, kings of Heshbon and Bashan

B. Prophecy on the plains of Moab (Chapters 22–24)

    1. King Balaak tells Balaam to curse Israel

    2. Balaam's oracles of blessing

        a. "A shout of a king is among them" (23:21)

        b. "A scepter shall rise out of Israel" (24:15-17)

        c. New Testament Connection: Herod and the Holy Innocents

C. Israel sins: the worship of Baal of Peor (Chapter 25)

    1. Israel becomes involved in cult prostitution

    2. Phineas fights back, is given a special priesthood

VII. Preparing to Enter the Promised Land (Numbers 26–36)

A. Reuben and Gad ask to stay on the eastern side

B. Final instructions

    1. Forty stages of the journey, instructions for conquest (Chapter 33)

    2. Territorial boundaries (Chapter 34)

  3. Levitical cities (Chapter 35)

  4. Half-tribes of Ephraim and Manasseh

  5. Deuteronomy: "second law" (Moses' farewell message)

    a. Laws instituted because of hardness of hearts

      i. Example: divorce (Chapter 24)

    b. Provision for a place of worship and a king (Chapter 17)

      i. Prohibition on multiplying chariots, wives, gold

    c. Two keys to survival in Canaan

      i. The Lᴏʀᴅ is One (the *Shema*)[1]

      ii. Teach your children (Deuteronomy 6:6-9) – *mazuzah,* "doorposts"

 C. The death of Moses

---

[1] The *Shema* is the central prayer of the Jewish prayer book. Recited twice daily, it begins, "*Shema Yisrael …*": "Hear, O Israel; the Lᴏʀᴅ our God, the Lᴏʀᴅ is one" (Deuteronomy 6:4).

THE BIBLE
TIMELINE
The Story of Salvation

A. Establish the Context

The period called Desert Wanderings began full of promise. Israel had spent a year with God at the foot of Mount Sinai, during which time God was equipping them to become his people. They also had a number of very dramatic lessons and demonstrations of who God is: He is YHWH—I AM; he is mightier than all other gods; he fights their battles; he provides miraculously and faithfully for their needs. But the question remained for them, just as it was in the beginning for Adam and Eve: Do you trust God? And despite all God's promises and miracles on their behalf, when they got hungry and tired or saw the size of their enemies, Israel failed to have faith. As a result, they wandered forty years in the desert until the doubting generation died out and their children grew up having to depend on God and learning to trust him.

Remember this time period by the color tan for the hot desert sands Israel wandered through for forty years. It stands in sharp contrast to the triumphant red of deliverance of Egypt and Exodus and the lush green of the hills of Canaan, the setting for Conquest and Judges.

Before we leave Desert Wanderings, it is worthwhile to note these words of Moses to the people as he renewed God's covenant with them on the plains of Moab shortly before his death:

> Hear, O Israel: The LORD our God is one LORD; and you shall love the LORD your God with all your heart, and with all your soul, and with all your might. And these words which I command you this day shall be upon your heart; and you shall teach them diligently to your children. … Take heed lest you forget the LORD, who brought you out of the land of Egypt, out of the house of bondage. … You shall not go after other gods, of the gods of the peoples who are round about you. … And you shall do what is right and good in the sight of the LORD, that it may go well with you, and that you may go in and take possession of the good land which the LORD swore to give to your fathers (Deuteronomy 6:4-7, 12, 14, 18).

Will they remember? Will they continue to test God, or will they trust him? And will they teach their children? We will find out as we watch Israel move into and settle in the Promised Land in the period of Conquest and Judges.

B. Read the Story

The first part of the period of Conquest and Judges, in which Joshua leads the children of Israel victoriously into the Promised Land, is told in the book of Joshua. Read **Joshua 1–4, 6–8, and 23–24.** These passages tell how Israel crosses the Jordan and defeats Jericho; about Achan's sin and the taking of Ai; and about Joshua's final address to the nation. Trace the action in the center section of your *Bible Timeline* Chart. Identify the main characters, and notice the flow of key events and where they take place. Any questions? Jot them down.

Going Deeper (optional): To get the entire story of this period, read the whole book of **Joshua.**

As always, pray before you read.

C. Take a Deeper Look

Answering these questions will draw you into the heart of the story. If you do not understand something, make a note of it to bring up in the discussion.

Preparation and Entry (Joshua 1–5)

1. As Israel prepares to cross the Jordan into the Promised Land, Joshua takes over the leadership of God's people. According to **Joshua 1:1-9,** what will be the key to his success and theirs?

2. In **Joshua 2,** God uses a Canaanite prostitute, Rahab, to help Israel in its mission.

    a. Why do you think Rahab is eager to help Israel?

    b. According to **Hebrews 11:31** and **James 2:24-26,** how will Rahab be remembered?

3. What is the significance of the twelve stones God has Israel set up at its camp on the far side of the Jordan? (See **Joshua 4.**)

Conquest (Joshua 6–12)

4. Read **Joshua 6.** Describe the marching order and plan of attack to conquer Jericho. What kind of warfare is this? What spiritual message should this send to Israel?

5. a. Read **Joshua 7–8.** What happens in the aftermath of Jericho that causes God to withdraw his support so that the Israelites lose their first battle against Ai?

    b. How does Achan's failure illustrate what St. John Paul II spoke of as a "communion of sin," whereby one person's sin, no matter how private, affects the rest of the Church?

Note: Strategically speaking, Israel's first few moves in conquering Canaan are brilliant. By thoroughly defeating Jericho, Ai, and other cities in the central region and striking fear into all the others, Joshua effectively drives a wedge among the rival kingdoms before they can band together against him. Israel now is able to take on kingdoms in the North and South separately. The story of their conquest is told in Joshua 10–12.

Division of the Land (Joshua 13–22)

Joshua 13–21 tells how the land is divided among the tribes as shown in the map to the right. Make sure you know where Jerusalem is (in the approximate center of the land). Judah, which eventually absorbs Simeon, is the large area to the south of Jerusalem. The two tribes of Joseph (Ephraim and half of Manasseh) are given land to the north of Jerusalem and west of the Jordan and are the prominent tribes there. To the east of the Jordan, are Reuben, Gad, and the other half of Manasseh, which were promised to them by Moses when they conquered that land before crossing the Jordan. The rest of the land is divided by lot among the remaining tribes. The Levites are given forty-eight cities scattered throughout the land, including six "cities of refuge" to provide a fair method of trying people accused of manslaughter.

6.   Read **Joshua 21:43-45.** Where does Israel stand in seeing the fulfillment of God's promises?

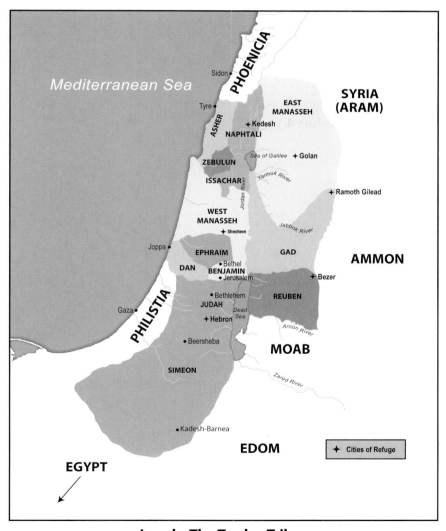

Israel – The Twelve Tribes

Covenant Renewal (Joshua 23–24)

7. Joshua's farewell address is recorded at the close of the book. Read **Joshua 23–24.**

    a. What is Joshua's warning to the leaders? (See **Joshua 23.**)

    b. What is the central message of his general address? (See **Joshua 24.**)

8. **Think About It:** Israel's conquest and occupation of the Promised Land anticipates the Church's warfare against the powers of the world and its efforts to establish and spread the kingdom of God on earth. The apostles Paul and Peter encourage the early Christians in this battle. Read the following passages from their letters, and note what they say about the nature of the battle and the weapons God gives us to fight it. Relate them to the book of Joshua if you can.

    a. **2 Corinthians 10:3-4:**

    b. **1 Peter 2:11:**

    c. **1 Timothy 6:11-12:**

    d. **Ephesians 6:11-18:**

So ... What About All This Fighting?

Many people read this far in the Bible only to put it down, put off by what seems to be excessive bloodshed. How can the God pictured here be the God of love and forgiveness? There is no easy answer to such questions. The best way to move forward may be to back up and review the big picture.

The God we met at Creation is a God to whom goodness is paramount. The God who called Abram is a God of promise and abundant blessing. The story so far has shown us how people who reject God's goodness and blessing live: Cain kills his brother, and his descendants prize vengeance (Genesis 4). Pharaoh oppresses the Hebrews and kills their children. God has just pulled the children of Israel out of the frying pan of Egypt. If they are to survive in Canaan, the "fire" represented by the culture there must be put out. God has allowed the people of Canaan hundreds of years to repent of their wickedness (see Genesis 15:16). The Red Sea crossing and Israel's victories on the way to Canaan send a final set of warnings, which the people understand but do not heed—except for Rahab and the Gibeonites, who listen and are saved (see Joshua 2:8-13).

At the time of the Conquest, there is not yet a remedy for the problem of sin, but there are visible consequences for it. God is not only merciful—he is just. His directions to Israel in the Conquest are concise and specifically directed to apply in particular situations, not to every battle. Today, under the New Covenant, we must still work to possess "the land" of the kingdom, but as St. Paul is careful to point out (see 2 Corinthians 10 and Ephesians 6), our enemies are no longer other nations but spiritual forces of evil. The battle begins in our hearts and minds, and we must destroy every sinful thought with the ruthlessness Israel was meant to show the inhabitants of those cities God put under the ban.

D. Application

These questions will help you apply one of the key themes of the session to your life. After meditating on them, respond to God with a brief written prayer if you choose.

Think about what the people of Israel are up against when they set out to conquer Canaan and about the methods and instructions God gives Joshua to guide the people in that task. What strongholds are you up against as you seek to "enter the rest" of God's kingdom on earth? What makes it hard for you to push out the enemy? Are there any basic principles you can apply from this session to the battle in your life?

Dear Lord ...

Session 9 Talk Notes

Conquest and Judges – Part 1

I. Introduction to Conquest and Judges – Part 1: Conquest

A. The land of Canaan
1. Approximately fifty times 150 miles
2. Influential "land bridge"
3. Four ecological zones converge

B. The people of Canaan
1. Multiple sovereign city-states
2. Advanced material culture
3. Strong fortifications
4. Religion
   a. El and Ashtora, Baal (fertility cults, cult prostitution)
   b. *Tophet = Molech* (child sacrifice)[1]

II. Entering the Land (Joshua 1:1–5:12)

A. Spies sent into Jericho (Chapter 2)

B. Rahab's testimony and decision

1. Canaanites "melting with fear" (contrast Numbers 13–14)
2. Exodus 23:28-30: God's intent to drive out the Canaanites before Israel
3. Rahab becomes ancestress of David

C. Crossing the Jordan (Chapters 3–4)

1. Preparation

2. The waters rise up "in a heap"

3. Passover, circumcision

   a. *Gilgal* ("rubble, stone heap" – a fortified camp)

   b. Manna stops

III. Conquering the Land (Joshua 5:13–12:24)

A. Initial conquests: Jericho and Ai

1. Instructions: Take nothing for yourselves ("herem warfare")

2. Victory at Jericho (Chapter 6)

3. Defeat at Ai (Chapters 7–8)

   a. Achan's sin

---

[1]   Jeff Cavins quotes from Rashi's commentary on Jeremiah 7:31 (See *The Complete Jewish Bible with Rashi Commentary* at chabad.org/library/bible_cdo/aid/16004/showrashi/true).

    B. *Kherem*[2] warfare = "devoted to destruction" or "put under the ban"

        1. A type or picture of purgatory

            a. Keep only what passes through fire; give that to God (no plunder)

            b. 1 Corinthians 3:12-15

            c. Hosea 2:15 on the "Valley of Achor" (*ha tikva* = "the hope")

        2. Four hundred years of opportunity (Genesis 15:14-16; Leviticus 18:24-25)

        3. No more "ban" after Ai

        4. God is not arbitrary ("nominalism" heresy)

            a. CCC 271

            b. Hearing demands a response

                i. Ezekiel 18:32, 33:11 – God takes no pleasure in death

                ii. CCC 142–143 – our response

            c. Trust rests on God's actions in history (CCC 2738)

    C. Victory and covenant renewal: blessings and curses on Mounts Ebal and Gerazim (Chapter 8)

    D. Military strategy: divide and conquer

        1. Southern campaign (Chapters 9–10)

            a. Treaty with the Gibeonites, the sun standing still (10:13)

        2. Northern campaign (Chapter 11)

IV. Dividing the Land (Joshua 13–21)

    A. Areas yet to be conquered (13:1-7)

    B. Tribal allotments (13:8–19:51)

        1. No allotment for the Levites

        2. Joseph's allotment: half-tribes of Ephraim and Manasseh

    C. Cities of refuge (Chapter 20) and levitical cities (Chapter 21)

V. Resting in the Land (Joshua 22–24)

    A. Joshua's final address (Chapter 23): Do not marry foreign wives

    B. Joshua's covenant (24:15): "Choose this day whom you will serve"

---

2   Also spelled *cherem* or *herem*.

THE BIBLE
TIMELINE
The Story of Salvation

A. Review the Context

The period of Conquest and Judges began with a glorious display of God's power as Joshua led the new nation across the Jordan on dry ground and felled the walls of Jericho with a mighty shout. God was with them as they conquered first an area in the South and then turned to the North to establish a presence there. God's promise to give them the land of Canaan had come to pass; they had only to push out the remaining inhabitants, tear down the false altars, and occupy it completely. At the end of his life, Joshua reminds the people that God is with them and will continue to be so, if only they will remember to love and obey him. God freed them from serving Pharaoh so they could serve him; now it is up to them to choose to serve him over the gods of the inhabitants of the land.

Part 2 of Conquest and Judges shows how they live up to this challenge.

Before continuing with this session, look at the Conquest and Judges section on your *Bible Timeline* Chart. It is green to remind you of the green hills of Canaan. Notice that the book of Joshua takes up only a small part of this time period but covers five key events (30-35) on the Chart. In the "12 Judges" box on the Chart, you will find a diagram of the cycle of sin that characterizes this time period as well as the names of the main people you will read about in the book of Judges. In your reading for this session, do not worry about memorizing names and other information; just get a general feel for the tenor of the time period.

B. Read the Story

The book of Judges chronicles Part 2 of Conquest and Judges, in which the children of Israel fall into a pattern of sin and are rescued by a series of judges sent by God. Read **Judges 1:1–3:6,** which summarizes the time period; **Judges 6–7,** the story of the judge Gideon; and **Judges 17–21,** which shows the result of the people's stubborn insistence on going their own way. Later in the session, you will be asked to read the book of **Ruth,** which was written during this time period and should be read in its context. Be advised that some of the events described in Judges, and particularly those in Chapters 17–21, make for tough reading. They provide an unvarnished picture of the ultimate fruits of sin.

After reading, trace the action in the center section of your *Bible Timeline* Chart. Identify the main characters and notice the flow of key events and where they take place. Any questions? Jot them down.

Going Deeper (optional): To get the entire story of this period, read the books of **Judges** (the narrative book for this time) and **Ruth** (a "supplemental" book for this period).

As always, pray before you read.

C. Take a Deeper Look

Answering these questions will draw you into the heart of the story. If you do not understand something, make a note of it to bring up in the discussion.

> ## The Structure of Judges
>
> The time of the Judges is summarized twice in what might be called the "prologue" to Judges (1:1–3:6). Chapters 1:1–2:5 focus on how Israel fights the remaining inhabitants of the land. They also tell us how Israel fares in keeping the covenant (2:6–3:6). Most of the rest of the book describes the recurring cycles of sin and salvation that characterize the time. Then, the "epilogue" (the final three chapters) describes two incidents that most likely happen toward the start of the time period. We will look at the "prologue" and "epilogue" first before addressing the cycle described in the "12 Judges" box on the *Timeline* Chart.

Israel's Occupation of Canaan: Prologue (Judges 1:1–3:6)

1. Read **Judges 1:1–3:6.**

   a. After the initial victories God gives to Israel on entering the land, it remains Israel's task to fully occupy it by driving the people out and breaking down their altars. Compare the way Judah and Simeon set out to occupy their tribal area in the South with the way the other (Northern) tribes occupy theirs.

   b. What is God's response? (See **Judges 2.**)

2. In Moses' final words to the people in **Deuteronomy 11,** he warns them to be careful to *teach God's words to their children,* and God will drive out the nations before them. Read **Judges 2:10-15.** What is the result of that generation's failure to do this?

Israel's Occupation of Canaan: Epilogue (Judges 17–21)

3. The closing chapters of Judges are flanked with this phrase: "In those days there was no king in Israel; every man did what was right in his own eyes" (see **Judges 17:6 and 21:25**).

   a. This might sound like a recipe for freedom, but what is the result in Israel, based on the stories in **Judges 17–21?**

b. The *Catechism* states that, "there is no true freedom except in the service of what is good and just. The choice to disobey and do evil is an abuse of freedom and leads to 'the slavery of sin'" (CCC 1733; cf. Romans 6:17). How does Israel's history so far illustrate this truth? (For more on what the Church has to say about man's freedom, read all of **CCC 1730–1748.**)

Seven Cycles of Sin and Deliverance (Judges 3:7–16:31)

The central part of the book of Judges details a sevenfold cycle in which Israel falls into sin, servitude, supplication, salvation, and then a period of silence before the cycle begins again. In each cycle, God allows his people to fall into bondage because of their disobedience, and then when they cry to him for help, he raises a judge to save his people. These are warrior heroes, not legal judges the way we know judges today. There are twelve judges in all, but the main ones are: Othniel (3:7-11), Ehud (3:12-30), Deborah (4–5), Gideon (6:1–8:32), Jephthah (10:6–12:7), and Samson (13–16). Each provides a brief picture of life during this time period.

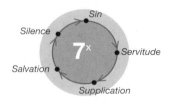

4. Choose the story of one judge, and use it to describe the cycle. (Othniel is the simplest and shortest example, but the others are more interesting.)

5. The story of Gideon is in **Judges 6–7.**

    a. What do these two chapters tell you about the ways of God in the midst of seemingly inevitable defeat?

    b. Gideon is so successful a deliverer that the Israelites ask him to rule over them. Read **Judges 8:22-23.** How does Gideon's reply focus on one of the main issues of this time?

6. **Think About It:** Human nature is no different today than it was then. We can find ourselves slipping into the same cycle of sin, servitude, supplication, salvation, and silence all too easily. What do we have available to us in the New Covenant that Israel did not have and that will help us break the cycle? (See **John 20:23** and **CCC 1210–1213, 1325, 1426, and 1446** for help.)

7. All through the book of Judges, we see the influence pagan nations and false gods have on Israel. Read **Psalm 115:1-9** and **CCC 2085–2086 and 2112.** What distinguishes the pagan gods from the One, True God?

8. Judges paints a dark picture of the unfaithfulness and moral and religious decline of this period when, if it were not for God's covenant faithfulness, Israel might be swallowed up by the pagan nations. All is not dark, however. The book of **Ruth,** written during this time, provides a welcome counterpoint to the closing chapters of Judges. Read the entire book (it is only four chapters long). How is Ruth's story the opposite of the one told in Judges?

Note: The end of Conquest and Judges overlaps somewhat with the period of the Royal Kingdom. This overlap, including the birth of the last and greatest judge and prophet—Samuel—and the time when Israel asks for a king (both of which appear on *The Bible Timeline* Chart in the Conquest and Judges period) will be included in the next session.

D. Application

These questions will help you apply one of the key themes of the session to your life. After meditating on them, respond to God with a brief written prayer if you choose.

What similarities do you see between our time and the time of the Judges? Think about the pressures and influences you face today compared with the pressures Israel faced. Where did the people of Israel go wrong? What have you learned from them that you can use to avoid getting caught up in the same never-ending cycle?

Dear Lord …

E. Wrap-Up

Conclude your study of Conquest and Judges, and fix it in your mind by doing the following:

1. Recall the color of this period, green, and think of it in terms of your reading to help you remember it.

2. Quickly review Sessions 9 and 10. Write a brief summary of what the Conquest and Judges period is about or its significance as part of the "big picture."

Session 10 Talk Notes

Conquest and Judges – Part 2

I. Introduction to Conquest and Judges – Part 2: Judges

A. Every man does what is right in his own eyes
B. Death of Joshua (Joshua 2:8)
C. There arises a generation that does not know God; they forsake him and serve the Baals

II. Cycles of Sin and Salvation: Twelve Judges

A. Cycle: sin – servitude – supplication – salvation – silence (Judges 3–16)

B. Twelve judges: warrior leaders
1. Major and minor judges
2. Understanding the cycle (Judges 3:7-11)

Cycle	Reference in Judges	Oppressor	Years Oppressed	Judge	Years of Peace
1	3:7-11	Mesopotamians	8	Othniel	40
2	3:12-30, 3:31	Moabites	18	Ehud Shamgar	80
3	4:1–5:31	Canaanites	20	Deborah and Barak	40
4	6:1–8:32	Midianites	7	Gideon	40
5	8:33–10:5	Abimelech	3	Tola and Jair	45
6	10:6–12:15	Ammonites	18	Jephthah, Ibzan, Elon, Abdon	31
7	13:1–16:31	Philistines	40	Samson	20

III. Judges Save Israel

A. Deborah and Barak versus Sisera (Judges 4–5)
1. Deborah = "buzzing bee"

B. Gideon (Judges 6–7)

1. God calls the unlikely

a. God calls when Gideon is about his daily work

b. 1 Corinthians 1:27: God chooses what is foolish to confound the wise

2. The sign of the fleece (6:36)

3. Gideon's triumph

        a. The people seek to make him king

C. Samson (Judges 13–16)

    1. Tribe of Dan near Philistine cities

    2. Samson (from *shimshon,* "sunshine")
        a. Samson's story: a microcosm of Israel at the time

        b. Nazirite vow (13:5)
           i. Consecrated to service, holiness
          ii. Uncut hair an outward sign of fidelity

    3. Delilah (Chapter 16)
        a. A Philistine

        b. *Lilah* is Hebrew for "night"

        c. Seduces Samson to tell his secret

    4. Toying with sin

        a. Cutting his hair: a reversal of the initiation of the rite

        b. Presumption

    5. Triumph
        a. Repentance leads to regained strength

IV. Ruth: A "Supplemental" Book Provides Contrast

A. Judges is the story of Israel forsaking God for Canaanite gods; Ruth tells of a Moabite woman turning to God

B. Naomi and Elimelech, Chilion and Mahlon

C. Orpah stays; Ruth accompanies Naomi (Ruth 1:16)

D. Boaz ("kinsman redeemer") marries Ruth; become ancestors of David

V. The Tribes of Dan and Benjamin During the Judges (Judges 17–21)

A. 19:22 – "base fellows": Hebrew, "the sons of Beliel" (1 Corinthians 6:15, means Satan)

B. Do not allow venial sins to go unchecked

A. Establish the Context

The land had not all been conquered by the end of Joshua's life. Joshua assured Israel that God would drive out the remaining people as he had those already defeated if Israel did its part and stayed true to God. But if they turned back and allied themselves with those who remained, "they shall be a snare and a trap for you, a scourge on your sides, and thorns in your eyes, till you perish from off this good land which the LORD your God has given you" (Joshua 23:13). The book of Judges shows in living color what happened when Israel chose not to drive out the Canaanites. The people of Israel chose their way over God's way. They did not teach their children what they had learned. Every man did what was right in his own eyes. And the inhabitants of the land became a snare and a trap to them. The Israelites joined with the Canaanites. They married them; they worshiped like them; they became like them. The horrors narrated in the final three chapters of Judges paint a vivid picture of just how far they fell. The type of nation they started to become puts into perspective God's command to drive the others out.

Judges has its high points, its examples of faith and of God's faithfulness to his children. But the roller coaster of sin, supplication, and salvation leaves us wondering: Just what will it take to break the cycle? And where is the kingdom God promised? Other than the twelve Judges, there has been no real leader over Israel for nearly two hundred years. They have arrived in Canaan, but have a tenuous hold over the land. In the closing words of Judges: "In those days there was no king in Israel; every man did what was right in his own eyes." Session 11 picks up the tail end of that period with the rise of the last and greatest prophet, Samuel, and Israel's request for a king. The next period is the Royal Kingdom, which is told in 1 and 2 Samuel and part of 1 Kings. This is the long-awaited time in which God establishes Israel as One Holy Kingdom through a man after God's own heart—King David. His people may be fickle, but God never forgets his promises.

B. Read the Story

Read **1 Samuel 1–4, 7–12, 15–16, and 26** to become familiar with some of the highlights of Part 1 of the Royal Kingdom. This session starts with the rise of the monarchy under Samuel and continues through the reign of Saul and the anointing of David. Part 2 will cover the reigns of David and Solomon. After reading, trace the action in the center section of your *Bible Timeline* Chart. Notice the development in God's "family plan" and the color purple, which should remind you of royalty. Any questions? Jot them down.

Going Deeper (optional): To get the entire story of this half of the Royal Kingdom, read the entire book of **1 Samuel.** Read it like a story, enjoy the flavor of it, and do not worry too much about the details. It will be worth the extra time you spend on it.

As always, pray before you read.

C. Take a Deeper Look

Answering these questions will draw you into the heart of the story. If you do not understand something, make a note of it to bring up in the discussion.

The Call of Samuel (1 Samuel 1–7)

1. a. Hannah is barren until God blesses her with a son she names Samuel, a child who will become the last and the greatest of all the judges. Can you remember any other great figures in the Bible who were born of women whose bodies were unable to conceive until God intervened? (For help with this question, see **Genesis 21:1-3, 25:21, and 30:22-24; Judges 13:2, 24;** and **Luke 1.**)

    b. Is this coincidence? Why do you think the authors make it a point to describe the circumstances of these men's births?

2. What in the description of Samuel's early life gives further proof of God's initiative and purpose for Samuel?

3. a. In **1 Samuel 4–6,** the people of Israel send for the Ark of the Covenant when the Philistines defeat them. Is this the wrong thing to do? After all, God had them march against Jericho led by the Ark. Why does God deliver them to the Philistines and allow the Ark to be taken?

    b. By Chapter 7, twenty years have passed. The Ark of the Covenant has been returned to Israel, but the people are still oppressed by the Philistines. Samuel calls an assembly at Mizpah and prepares to do battle. How do you account for Israel's victory? How are their actions in this battle different from their actions in the earlier battle described in **1 Samuel 4?**

Israel Asks for a King (1 Samuel 4–8)

4.   Read **1 Samuel 8.**

   a.   It is the end of the era of the judges, and the people ask for a king. Why do they want a king, and what does this say about their relationship with God?

   b.   What does God tell Samuel the outcome will be if they have a king?

The First King of Israel: Saul (1 Samuel 9–31)

5.   **Think About It:** In Chapter 9, Samuel anoints a man named Saul of the tribe of Benjamin to be king. Look at the "Twelve Tribes" map on page 65. Think back to what you learned about the tribes in the book of Joshua. Is there anything significant about the location of the tribe of Benjamin that makes it a good place for Israel's first king to be from?

6.   Israel now has a king like the other nations. But is its king going to be like those of other nations? Read **1 Samuel 12:12-15** (part of Samuel's farewell speech to the nation) and **Psalm 47 and Psalm 2.** (Psalms is a supplemental book for this time period, and many psalms were written during the time of the Royal Kingdom.) How will Israel's king be radically different from those of other nations?

7.   Read **1 Samuel 13:1-14 and 1 Samuel 15.** What sins does King Saul commit, and what does he lose because of his serious sin?

8. Samuel anoints the young David as the next king of Israel, although Saul will remain "acting" king until his death. Soon afterward, Goliath, a mighty champion of the Philistines, taunts Israel (Chapter 17). How do you explain David's confidence that he, a mere boy, can defeat Goliath, especially when the experienced soldiers are all so afraid?

9. Saul has been chosen by God, anointed by Samuel, and divinely equipped for the position of king (see **1 Samuel 10:6**). Even when Saul disobeys God and tries to kill David because he is jealous of him—and even though David knows he himself has also been anointed king—how does David show his respect for Saul, God's anointed one? What does this say about David's relationship with God? (See **1 Samuel 23–24 and 26.**)

D. Application

These questions will help you apply one of the key themes of the session to your life. After meditating on them, respond to God with a brief written prayer if you choose.

Israel's request for a king is a refusal of God's kingship and reflects Israel's desire to be "like the other nations." Are you looking to anyone other than God to be king in your life? Do you have trouble trusting in him and so try to take things into your own hands the way Saul did? Look through the psalms, and find one that speaks to your heart. Many of the early psalms were written by David. They speak strongly and with great beauty of God's kingship. Meditate on one of them, and make it your prayer.

Dear Lord …

Session 11 Talk Notes

Royal Kingdom – Part 1

I. Introduction to the Royal Kingdom – Part 1

II. Samuel

    A. Samuel's birth to Elkanah and Hannah (1 Samuel 1)

        1. Samuel is a prophet and a priest

        2. Hannah: a model mother who gives her son to God

    B. Samuel called by God (1 Samuel 2–3)

        1. Samuel serves high priest Eli at Shiloh

        2. CCC 2578: Cultivate sensitivity to God's voice

    C. The Ark of the Covenant (1 Samuel 4–7)

        1. Philistines[1] capture the Ark

            a. The Ark in the house of Dagon (Chapters 5–6)

            b. Victory

        2. The Ark in Kiriath-jearim (Chapter 7)

            a. Statue of Ark with Blessed Virgin Mary, the new Ark of the Covenant (see Revelation 11–12)

III. Israel Asks for a King (1 Samuel 8)

    A. A king "like all the other nations" versus God as King

        1. God accommodates himself to their weakness ("divine accommodation," or condescension) and gives them a king

        2. Typology: the earthly king as a type of their heavenly king

    B. Provision for a king and warnings

        1. Deuteronomy 17:14ff: Do not multiply wives, horses, silver, or gold

        2. 1 Samuel 8:11-15: Kings will tax you; take your children, vineyards

IV. King Saul Unites the Kingdom

    A. From tribe of Benjamin

    B. Samuel anoints Saul (1 Samuel 10)

---

[1]   Philistia lay along the southwest coast of Canaan in what is now known as the Gaza Strip. There were five major Philistine cities: Ashkelon, Ashdod, Ekron, Gath, and Gaza.

 C. Saul's downfall (1 Samuel 13–15)

  1. Saul's weakness: a fear of the people
   a. Disobeys and offers sacrifice

  2. The kingdom is taken from Saul
   a. Trades the eternal for things of this earth
   b. Disobeys again: spares the Amalekite king
    i. "To obey is better than sacrifice" (15:22)

  3. Saul's response: "Honor me now before … Israel" (verse 30)

V. David

 A. David, son of Jesse, anointed as king (Chapter 16)

 B. Saul's torment
  1. David plays his harp

 C. David rises to prominence

  1. David and Goliath (Chapter 17)
   a. Battle in the Valley of Elah
   b. David challenges Goliath (verse 45)

 D. Saul seeks David's life (Chapter 18ff)
  1. Saul's son Jonathan is David's best friend
  2. David hides in En-gedi
  3. Many psalms of David refer to this period
  4. David spares Saul's life, respects the office of the king

VI. The Place of 1 and 2 Chronicles ("Supplemental" Books)

 A. 1 Chronicles parallels 2 Samuel

 B. 2 Chronicles parallels 1 and 2 Kings from the perspective of the Davidic throne

VII. The Death of Saul (1 Samuel 31)

 A. Philistines slay Saul on Mount Gilboa[2]

---

[2] Mount Gilboa rises above the Jezreel Valley (also known as the Valley of Esdraelon or Armageddon). Running through that valley was the inland branch of the *Via Maris* (the "Way of the Sea"), an ancient trade route linking Egypt with the lands to the north of Canaan.

A. Review the Context

By the end of the time of the Judges, the children of Israel had had enough of being ruled by random judges and prophets. They wanted a king like all the other nations around them. In answer, God gave them Saul—but only after warning them that a king would take their children into his military, take the best of their fields, produce, and cattle for himself, and make them his slaves. Having a king was more important to them than these things, and God gave them their desire. But Israel's king would be a different kind of king: He would be subject to God—their true Ruler—and to his Word. Saul did not live up to those requirements but put his own wishes before God's. He lost the kingdom as a result. And although he continued to rule, the kingdom would not be established on him and his descendants. In this session, we will see God choose "a man after his own heart"—the boy David—on whom to build the promised kingdom. In 1 Samuel, David shows himself to be strong where Saul was weak. He puts his trust in God to fight his battles and is willing to wait on God. The kind of king he is—and the kind of kingdom that will be founded on him—is the focus of Royal Kingdom – Part 2.

Before continuing with the session, take a look at the Royal Kingdom portion of your *Bible Timeline* Chart. Notice the purple bar marked "Davidic Dynasty." A dynasty is marked by a succession of kings in the same family. It is sometimes known as a "house," as in England's House of Windsor. You will want to watch for the wordplay in 2 Samuel 7 as David wants to build God a "house" (temple), and God says he will build a "house" (dynasty) for David. The covenant God makes with David is the fifth in our study and is crucial to our understanding of future events.

Also notice the supplemental books listed in the section at the bottom of your *Timeline* Chart. 1 and 2 Chronicles parallel the narrative books for this time period from the point of view of the South, focusing on the kings of Judah (the Davidic throne) and the impact of events during that time on liturgy and worship. Psalms, Proverbs, Ecclesiastes, and Song of Songs are examples of what is called "wisdom literature." (Job, Sirach, and the book of Wisdom also fit into this category.) These four books of wisdom are placed within the context of the Royal Kingdom period not because they were written then (the dating of these books is uncertain and complex), but because they reflect on the Davidic kingship and kingdom, whose ultimate purpose was to lead others to God and his wisdom.

B. Read the Story

In the Royal Kingdom – Part 2, God establishes Israel as a kingdom through a covenant with King David, and his son Solomon builds the Temple. This is narrated in 2 Samuel and in 1 Kings 1–11. Read some of the highlights of David's reign in **2 Samuel 5–7 and 11:1–12:25** and about Solomon's reign in **1 Kings 2:1-12, 3, 6:1–7:19, 10:23-29, and 11.** Any questions? Jot them down.

Going Deeper (optional): To get the entire story of this period, read all of **2 Samuel** and **1 Kings 1–11.**

As always, pray before you read.

C. Take a Deeper Look

Answering these questions will draw you into the heart of the story. If you do not understand something, make a note of it to bring up in the discussion.

King David (2 Samuel)

1. After Saul's death, David is anointed king first over Judah in the South and then over all Israel (see **2 Samuel 2, 5**). The first thing he does is to conquer Jerusalem and establish it as his royal city. Jerusalem was on the border of the northern and southern halves of the nation but was controlled by neither, so it was an ideal city to unite the kingdom. After defeating the Philistines, David moves the Ark of the Covenant from its resting place in Kiriath-jearim to Jerusalem with great fanfare (see **Chapter 6**). What is the significance of this first royal action?

2. A thousand years earlier, in this same place (then called Salem), the priest-king Melchizedek brought out bread and wine and blessed Abram, who paid him a tithe (see **Genesis 14:18-20** and the boxed note on page 27). Here, after the Ark of the Covenant is returned to its place, David blesses the people and gives them meat and cakes of bread and raisins. Read **2 Samuel 6:12-22**. Does anything make you believe David is acting as much like a priest as a king? Why is this significant? (See **Hebrews 7:1-4, 14-17** and **Psalm 110:4**.)

3. David is a conquering king, and under his rule, Israel is at its strongest in terms of power and size. Read **2 Samuel 7**. Once David is given rest from his enemies, he wants to build a permanent dwelling place for the Ark. What is God's response to David, and how does it relate back to his promise to Abraham?

4. Although David is "a man after God's own heart," he is not without sin. In **2 Samuel 11,** we read of his sin with Bathsheba and Uriah. What are the consequences for David and his family? (Nathan's warning is in Chapter 12.) **Optional:** See how the consequences play out by reading **Chapters 12–20.**

5. Even though God punishes David for his sin, he does not withdraw the kingdom. In contrast, when King Saul disobeyed God, he took the kingdom from him (1 Samuel 15). Why the difference? (For David's response to God's rebuke, read **2 Samuel 12:15-23** and **Psalm 51,** which records his prayer. Read also **CCC 1847 and 1850.**)

King Solomon (1 Kings 1–11)

6. Solomon is perhaps twenty years old when he assumes the throne of Israel after his father, David.

    a. When God tells him to ask for anything he wants, how does he respond? (See **1 Kings 3.**)

    b. What is God's response to Solomon's request?

7. In 1 Kings, we learn that, "King Solomon excelled all the kings of the earth in riches and in wisdom" (10:23). He wrote thousands of proverbs, many of which are preserved in the book of Proverbs, one of the supplemental books for the Royal Kingdom time period. Read **Proverbs 1:1-7 and 2:1-11.** What do these Scripture passages teach us about wisdom?

8. a. Once Solomon is given peace on all sides, he builds a magnificent Temple for the Name of God, a permanent place for God to dwell among his people. Read **CCC 2580–2581.** What will the king do there, and what is the Temple meant to be for God's people?

    b. **Think About It:** What is the relationship between the Tabernacle, the Temple, Jesus Christ, the Church, and individual believers? (Read also **Matthew 12:6 and 26:61** and **1 Corinthians 3:16 and 6:19.**)

9. God consecrates the Temple Solomon has built for his Name and reminds Solomon of the importance of keeping the covenant in order to continue enjoying its blessings. In **1 Kings 9:10–11:13,** we learn about the rest of Solomon's reign. Read Moses' instructions for the king in **Deuteronomy 17:16-17.** How does Solomon fare, and what is the result?

10. Read **1 Kings 11:26-43.** Describe Ahijah's prophecy to Jeroboam, whom Solomon has put in charge of laborers from the Northern tribes on his building projects. What hope is given in this prophecy for the long-term outlook of David's dynasty and the kingdom?

D. Application

These questions will help you apply one of the key themes of the session to your life. After meditating on them, respond to God with a brief written prayer if you choose.

God gave Solomon "wisdom and understanding beyond measure, and largeness of mind like the sand on the seashore, so that Solomon's wisdom surpassed the wisdom of all the people of the east, and all the wisdom of Egypt" (1 Kings 4:29-30). How could the wisest man in the world fail so miserably? What turned his heart away from God? What does this say about our own vulnerability to error, and how can we avoid Solomon's error? Think about the example of David, who may not have been as wise as his son, but who was called "a man after God's own heart" (1 Samuel 13:14).

Dear Lord …

E. Wrap-Up

Conclude your study of the Royal Kingdom, and fix it in your mind by doing the following:

1. Recall the color of this time period, purple, and think of it in terms of your reading to help you remember it.

2. Quickly review Sessions 11 and 12. Write a brief summary of what the Royal Kingdom period is about or its significance as part of the "big picture."

Session 12 Talk Notes

Royal Kingdom – Part 2

I. Introduction to Royal Kingdom – Part 2

II. War Between the Houses of David and Saul (2 Samuel 1–4)

A. Saul's death: "Cursed be Mount Gilboa" (David; 1:21)

   1. Valley of Esdraelon, (also known as Jezreel, Armageddon)

III. David Becomes King Over Judah (2 Samuel 2–4)

A. Saul's son Ishbosheth reigns over the North

B. War between the two houses

C. David makes Jerusalem the capital

IV. David Becomes King Over All Israel (2 Samuel 5–6)

A. The city of David established at Jerusalem (5:6-9)

B. The Ark of the Covenant moved to Jerusalem (Chapter 6)

V. God Makes a Covenant with the House of David (2 Samuel 7)

A. Establishes the family of God as One Holy Kingdom

B. David's offer and God's promise

   1. "I will make for *you* a great name" and a house
     a. "house" = royal dynasty
   2. God's reign through his appointed king (cf. messianic psalms)
   3. An everlasting kingdom
   4. "I will raise up your offspring after you"
     a. Literal and spiritual (allegorical, moral, anagogical) senses (CCC 115–120: Solomon, Jesus)

C. A change in priesthood under David from Abiathar to Zadok (8:15-17)

D. David shows kindness to Mephibosheth, son of Jonathan (9:1-13)

VI. David's Sin (2 Samuel 11)

A. David seduces Bathsheba

B. David sends Uriah to his death

C. Nathan confronts David (2 Samuel 12)

D. David's response: "I have sinned" (see Psalm 51)

VII. David's "Mighty Men" Illustrate Tenacity (2 Samuel 23:8, 9, 11)

A. Adino (Josheb-basshebeth, a Tah-chemonite) slew eight hundred
   1. Tenacity in the face of overwhelming odds

B. Eleazar, the son of Dodo

    1. Tenacity in the face of overwhelming fatigue

C. Shammah, the son of Agee the Hararite

    1. Tenacity even in a seemingly insignificant task

VIII. Supplemental Books (1 and 2 Chronicles)

A. 1 Chronicles parallels 2 Samuel (David's reign)

B. 2 Chronicles parallels 1 and 2 Kings (Solomon and later kings of Judah)

IX. Bathsheba: The Queen Mother (1 Kings 1–2)

A. The role of Queen Mother in the kingdom of David (1 Kings 1:11-13, 28-30)

    1. Hebrew *Gebirah* (1 Kings 15:9-13)
       a. Advocate and intercessor
       b. Throne
       c. Babylonian exile: exiled and chastised along with the king

    2. Not wife but mother of the king (ancient near East)

B. New Covenant fulfillment: the Blessed Virgin Mary

    1. Mary visits Elizabeth at Ein Kerem
    2. "Flock" given to the king and the queen mother (Jeremiah 13:18ff)

X. Solomon ("Peace") Becomes King

A. Solomon the builder (1 Kings 5–8)
    1. Temple (seven years) and palace (thirteen years)

B. Solomon's wisdom and wealth (1 Kings 10)
    1. Wisdom literature

C. Solomon's downfall (1 Kings 11)
    1. Moses' prophetic warning (Deuteronomy 17)
       a. Do not multiply gold, chariots, wives

    2. Samuel's warning (1 Samuel 8)
       a. A king will tax people, take children and property

    3. Solomon's kingship
       a. Tyrannical
       b. Heart turned to other gods
       c. Seven hundred wives, three hundred concubines, 666 talents of gold

    4. Ends in ruin

A. Establish the Context

We are halfway finished our journey through the Bible. Take a moment to review the story. Among many important events, three stand out as "mountain peaks": God's covenant with Abraham and its threefold promise of land, kingdom, and worldwide blessing; the Exodus, in which God liberated the people of Israel from slavery so they could live as free children of God; and God's covenant with David and the establishment of an eternal royal throne, or dynasty.

In the Royal Kingdom period, Saul united the kingdom under a single ruler. David then expanded it, and Solomon built it up. At the height of its glory, Israel must have looked like a near-final fulfillment of God's promises to Abraham: It possessed most of the strategic land of Canaan and was in a position to bless the surrounding nations. God dwelt among them in a magnificent Temple in Jerusalem. Their king was the wisest and wealthiest man on earth. The nation was blessed, and the people prospered. Most of all, God had promised to establish David's throne forever. What could go wrong?

What indeed. At the close of the Royal Kingdom, God promised to tear away the bulk of the kingdom from Solomon's son because of Solomon's sin. The resulting split will launch Israel into the period of the Divided Kingdom. This period's color is black because it is Israel's darkest hour. (Flip over your *Timeline* Chart and notice how the central purple bar representing the Davidic dynasty remains toward the south while a new, black "Northern Kingdom" branches upward.) The story is told in 1 Kings 12–22 and in 2 Kings. The supplemental book of 2 Chronicles gives a parallel history of the reigns of the kings of Judah; the other supplemental books during this time are writings and oracles of the prophets God sent with messages to the two kingdoms and to other nations. Looking forward, we see that the next period is Exile—the tragic result of this dark time. There will be no further development in God's family plan until it culminates in Jesus Christ.

Notice on your Chart that the action takes place in the land of Canaan, within the kingdoms of Israel (in the North) and Judah (in the South). There is an overlap with the time of Exile, which begins in 722 BC for the Northern Kingdom and in 587 BC for the Southern Kingdom. During this time, we also see the first change in "world power" at the bottom of the Chart: Where Egypt has been the leading power since the start of the story, Assyria rises to power around 900 BC and remains dominant until Babylon takes over shortly before 600 BC. Elsewhere in the world, the city of Rome is founded, the first Olympic Games are held in Greece, and Homer writes the *Iliad* and the *Odyssey*.

B. Read the Story

The narrative books of 1 and 2 Kings tell how the nation of Israel came to be divided into two kingdoms and the subsequent history of each kingdom. Divided Kingdom – Part 1 will look at the readings pertaining to the Northern Kingdom (Israel), and Part 2 will cover events in the Southern Kingdom (Judah). Because the narrative jumps back and forth between the two kingdoms, **the reading will not be done up front** but will instead be interspersed with the questions.

Going Deeper (optional): To get the entire story of this period (which is covered in this session and the next), read **1 Kings 12–22** and **2 Kings.**

As always, pray before you read.

C. Take a Deeper Look

Answering these questions will draw you into the heart of the story. If you do not understand something, make a note of it to bring up in the discussion.

The Kingdom Divides

The kingdom divides in half above Jerusalem, splitting the tribe of Benjamin. The territory to the north continues to be called Israel. The territory to the south remaines loyal to the Davidic throne and to David's son Rehoboam and is called Judah.

1. Read **1 Kings 12:1–14:20,** which begins with Rehoboam ascending the throne after the death of his father, Solomon. What is the immediate cause of the division of the kingdom?

2. Jeroboam, king of the Northern Kingdom (Israel), is faced with a major dilemma in that Jerusalem, the center of worship, is in Judah to the south.

    a.   What is he afraid will happen, and what does he do to solve this problem?

The Divided Kingdom

b.   What is the result of his disobedience?

The Kings of Israel

3.   Read **1 Kings 15:25–16:34 and Chapter 21,** which tell about the first eight kings of the Northern Kingdom. (If you have time, read about the others in **2 Kings 15:8-31 and 17:1-2.**)

a.   The same refrain appears nearly verbatim in the account of each king. What is it? (See **1 Kings 15:34.**)

b.   What kind of men are these rulers, and what is Israel like under their rule?

c.   Look at the "Kings of Israel (Northern Kingdom)" chart on page 93. It names every king of the Northern Kingdom and tells when and for how long each reigned, whether he was a bad or good king (B/G), and his relationship to his predecessor. It also includes information on the way he died and where his reign is recorded in Scripture. From Jeroboam I to Hoshea, how many dynasties ruled Israel in the North? (A "dynasty" is a series of rulers from the same family. Do not figure Tibni in your count; he struggled with Omri for control but lost after several years of a split "reign.") What does the way many of these kings died seem to indicate?

Prophets Sent to the Northern Kingdom

4. One of the greatest prophets during this time was Elijah, whose main ministry was during the reign of Ahab—a man who "did more to provoke the LORD, the God of Israel, to anger than all the kings of Israel who were before him" (1 Kings 16:33). What is God's message to Israel through Elijah, especially as it is dramatized at Mount Carmel? (See **1 Kings 18:16-39;** if you have time, read the entire account of Elijah in **Chapters 17–19.**)

5. Elijah's mantle—and a double portion of his spirit—falls (literally) on Elisha when the older prophet is taken up to heaven. Read **2 Kings 2, 4, and 5,** which record this and some of the miracles Elisha does in Israel. How do these miracles show God's grace and desire to bless those who follow him?

6. Read **CCC 2582–2584.** How do Elijah and the other prophets find strength for their often-dangerous missions?

7. Under the reign of Jeroboam II (2 Kings 14:23-29), the king is able to restore Israel's northern borders, and Israel enjoys a time of relief from foreign pressure. The people become complacent, worship other gods, and fail to follow God's commands. God sends Amos and Hosea during this time to announce that he will not spare them forever but will send them into exile to Assyria, the new world power to the north. Read **Hosea 1–3.**

    a. What does God tell Hosea to do at the start of Chapter 1, and why?

    b. List the names of Hosea and Gomer's children along with their meanings. What message does God send Israel through these names?

    c. How will God treat Israel for its unfaithfulness, as symbolized by the way he tells Hosea to treat Gomer in Chapter 2?

8. **Optional:** Around this same time, God calls on the prophet Jonah to bear a message to the Assyrian capital of Nineveh. Read the book of **Jonah** (it has just four chapters). What does this story tell you about God?

D. Application

This question will help you apply one of the key themes of the session to your life. After meditating on it, respond to God with a brief written prayer if you choose.

Are there ways you are unfaithful to God? Meditate on God's love for you as expressed in Hosea 11 and 14. Make your confession, and be reconciled to your Father.

Dear Lord …

KINGS OF ISRAEL (NORTHERN KINGDOM)
930–722 BC: Nine Dynasties*

No.	King	Date BC	Bad/Good	Years Reigned	Relation to Predecessor	End of Reign	Scripture Reference
1	Jeroboam I	930–909	Bad	22		Stricken by God	1 Kings 11:26–14:20
2	Nadab	909–908	Bad	2	Son	Killed by Baasha	1 Kings 15:25–28
3	Baasha	908–886	Bad	24	Son of Ahijah	Died	1 Kings 15:16–16:7
4	Elah	886–885	Bad	2	Son	Killed by Zimri	1 Kings 16:6–14
5	Zimri	885	Bad	7 days	Captain of Chariot	Suicide by Fire	1 Kings 16:9–20
6	(Tibni)**	885–880	Bad	7	Son of Ginath	Died	1 Kings 16:21–22
7	Omri	885–874	Bad	12	Captain of Army	Died	1 Kings 16:23–28
8	Ahab	874–853	Bad	22	Son	Wounded in Battle	1 Kings 16:28–22:40
9	Ahaziah	853–852	Bad	2	Son	Fell to His Death	1 Kings 22:40–2 Kings 1:18
10	Joram	852–841	Bad	12	Brother	Killed by Jehu	2 Kings 3:1–9:25
11	Jehu	841–814	Bad	28	(none)	Died	2 Kings 9:1–10:36
12	Jehoahaz	814–798	Bad	17	Son	Died	2 Kings 13:1–9
13	Jehoash	798–782	Bad	16	Son	Died	2 Kings 13:10–14:16
14	Jeroboam II	793–753	Bad	41	Son	Died	2 Kings 14:23–29
15	Zechariah	753	Bad	6 months	Son	Killed by Shallum	2 Kings 14:29–15:12
16	Shallum	752	Bad	1 month	(none)	Killed by Menahem	2 Kings 15:10–15
17	Menahem	752–742	Bad	10	(none)	Died	2 Kings 15:15–22
18	Pekahiah	742–740	Bad	2	Son	Killed by Pekah	2 Kings 15:22–26
19	Pekah	740–732	Bad	20	Captain of Army	Killed by Hoshea	2 Kings 15:27–31
20	Hoshea	732–722	Bad	9	(none)	Exile to Assyria	2 Kings 15:30–17

* Shading indicates divisions between the nine dynasties that ruled the Northern Kingdom.
** Tibni, who unsuccessfully contended with Omri for the throne after Zimri's death, does not count as a separate dynasty. His name is in the chart because his reign is mentioned in the Bible, and he is included in some lists of kings of Israel.

PROPHETS OF THE NORTHERN AND SOUTHERN KINGDOMS
870–424 BC

No.	Prophet	Date BC	Pre-/Post-Exile	Audience	World Ruler	Scripture Reference
1	Elijah	870	Pre-Exile	Israel	Assyria	1 Kings 17–2 Kings 2:15
2	Elisha	850	Pre-Exile	Israel	Assyria	1 Kings 19:1–2 Kings 13:21
3	Jonah	800–753	Pre-Exile	Assyria	Assyria	2 Kings 13:10-25, 14:23-29 *
4	Amos	760–753	Pre-Exile	Israel	Assyria	2 Kings 14:23–15:7 *
5	Hosea	750–715	Pre-Exile	Israel	Assyria	2 Kings 14:23–18:12 *
6	Isaiah	740–680	Pre-Exile	Judah	Assyria	2 Kings 15:1–20:21; 2 Chronicles 26:16–32:33 *
7	Micah	735–700	Pre-Exile	Judah	Assyria	2 Kings 15:32–19:37; 2 Chronicles 27:1–32:23 *
8	Joel	c. 722-701	Pre-Exile	Judah	Assyria	2 Kings 17-22; 2 Chronicles 29-33 *
9	Nahum	664–654	Pre-Exile	Assyria	Assyria	2 Kings 21:1-18; 2 Chronicles 33:1-20 *
10	Zephaniah	632–628	Pre-Exile	Judah	Assyria	2 Kings 22:1-2; 2 Chronicles 34:1-7 *
11	Jeremiah	625–580	Pre-Exile	Judah	Assyria/Babylon	2 Kings 22:3–25:30; 2 Chronicles 34:1–36:21 *
12	Habakkuk	610–605	Pre-Exile	Judah	Babylon	2 Kings 23:3–24:7; 2 Chronicles 36:1-8 *
13	Baruch	600	Exile	Judah	Babylon	2 Kings 24:8–25:30; 2 Chronicles 36:9-21 *
14	Daniel	605–535	Exile	Exiles	Babylon/Persia	2 Kings 23:34–25:30; 2 Chronicles 36:4-23 *
15	Ezekiel	590–571	Exile	Exiles	Babylon	2 Kings 24:8–25:30; 2 Chronicles 36:9-21 *
16	Obadiah	c. 586	Exile	Edom	Babylon	2 Kings 24:8–25:30; 2 Chronicles 36:9-21 *
17	Haggai	520	Post-Exile	Judah	Persia	Ezra 5:1–6:15 *
18	Zechariah	520–480	Post-Exile	Judah	Persia	Ezra 5:1–6:15 *
19	Malachi	432–424	Post-Exile	Judah	Persia	Ezra 5:1–6:15 *

*These prophets also have Old Testament books named after them.

Session 13 Talk Notes

Divided Kingdom – Part 1

I. Introduction to Divided Kingdom – Part 1 (Northern Kingdom, Israel)

II. The Kingdom Divides (1 Kings 12)

A. Ahijah's prophecy (1 Kings 11:29ff): ten tribes to Jeroboam

    1. Jeroboam (an Ephraimite) challenges Solomon's son

    2. Rehoboam's reply

B. The kingdom divides in two (930 BC; 1 Kings 12:16)

    1. Northern Kingdom: Israel (King Jeroboam, capital Samaria, ten tribes)

    2. Southern Kingdom: Judah (King Rehoboam, Solomon's son; capital Jerusalem; two tribes)[1]

    3. Jeroboam's problem: The Temple is in Judah

    4. Jeroboam's solution: an apostate cult (new feast days, new priests, two golden calves)

    5. Importance of Magisterium

C. Differences between North and the South
    1. Messianic promise through Judah, Davidic dynasty
    2. Nine dynasties in the North (Israel), one in the South (Judah)
    3. Authority for the taking in the North, established authority in the South

D. Review of charts of kings ("Kings of Israel" on page 93 and "Kings of Judah" on page 101)

III. Kings of Israel, the Northern Kingdom (Examples)

A. Omri (1 Kings 16:23-28)

B. Ahab, "the worst" (1 Kings 16:28–22:40)
    1. Wife Jezebel
    2. Confronted by prophet Elijah
    3. Worships Baal
    4. Wickedness angers God

C. Jehu, "best of the bad" (2 Kings 9:1–10:36)

D. Sins of the Northern kings

---

[1] The precise division of tribes into the Northern and Southern Kingdoms is not easily defined. For simplicity's sake and to be consistent with the traditional division and the prophecy in 1 Kings 11:31-35, *The Bible Timeline* presents them as ten tribes in the North and two tribes (Judah and Benjamin) in the South.

IV. The Prophets

    A. Understanding the prophets

        1. Sent to warn and woo

        2. Difference between God's prophets and other ancient prophets
            a. Prophets were not normally priests
            b. Methods of finding God's will
            c. Purpose: move hearts to obedience

        3. Messages of the prophets
            a. Unusual methods
            b. Prophecy to North

            c. Prophecy to South

        4. Review the "Prophets of the Northern and Southern Kingdoms" chart (page 94)

    B. Non-writing prophets

    C. Prophets sent to the North (examples)

        1. Amos warns against the apostate cult

        2. Elijah defeats prophets of Baal on Mount Carmel (see 1 Kings 18ff)

        3. Hosea addresses infidelity in the North
            a. "God is your husband"
            b. Warnings of exile and God's faithful love
            c. Hosea lives out Israel's situation (marries Gomer)

V. Rise of Assyria and End of the Northern Kingdom (2 Kings 17)

    A. Assyria conquers and scatters Israel (722 BC)

    B. Samaria resettled with people from five other nations

        1. "Samaritans" in North, "Jews" from Judah in South

        2. New Testament Connection: John 4:4-20, the woman at the well

        3. God has not forgotten the ten tribes (apostle Paul goes to the Gentiles)

VI. Conclusion

A. Review the Context

When Solomon's kingdom divided into Israel (North) and Judah (South), the Northern Kingdom sank almost immediately into apostasy as Jeroboam set up golden calves at new centers of worship in Dan and Bethel. A quick, violent succession of kings followed, none of whom tore down the false altars or led the people back into the covenant with God. Ahab's reign in particular stood out as a time of gross infidelity. The prophet Hosea married a harlot to symbolize Israel's spiritual adultery and prophesied the Northern Kingdom's inevitable end in exile. Meanwhile, in Judah, Solomon's son Rehoboam sits on the throne. Even though the once-glorious kingdom has been reduced to a shadow of its former glory, he is still the heir to the throne of David, and God's presence still dwells in the Jerusalem Temple. Did he learn a lesson in the split? How the Southern Kingdom fares is the subject of this session.

Before reading, you may find it helpful to examine the chart on page 101: "Kings of Judah (Southern Kingdom)." Compare it with the "Kings of Israel (Northern Kingdom)" on page 93. What differences do you see in how long the kingdoms last and in the type of kings who reign? This session does not look at every king, but Scripture references are listed on the charts if you want to read about them.

B. Read the Story

Divided Kingdom – Part 2 covers only the parts of 1 and 2 Kings that pertain to the Southern Kingdom (Judah), which means going back through chapters covered in Session 13 and reading the parts that were skipped. If you did not already mark the section headings that name the kings of Judah with a crown, you may want to do it before you read so you do not get confused when the text jumps back and forth between the Northern and Southern Kingdoms. Once again, the reading will not be done ahead of time but will be assigned along with the questions that pertain to each reading. The session and readings have been divided into sections for the sake of clarity.

Going Deeper (optional): To get the entire story of the Divided Kingdom, finish reading all of **1 Kings 12–22** and **2 Kings.**

As always, pray before you read.

C. Take a Deeper Look

Answering these questions will draw you into the heart of the story. If you do not understand something, make a note of it to bring up in the discussion.

Kings of the Southern Kingdom

Read **1 Kings 14:21–15:8.**

1. a. What is Judah like under Rehoboam's rule? Read also **2 Chronicles 11:5–12:1.**

b. What fact is recorded twice in **1 Kings 14:21 and 14:31** that might explain why Judah turns from God? (Make sure to use an RSV-CE or NAB Bible; the wording in others may differ.)

2. In spite of the evil done by kings of Judah, God again promises to maintain a "lamp" for David in Jerusalem forever (the first time he promised this was in **1 Kings 11:34-36**). What does that mean, and why does God do it?

3. Read **2 Kings 8:16-29 and Chapters 11 and 12.** After sixty-six years of good kings (whose reigns are not included in this session's reading) and peace, an evil king, Jehoram, takes the throne (see **2 Kings 8**).

    a. How do you account for the dramatic change?

    b. How tenuous does the situation become in just fifteen years? (See **2 Kings 11–12.**)

    c. Is Athaliah ultimately successful in her attempt to destroy the royal line? Explain.

Following Queen Athaliah are four generations of good kings, reigning a total of 137 years. During this time, they do what is right but fail to remove the high places set up during the time of Rehoboam. This reading focuses on the later reigns of Hezekiah and Manasseh—arguably the best and worst kings of the Southern Kingdom respectively.

4. Read **2 Kings 18:1–21:18.** King Hezekiah (Chapters 18–20) trusts God and does what is right in his eyes. God gives him success during his twenty-nine-year reign. Among other things, Hezekiah removes the high places dedicated to Baal and cuts down the Asherah poles. Sennacherib, king of Assyria, deports people from the Northern Kingdom during Hezekiah's reign and then comes down and marches against Jerusalem.

    a. Think back for a moment. What options does God set before the people before they enter the Promised Land? (Read **Deuteronomy 30:15-20.**)

b. Now read **2 Kings 18:28-35.** What options does Sennacherib present to them? How does Sennacherib's "offer" compare or contrast with God's?

c. Do you hear in Sennacherib's words any echo of the voice of the Serpent to Adam and Eve?

d. How does Hezekiah respond, and what is the result?

5. Hezekiah's son Manasseh follows him as king. What are the sins of Manasseh, and how does God say he will judge them? (See **2 Kings 21:1-18.**)

The Sins of Manasseh

One of the most shocking things that Manasseh did was to erect pagan altars in the Temple, turning it into a place for worshiping the stars. Think back on the significance of the Temple in Jerusalem. Like the Tabernacle that preceded it, the Temple was God's house—the place he chose to dwell among his people, the place where he met with man. The Ark of the Covenant in the Holy of Holies was his earthly throne. It is hard to imagine the desecration.

It is worth considering: If the Church today is the New Jerusalem, and if we are temples of the Holy Spirit with Christ present in us in the Eucharist, are there ways in which we have built altars to other gods in our churches or in the tabernacles of ourselves? Let us not repeat the sins of Manasseh.

---

6. **Think About It:** The Davidic kingdom may have been flawed, but it had been established by God and had become, in some ways, a model for the heavenly kingdom, the Church. Several places in 1 and 2 Kings mention the office of a steward or vicar in charge of the king's palace and properties. Much like a prime minister is today, he was second only to the king in power and authority and acted with the king's authority in his absence.

a. Read about the steward in **Isaiah 22:15-24,** and record what you learn?

b. Now read **CCC 552–553.** What continuity do you see between this Old Testament office and the office of the papacy?

Prophets Sent to the Southern Kingdom

7. Isaiah is perhaps the greatest Old Testament prophet. He is quoted more often in the New Testament than any book except Psalms. His book is given pride of place in Scripture, appearing first in the section devoted to the prophets. Isaiah lived in Jerusalem and wrote primarily to the Southern Kingdom. Read **Isaiah 5–6.**

    a. What does Isaiah say is going on in Judah that gives God concern?

    b. How will God deal with the sins of the Southern Kingdom? (Read also **2 Kings 20:16-18,** in which Isaiah tells King Hezekiah this directly.)

8. Micah is another prophet sent by God around the time of Isaiah. He prophesies during the reigns of Jotham, Ahaz, and Hezekiah (find them on your *Bible Timeline* Chart) and speaks to the conditions prior to Hezekiah's reforms. Up until now, we have been reading a lot about what God's people are not supposed to do. Read **Micah 6:1-8.** What does God want from them more than burnt offerings?

D. Application

These questions will help you apply one of the key themes of the session to your life. After meditating on them, respond to God with a brief written prayer if you choose.

Are there voices in this world that hold out the enticements of life, love, or goodness apart from God? What are they? Do you hear any echoes of Sennacherib's offer to Hezekiah or the Serpent's questions to Eve? Hear the words for what they are. What can you learn from Hezekiah's example to help you fight their allure?

Dear Lord …

E. Wrap-Up

Conclude your study of the Divided Kingdom, and fix it in your mind by doing the following:

1. Recall the color of this time period, black, and think of it in terms of your reading to help you remember it.

2. Quickly review Sessions 13 and 14. Write a brief summary of what the Divided Kingdom period is about or its significance as part of the "big picture."

KINGS OF JUDAH (SOUTHERN KINGDOM)
930–586 BC

No.	King	Date BC	Bad/Good	Years Reigned	Relation to Predecessor	End of Reign	Scripture Reference
1	Rehoboam I	930–913	Bad	17	Son of Solomon	Died	1 Kings 11:42–14:31
2	Abijah	913–910	Bad	3	Son	Died	1 Kings 14:31–15:8
3	Asa	910–869	Good	41	Son	Died	1 Kings 15:8-24
4	Jehoshaphat	872–848	Good	25	Son	Died	1 Kings 22:41-55
5	Jehoram	848–841	Bad	8	Son	Stricken by God	2 Kings 8:16-24
6	Ahaziah	841	Bad	1	Son	Killed by Jehu	2 Kings 8:24–9:29
7	Athaliah	841–835	Bad	7	Mother	Killed by Army	2 Kings 11:1-20
8	Joash	835–796	Good	40	Grandson	Killed by Servants	2 Kings 11:1–12:21
9	Amaziah	796–767	Good	29	Son	Killed by Court	2 Kings 14:1-20
10	Uzziah	792–740	Good	52	Son	Stricken by God	2 Kings 15:1-7
11	Jotham	750–732	Good	16	Son	Died	2 Kings 15:32-38
12	Ahaz	735–715	Bad	16	Son	Died	2 Kings 16:1-20
13	Hezekiah	715–686	Good	29	Son	Died	2 Kings 18:1–20:21
14	Manasseh	697–642	Bad	55	Son	Died	2 Kings 21:1-18
15	Amon	642–640	Bad	2	Son	Killed by Servants	2 Kings 21:19-26
16	Josiah	640–609	Good	31	Son	Wounded in Battle	2 Kings 22:1–23:30
17	Johoahaz	609	Bad	3 Months	Son	Exiled to Egypt	2 Kings 23:31-34
18	Jehoiakim	609–598	Bad	11	Brother	Died in Siege	2 Kings 23:34–24:5
19	Jehoiachin	598–597	Bad	3 Months	Son	Exiled to Babylon	2 Kings 24:6-16
20	Zedekiah	597–586	Bad	11	Uncle	Exiled to Babylon	2 Kings 24:17–25:30

Session 14 Talk Notes

Divided Kingdom – Part 2

I.   Introduction to Divided Kingdom – Part 2 (Southern Kingdom, Judah)

II.   The Kings of Judah (Davidic Monarchy) – Examples

A.   Rehoboam, son of Solomon (1 Kings 15)

B.   Jehoram, son of Jehoshaphat (2 Kings 8)

1.   Marries Ahab and Jezebel's daughter Athaliah (from Israel)

2.   Royal line narrows to one child: Joash

C.   Uzziah (also known as Azariah; 2 Kings 15:1-7)

1.   Reigns fifty-two years in Jerusalem

2.   Stricken with leprosy; son "over the household" (Heb., *al ha-bayit*)

3.   Chronicles of the kings

D.   Ahaz, Hezekiah (2 Kings 18)

1.   Ahaz does not listen to God or pray

2.   Hezekiah embodies the condition and fate of his people

3.   Isaiah 38: a hymn of thanksgiving to God from Hezekiah

E.   Manasseh, Josiah (2 Kings 22)

1.   Manasseh

2.   Josiah

a.   Reform

i.   Josiah devoted to Temple and *Torah*

b.   Response to *Torah:* rending garments

c.   Sirach 49:1-3 speaks of Josiah

i.   As sweet as honey (love of *Torah*)

ii. A blending of incense (devotion to Temple)

III. Prophets Sent to Judah ("Prophets of the Northern and Southern Kingdoms")[1]

A. "Major" versus "minor" prophets

B. Isaiah

1. Two "books" can be seen within its sixty-six chapters

   a. "Book of Woe" (Chapters 1–39)

   b. "Book of Consolation" (Chapters 40–55)

2. Isaiah sheds light on ministries of John the Baptist and Jesus

   a. Looking for "the consolation of Israel" (Simeon, Luke 2:25)[2]

   b. A voice in the wilderness: "Prepare the way of the LORD" (Isaiah 40:3)

3. "Book of Woe" (Chapters 1–39)

   a. Woes: "Until cities lie waste" (6:1-11)

   b. Behold, a sign: *almah* – "virgin," "young maiden" (7:10-17)

   c. Zebulun and Naphtali (9:1-7)

      i. The highway, the "Way of the Sea"

      ii. The people who dwell in darkness shall see a great light

      iii. Matthew 5:14: "You are the light of the world"

   d. Installation of a new steward or "prime minister" (Isaiah 22)

      i. *Al ha-bayit,* "over the household"

      ii. Rules in the king's absence

      iii. Receives keys to the kingdom

      iv. Authority to bind and loose

      v. A father or "papa"

---

[1]   This chart is on page 94.

[2]   "The consolation of Israel" was a name used by Jews for the Messiah, possibly based on Isaiah 12:1 and 49:13.

      vi. New Testament: St. Peter as "prime minister" (Matthew 16)

    4. "Book of Consolation" (Chapters 40–55)

      a. Isaiah 40

      b. Isaiah 53

IV. Micah's Message to Judah (Micah 4:1-2)

A. "Come, let us go up to the mountain of the LORD"

B. Jeremiah

   1. His message

   2. Predicts exile and return

     a. Jeremiah 25:11-12

     b. Jeremiah 29:10-14

   3. Prophecy of the New Covenant (31:31-34)

     a. Reasons for exile (34:8-21)

V. The End of the Southern Kingdom (2 Kings 25)

VI. Conclusion

A. Establish the Context

Israel at last was a kingdom, but it quickly ran aground when Solomon turned his eyes from God and focused on building for himself. His son Rehoboam only made things worse, precipitating a drastic split. David's Royal Kingdom of Israel became two separate kingdoms. Judah encompassed Jerusalem and the land to its south. Israel comprised the tribes to its north (tribes which seceded from the original kingdom and which wanted nothing to do with the house of David). Israel's king, Jeroboam, set up golden calves at two centers of worship to replace the Temple, appointed his own priests, and established new festivals. Under this alternate religion, Israel quickly foundered. About two hundred years of apostasy, violence, and Baal worship followed. Twenty kings jostled for power during that time, and not one followed God. This was despite repeated warnings from prophets who spoke against the apostate cult and called the people back to spiritual fidelity, even as they gave assurance that God still loved them and would forgive them and take them back. By 722 BC, the time for punishment had come. The people of Israel would be conquered by Assyria and scattered in exile.

Judah fared somewhat better, with good kings periodically calling the people back to God. The Temple was there, and for the most part, God was worshiped there. God kept his promise, and for about 350 years, David's dynasty continued. However, the people continued to fall into idol worship and various types of apostasy. They had God's presence among them in the Temple but were complacent and failed to follow his Law. They, too, received messages from God's prophets—calls to return to their Father—but heeded them only sporadically. Around the time the Northern Kingdom fell, Isaiah foretold that Judah, too, would be punished with exile, this time to Babylon. This was a remarkable prophecy considering that Assyria was in power in those days, and Babylon was no noticeable threat.

The dark, black days of the Divided Kingdom are about to spill into the baby blue of the Exile (see your *Bible Timeline* Chart). The times of exile are depicted by the blue arrows going northward from the two kingdom bars. You can remember the color of this period by thinking of Judah "singing the blues" in "Baby-lon." This is a time of deep sadness, mourning, and reflection but also a time of hope. God's punishment of his children—just as it was in Eden—is remedial. Whatever they do, he will keep his promises. It is not yet clear how he will do this, but his prophets hint at a light at the end of the tunnel. Pay attention to these messages. They apply to the kingdoms of Israel and Judah, certainly, but also to the coming heavenly kingdom and God's solution to the problem of sin.

B. Read the Story

The reading from the narrative books is light for the period of the Exile. Read **2 Kings 17 and 18:9-12** for the fall of Israel and **2 Kings 24–25** for the exile of Judah. Much of what we know about this period comes from the writings of the prophets, which appear as supplemental books on your *Timeline* Chart. (2 Chronicles provides an alternate narrative of the history of the kingdom of Judah. The book of Lamentations presents the prophet Jeremiah's account of the destruction of Jerusalem.) Take time to look at the prophets named among the supplemental books of the Exile on your Chart and then find them above in the middle section of the Chart, where you can get an idea of their audiences and when they spoke. Several readings from these supplemental books will be included with the questions in this session.

As always, pray before you read.

C. Take a Deeper Look

Answering these questions will draw you into the heart of the story. If you do not understand something, make a note of it to bring up in the discussion.

Israel (the North) Goes into Exile Under Assyria: 722 BC (2 Kings 17)

1. Read **2 Kings 17.** What reasons are given for Israel's exile to Assyria?

2. The king of Assyria (probably Sargon II) sends people from five other captured nations to repopulate Samaria after he exiles the Jews. Even though he sends a Jewish priest back to teach the people how to worship God, what is the result of repopulating the land in this way?

Israel, the Northern Kingdom

When you read the Prophets, take care to identify who is meant by "Israel." During the time of the Divided Kingdom, "Israel" was the name of the Northern Kingdom. After the people of the North were deported, only Judah (whose people come to be called "Jews") remained—and the prophets once again started referring to the people as a whole as "Israel." Clearly, the word has a connotation that means "God's people" and is not confined to geographic boundaries.

The messianic hopes of Israel included the belief that the twelve tribes of Israel would be fully restored under the rule of a Davidic king. Thus, in the New Testament, when the apostle Paul says that "all Israel" will be saved (Romans 11:25-27), he is referring to all of the twelve tribes, including the people of the Diaspora—those who were scattered in exile.

Judah's Failure to Proclaim Liberty

To properly understand the exile of Judah, we need to remember the freedom from bondage that was at the heart of Israel's identity. Every seventh day was meant to be a day of rest. As an extension of this, there were specified years (at seven-year intervals) of rest for the land, of forgiveness of debts, and freedom for Hebrew slaves. Every fiftieth year was a year of Jubilee, a joyous memorial of God's redemption in which the people were to grant others what God had given them: Debts of all kinds were to be canceled, all slaves were to be set free, and everyone was to return to the land of their inheritance and regain their ancestral property.

Such, at least, was the Law. Whether that law was followed is another story.

3. The prophet Jeremiah is sent by God toward the end of the Southern Kingdom to announce the imminent approach of judgment. Read **Jeremiah 34,** which is a final warning to Judah under King Zedekiah. What reason does Jeremiah give for the impending judgment?

4. a. **New Testament Connection:** Jesus tells a parable about a man who is unwilling to forgive the debt of another man. Read **Matthew 18:21-35.** What is Jesus teaching Peter with this parable, and how does it relate to the concept of Jubilee and the reason for exile?

    b. Read **CCC 2838–2845.** What does this add to your understanding of the importance of forgiveness in light of this lesson of the Jubilee and the Exile?

Judah (the South) Is Exiled to Babylon: 587 BC (2 Kings 24–25)

In 612 BC, the Assyrian capital of Nineveh fell to the Babylonians, who pressed southward to meet hostile advances from Egypt. Judah got caught in these battles that marked the rise of the new world power. Eventually, the Southern Kingdom was exiled in three deportations (see your Bible Timeline Chart*). The first exile occurred in 605 BC under the reign of Jehoiakim (2 Kings 24:1-7). From the book of Daniel, we know that at this time, Nebuchadnezzar carried off some of the best and brightest young men to work in his kingdom. The second and main exile was in 597 BC (2 Kings 24:8-16). Jerusalem was captured, King Jehoiachin was exiled, and ten thousand Jews were deported to Babylon. Finally, in 587 BC (2 Kings 24:17–25:21), Jerusalem was destroyed, much of the royal family and many high officials were executed, and King Zedekiah and most of the remaining people were exiled. If you have not done so already, read about it in* **2 Kings 24–25.**

5. The first deportation: Read **Daniel 1–7.** Daniel is one of the bright young men taken to Babylon after Nebuchadnezzar's initial foray into Judah. The book of Daniel, which is part historical narrative and part apocalyptic literature, is an important supplemental book of this time period.

    a. In Chapter 2, Daniel's vision of the five kingdoms gives us a road map for the rest of the story. Re-read Nebuchadnezzar's dream and the interpretation God gives to Daniel. What is the dream, and how does Daniel describe the kingdom that will one day be set up by God?

    b. **Daniel 7:1-14** relates a dream Daniel has during the reign of Nebuchadnezzar's son and successor, Belshazzar. Describe the "Son of Man" and his kingdom that the dream foretells (verses 13-14).

    c. Now read **Mark 14:60-65.** Why do you think Jesus' words prompt such a drastic reaction from the high priest?

6. The second deportation: Ezekiel is exiled to Babylon in the second deportation. As both a priest and a prophet, Ezekiel is called by God to minister to the exiles who are cut off from both the Land and Temple. Read **Ezekiel 34.**

    a. On whom does Ezekiel lay the weight of blame in this chapter?

    b.   What promise of consolation does Ezekiel offer?

7.   The third deportation: Read the account of Zedekiah's defeat in **2 Kings 25:5-7.**

    a.   How does the way in which he is carried off reflect the state of the people's hearts and spirits?

    b.   Find Babylon on the "Abraham's Journey" map on page 26. Think back through the history you have learned so far. What else has happened here? Is there anything notable or ironic about *where* God's people are taken into captivity?

Jeremiah begins to prophesy during the reign of Josiah and continues through the three deportations, finally fleeing with others to Egypt after the murder of Gedaliah, referred to in 2 Kings 25. He is a fiery preacher and a prophet of judgment who announces the pending destruction of Judah and the fulfillment of the covenant curses. But God also gives him a message of hope that his mercy will ultimately triumph.

8.   Read **Jeremiah 31 and 33.** What good news does he announce in these chapters? (Recall that "Ephraim" is sometimes used to refer to the Northern Kingdom.)

D. Application

These questions will help you apply one of the key themes of the session to your life. After meditating on them, respond to God with a brief written prayer if you choose.

Have you ever heard anyone condemn the Catholic Church because it holds itself up to be true? "Tolerance" in America has degenerated into condemnation of any religion that does not give others equal weight. How do you handle charges of "intolerance"? Is there anything in the pressures Israel and Judah faced during the Divided Kingdom or in the messages of the prophets that can help you stand strong?

Dear Lord …

E. Wrap-Up

Conclude your study of the Exile, and fix it in your mind by doing the following:

1.   Recall the color of this period, baby blue, and think of it in terms of your reading to help you remember it.

2.   Quickly review this session. Write a brief summary of what the period of the Exile is about or its significance as part of the "big picture."

Session 15 Talk Notes

Exile

I.   Introduction to the Exile

A. Assyrians take Israel into captivity (722 BC)

B.   Babylonians exile Judah (587 BC)

C. World powers

D. "Supplemental" books

II.   Judah (the South) Exiled to Babylon

A. Reason: Jeremiah 34 – failure to release slaves

1.   Matthew 18: forgiveness as release

B.   Summary of Babylonian Exile: three deportations

1.   605 BC (Daniel)

2.   597 BC (Baruch, Ezekiel)

3.   587 BC (Judah falls to Babylon; Temple destroyed)

III.   First Deportation (Daniel)

A. Character of the exile

1.   Stripping identity
2.   Taking the "best and brightest"
3.   Rise of dietary laws, importance of *Torah*

B.   Book of Daniel – part "apocalyptic"

C. Nebuchadnezzar's dream of the five kingdoms (Daniel 2)

1.   The dream: a four-part statue and a stone (verse 31ff)

a. Head: gold
b. Breast and arms: silver
c. Belly and thighs: bronze
d. Legs: iron; feet: iron mixed with clay
e. Stone cut out by no human hand – becomes a mountain

2.   The interpretation: five kingdoms (verse 37ff)

a. First kingdom: Babylon

b. Second kingdom: Persia (Medo-Persia)

c. Third kingdom: Greece

d. Fourth kingdom: Rome

e. Fifth kingdom (stone): the kingdom of God (verse 44ff)

    3. New Testament echo: a temple "not made with hands" in messianic age

        a. Jesus' trial (Mark 14:56-58)

        b. The stone is Christ (by extension, the Church built on Peter, rock)

  D. Daniel's dream of the four beasts and the Son of Man (Daniel 7)

    1. Four beasts (four kingdoms)

        a. Lion with eagles' wings – Babylon

        b. Bear – Persia

        c. Leopard – Greece

        d. Immense beast, extraordinary strength – Rome

    2. "One like a son of man"– consistent with the fifth kingdom

        a. Characteristics

        b. Given everlasting dominion

        c. Glory

        d. Kingdom shall not be destroyed

        e. All peoples will serve him

        f. Messianic title

  E. Daniel intercedes for Judah (Daniel 9)

    1. Ezekiel 22:30: no one to "stand in the gap"

    2. The result of their faithlessness: Seventy years will not be enough (Gabriel; verse 20)

        a. Meaning of "seventy times seven" (time until the Anointed One, Messiah)

           i. Number of completeness

          ii. Leads roughly to the time of Christ

        iii. Matthew 18:21-35: Jesus' use of "seventy times seven" – failure to release

IV. Second Deportation: 597 BC (Ezekiel)

  A. Ezekiel's message

    1. Shepherds not doing their job (Ezekiel 34)

    2. God himself will be the shepherd and bring back the lost

  B. Jesus alludes to Daniel and Ezekiel

    1. Luke 19:9-10 (use of *hekesh,* "to bang together") – "Today salvation has come to this house … for the son of man has come to seek and save the lost"

V. Third Deportation and the Fall of Jerusalem: 587 BC (2 Kings 25)

  A. Temple destroyed

  B. King Zedekiah deported

VI. Conclusion

  A. Symbolism of Daniel and the lion's den

A. Establish the Context

During the time period of the Exile, Israel (the Northern Kingdom) was conquered by Assyria (in 722 BC). Most of the people were deported and scattered. They settled elsewhere in the Assyrian kingdom and eventually intermarried with the people around them and were absorbed into other nations (sometimes these are called the "lost tribes of Israel"). In their place, King Sargon imported people from five other conquered nations and settled them in the area of Samaria. These people intermarried with the remaining Israelites. The mixed population of Samaritans that resulted developed its own religion: They worshiped the God of Israel right along with the gods they had brought from their homelands. This exile marks the end of the Northern Kingdom and the tribes that comprised it.

The Southern Kingdom fell during the period of the Exile, (in 587 BC) to the Babylonians who destroyed Jerusalem and the Temple and exiled many of the people of Judah to Babylon. God's faithfulness to his people and to his promises—despite the infidelity of the people—can be seen in the messages of the prophets of the time. Even though they prophesied destruction and exile, they held out hope, saying a remnant of the people would return to the land; a "righteous Branch" would reign wisely; God would establish an eternal kingdom; God would forgive them and make a new covenant with them and write it on their hearts.

This next time period, the Return, chronicles Judah's return home after seventy years of Babylonian exile. Remember it by the color yellow, which represents brighter days. The people return in three waves over a period of about a hundred years. They are represented on the Chart by yellow arrows pointing down from the Northern Countries into the land of Canaan. The story is told in the narrative books of Ezra (who describes the first two returns) and Nehemiah. The supplemental books add to our understanding of the period. These include Zechariah and Haggai (two prophets who minister to those who return) and Esther and Malachi.

Notice on your *Timeline* Chart that two new world powers come into play during this time. Persia gains ascendancy at the start of the period and is followed by Greece about two hundred years later. One way to remember the sequence of world powers is by using this memory aid: Eat **A** **B**ig **P**urple **GR**ape ("E" for Egypt, "A" for Assyria, "B" for Babylon, "P" for Persia, "G" for Greece, and "R" for Rome). This is the time of Plato, Socrates, and Aristotle. The first Greek translation of the Old Testament, the Septuagint, was made in Alexandria, Egypt, during this time, and the Great Wall of China was built.

B. Read the Story

Read **Ezra 1, 3–7 and 9:1–10:17** and **Nehemiah 2, 4:1–5:13, and 9:32–10:29** to become familiar with the main characters (King Cyrus, Ezra, and Nehemiah) and the events of the Return. Cyrus of Persia sends the exiles home to rebuild the Temple, and they begin rebuilding Jerusalem. After reading, trace the action in the center section of your *Bible Timeline* Chart. Identify the main characters, and notice the flow of key events and where they take place. Any questions? Jot them down.

Going Deeper (optional): To get the entire story of this period, read the books of **Ezra** and **Nehemiah.** You may also want to read the book of **Esther,** which is a "supplemental" book for this time period in the *Bible Timeline* Learning System and which is also included in the readings for this session.

As always, pray before you read.

C. Take a Deeper Look

Answering these questions will draw you into the heart of the story. If you do not understand something, make a note of it to bring up in the discussion.

The Return Foretold

1. The events recorded in Ezra were prophesied by Isaiah two centuries previously during the time of the Divided Kingdom. Read **Isaiah 44:24-28 and 45:1-6, 13.** Who does Isaiah mention by name, and what does he say will be this man's role in the restoration?

The First Return (Ezra 1–6)

2. a. Read **Ezra 1.** How is Isaiah's prophecy fulfilled?

   b. Why might God have given his people such exact information so far in advance?

> ### Cyrus the Great
>
> King Cyrus founded the Persian Empire by uniting the Medes and Persians. He captured Babylon in 539 BC but was perceived more as a liberator than a conqueror because of his tolerance and magnanimity toward those he conquered. At his coronation, he read a "charter of freedom" granting his people freedom from slavery, freedom of religion, and freedom from oppression.

   c. Ezra 1:1 mentions a prophecy by Jeremiah. Read **Jeremiah 29:10-14.** What is the prophecy?

3. **Think About It:** Judah was exiled for failing to learn the lessons of the Exodus. Do you see any parallels between this return and the way the children of Israel left Egypt originally?

4. a. Read **Ezra 3.** What is accomplished in the first return?

    b. Read **Ezra 4–6.** What kind of opposition do they face, and how are they helped?

        (Note: Remember the Samaritans? These were the poor people who remained when most of the North was exiled. They were mixed with the Gentiles that King Sargon relocated from foreign countries to repopulate the area.)

The Second Return (Ezra 7–10)

5. Read **Ezra 7.** A descendant of a high priestly line that goes back to the days of David and Solomon, Ezra returns with the next wave of exiles. He is also a scribe (or teacher of the Law of Moses) who has devoted himself to studying, observing, and teaching the Word of God.

    a. Why is Ezra sent back to Jerusalem, and what assistance is he given?

    b. Read **Ezra 9:1–10:17.** What does Ezra find when he arrives, and what kind of reform does he find it necessary to make?

The Third Return (Nehemiah)

6. The book of Nehemiah tells about the third wave of return from captivity.

    a. Read **Nehemiah 2 and 4.** Why does Nehemiah return, and how does he fare?

    b. Read **5:1-13.** What additional crisis does Nehemiah confront at this time?

c.   After the walls are built and the people are settled in their towns, Ezra brings out the Book of the Law and reads it to the assembled people. There is great joy as they celebrate the weeklong Feast of Tabernacles. Following this, they confess their sins and worship God, remembering all he has done for them through the ages. Read **Nehemiah 9:32–10:29.** What else do they do?

Life in Babylon After the Exile

7.   The book of Esther fits between the first and second returns (between Zerubbabel and Ezra). Many of the Jews do not return to Israel. Esther gives us a window into the lives of those who choose to remain in Persia. Read the book of **Esther.** Interestingly, God is not mentioned in the original Hebrew text (although he is in the "Preliminaries," also called "Chapters A–F" or numbered as Chapters 10:4–16:24. These Greek additions were retained in the canonical Catholic Bible but were removed from Protestant Bibles.) Does God forsake the people left behind in exile, or is he faithful yet?

D. Application

These questions will help you apply one of the key themes of the session to your life. After meditating on them, respond to God with a brief written prayer if you choose.

Have you ever had an experience where you strayed from the Lord, repented, and returned to him? This may be in a relationship or attitude. What rebuilding did you need to do?

Dear Lord …

E. Wrap-Up

Conclude your study of the Return, and fix it in your mind by doing the following:

1.   Recall the color of this period, yellow, and think of it in terms of your reading to help you remember it.

2.   Quickly review this session. Write a brief summary of what the period of the Return is about or its significance as part of the "big picture."

Session 16 Talk Notes

Return

I. Introduction to the Return

A. Review of the Exile

1. Three deportations
2. Daniel 9: seventy times seven years
3. Jesus: still need to return spiritually
4. Disorientation

B. Introduction to the Return

1. Ezekiel 33:10: "How shall we then live?"

2. Three returns reveal three-part reorientation
   a. Worship (Zerubbabel rebuilds Temple)
   b. Word (Ezra re-establishes prominence of *Torah*)
   c. Wall (Nehemiah rebuilds Jerusalem walls)

3. Ezra and Nehemiah were originally one book

4. Supplemental books
   a. Prophets: Haggai, Zachariah, Malachi
   b. Esther (key thought: 4:14)

5. New world power: Persia

II. Cyrus Permits the Return (Ezra 1:1–4)

A. Theme of exile in the Bible: comparisons with Exodus

B. Problem of complacency

III. First Return: Zerubbabel Rebuilds the Temple (Ezra 3:7–6:18)

A. Obstacles to building (Ezra 4:1-5)

1. Challenges from without: the Samaritans

2. Challenges from within

   a. Haggai's message (Haggai 1:9): Give worship priority

3. The Temple completed

4. Meaning for us (CCC 115–117)

    a. Literal sense (meaning to original audience)

    b. Spiritual senses (built on literal)
       i. Allegorical sense (significance in Christ)
          • Jesus as the new Temple

       ii. Moral sense (significance to us and our actions)
          • 1 Corinthians 3
          • 2 Corinthians 6:16
          • 1 Peter 2:5

       iii. Anagogical sense (eternal significance)

    c. Our challenges from within and without

    d. A tale of two stones

IV. Second Return: Ezra Returns and Teaches (Ezra 7:1–10:44)

    A. The need for the Law (*Torah,* Word)

       1. Ezra 7:10: set heart to study, do, and teach

       2. Nehemiah 8:7-8: the need for instruction

    B. Ezra addresses their intermarriage (Ezra 9:2ff)

       1. "Disparity of cult" (CCC. 1634)

       2. New Testament Connection: 1 Corinthians 7:10-15

V. Third Return: Nehemiah Rebuilds Jerusalem Walls (Nehemiah)

    A. The importance of walls

    B. Nehemiah's approach to challenges (4:16-17): shovel and sword

    C. Finding the spiritual sense for our lives

VI. Malachi ("My Messenger") Prophesies

    A. Failure to give God what is his (Malachi 3:7-11)

    B. God as "a refiner's fire" (3:1-2)

    C. The "Elijah who is to come" (4:5; NAB: 3:23; see Matthew 11:11-14)

VII. Conclusion

    A. *HaTikvah* – Israeli national anthem, "The Hope"

A. Establish the Context

Just as God used foreign nations to punish his people when they turned from him, he used a foreign nation to restore them. Cyrus the Great, king of Persia, in his own words, was "appointed" by God, not only to allow the people of Judah to return to Jerusalem, but also to equip them to rebuild the Temple so that God might again be worshiped in his city.

Seventy years is a long time to be away from home. Two new generations had grown up hearing their parents and grandparents lamenting the loss of Jerusalem and the Temple, steeped in the knowledge that their exile was a physical living-out of their spiritual separation from God. Torn from the land God had given them and living with the memory of his promises, they began to realize what they had lost and why. It was an enthusiastic group that returned to Jerusalem. Not everyone returned, however. Those who made the journey south did so in three stages. The first group returned in 538 BC and included Zerubbabel, a descendant of David, who oversaw the rebuilding of the Temple. A second return occurred between 525 and 457 BC during the time a priest and scribe named Ezra taught the people from the Law and led moral reforms. Nehemiah came with the last wave in 444 BC. He rebuilt the Jerusalem walls and led the people to confess their sins and make a binding agreement with God.

After this "remnant" of Jews returned to the land, they lived in relative peace for a century and were quite faithful to the Covenant. Around 336 BC, Alexander the Great swept across Asia, conquering nations and extending the rule of a new power—Greece. He aimed to unify the world under Greek language and culture—a process known as "hellenization" that required people to abandon their religions and allegiances and submit to him. The Jews refused. In 332 BC, Alexander came to Jerusalem intending to punish them. Impressed by what he saw, he instead allowed them to keep their own laws. Alexander died suddenly in 323 BC, and the Greek empire was divided among five of his generals. By 312 BC, two had emerged as leaders: Ptolemy over Egypt and Seleucus over Syria. First the Ptolemies and then the Seleucids took control over Palestine. (The times of their rules are represented by triangles on your *Timeline* Chart.) While the Ptolemies were tolerant of Jewish law and religion, the Seleucids were not. In 175 BC, Antiochus Epiphanes came to power and began a policy of radical hellenization under which he determined to eradicate the Jewish religion. This sets the scene for the events described in 1 Maccabees and for the final Old Testament period in our study, the Maccabean Revolt.

B. Read the Story

Read **1 Maccabees 1–6** to become familiar with the main characters and events of the Maccabean Revolt. In these chapters and those that follow, Mattathias and his sons lead a courageous and ultimately successful resistance to violent, terroristic suppression of their religion by their Seleucid rulers. The reading for this session is not always easy to take, particularly a passage assigned later in the session from the supplemental book, 2 Maccabees. It gives a painfully vivid picture of the cruelty Israel was up against, but shows an alternate path of resistance: that of martyrdom.

Going Deeper (optional): To get the entire story of this period, read all of **1 Maccabees.**

1 Maccabees is one of the deuterocanonical books rejected by the Protestant founders, as are 2 Maccabees and Sirach (portions of which are also assigned in this session). You must have a Bible version that includes the "Apocrypha," to read them. For more information on why certain books were excluded from Protestant Bibles, see the Catholic Encyclopedia's explanation of the Old Testament Canon (newadvent. org/cathen/03267a.htm) or one of the resources listed on page 2 of this study.

Trace the action of the Maccabean Revolt on your *Bible Timeline* Chart. Identify the main people, and notice the flow of key events and where they take place. Any questions? Jot them down.

As always, pray before you read.

C. Take a Deeper Look

Answering these questions will draw you into the heart of the story. If you do not understand something, make a note of it to bring up in the discussion.

1. **1 Maccabees 1** tells the story of Antiochus Epiphanes and his brutal suppression of the Jews and desecration of the Temple. This is not the first time Israel has faced serious opposition. How would you summarize the threat to Israel, and how the people respond to that threat?

2. Read **1 Maccabees 2.**

    a. When Mattathias sees what has been done to Jerusalem, he moves with his sons to Modein. What threat do they face there?

    b. What are Mattathias and his sons able to do against this threat?

    c. How does Mattathias strengthen his sons before he dies?

3. How do you explain the victories of Judas Maccabeus and his family over far greater armies? What is their attitude and motivation? (See **1 Maccabees 3 and 4.**)

4. After crushing their enemies, Judas and his brothers turn their attention toward home. Describe what they accomplish in **1 Maccabees 4:36-61,** and why it is important.

5. 2 Maccabees is a supplemental book for this time period. While it contains some of the same history (the fifteen years covered in 1 Maccabees 1–7), it is more of a theological commentary on the time and was written to help build morale. Read **2 Maccabees 7.**

    a. What enables these brothers and their mother to stand steadfast in the face of such cruelty? **Going Deeper (optional):** Read **CCC 988–996,** especially **CCC 992.**

    b. The book of Sirach, which is used extensively today in the liturgy, was written during this period. Read **Sirach 2,** keeping in mind the types of trials God's people were apt to face at the time. What strength and encouragement does it offer them—or anyone whose faith is being tested?

6. Read **2 Maccabees 12:38-46,** which follows an account of some of the battles of Judas Maccabeus.

    a. What does Judas Maccabeus do on behalf of those who have died?

    b. Read **CCC 957–958 and 1030–1032.** What does the Catholic Church say about the practice of offering prayers for the dead?

7. The Wisdom of Solomon was written well after the events of 1 Maccabees and fifty to one hundred years before Christ. Not surprisingly, it warns of the dangers to one's faith of living in a secular environment. The author may have had in mind the plight of such Israelites as the brothers of 2 Maccabees 7 when he wrote the beautiful words found in **Wisdom 3:1-8.** This passage is often used today in the Church's liturgy when martyrs are remembered. Read it, and meditate on God's loving care and our hope of everlasting life. What strikes you that you would like to remember?

D. Application

These questions will help you apply one of the key themes of the session to your life. After meditating on them, respond to God with a brief written prayer if you choose.

Think for a moment of the pressures hellenization placed on devout Jews to stifle their faith. Do you see any parallel in the spirit of the world today? What influences in today's society threaten to desecrate your life or home, and how are you putting up a fight? Is there anything you can learn from these stories to strengthen you in your life?

Dear Lord …

The End of the Old …

This concludes our study of the Old Testament. Scripture is silent about the final years of waiting before the coming of the Messiah. But this does not mean God is not present. Just as he worked quietly behind the scenes during the long years of slavery in Egypt, preparing the way to rescue his people, he is working during this silent time in preparation for his greatest saving act of all. Jesus will be a "new Moses," a "second Adam," and even a "New Israel." He will do everything his predecessors failed to do. And out of the silence of the end of the Old Covenant, will come a song of joy and deliverance for all people—not just from earthly oppression or slavery but from the heavier yoke of sin.

E. Wrap-Up

Conclude your study of the Maccabean Revolt, and fix it in your mind by doing the following:

1. Recall the color of this period, orange, and think of it in terms of your reading to help you remember it.

2. Quickly review this session. Write a brief summary of what the Maccabean Revolt period is about or its significance as part of the "big picture."

Session 17 Talk Notes

Maccabean Revolt

I.　Introduction to the Maccabean Revolt

II.　Rise of Greece to World Power

   A.　Alexander the Great (356–323 BC)

   B.　Hellenization (Greek culture and language)

   C.　Alexander's empire divided
      1.　Syria (North)
      2.　Macedonia (northern Greece)
      3.　Alexandria (Egypt)

   D.　The Ptolemies (Egypt) rule Israel
      1.　The Septuagint (LXX) – Old Testament translated into Greek
         a.　Followed by early Church and Catholics
         b.　Includes deuterocanonical books ("second canon");
            Protestant term = "apocryphal"; "false writings"
      2.　Luther returned to the Hebrew canon (lacking Greek books)

   E.　The Seleucids (Babylonia) take control (198 BC)
      1.　Early tolerance
      2.　Antiochus Epiphanes (175–164 BC): forced hellenization attacked
         a.　Worship – Jewish practices forbidden (Sabbath, circumcision)
         b.　Word – replace God's Word as law with that of the Greek empire
         c.　Wall – community expanded to the hellenistic world, not to be unique God's people

III.　Persecution

   A.　Temptation to join the Gentiles
      1.　The lure of the gymnasium (1:11-15); reversed circumcision

   B.　Forced hellenization (1:41-53)

   C.　Desecration of the Temple (1:54)

IV.　The Maccabean Revolt (166–142 BC)

   A.　Mattathias and his sons (challenge at Modein: 2:15-27)
      1.　Judas Maccabeus, Jonathan, Simon

   B.　The restoration and cleansing of the Temple
      1.　Feast of Dedication (Lights), Hanukkah

   C.　Mattathias' witness (2:49-61): recounting salvation history

   D.　Meaning for us: response to pressure to conform to the world?

V. The Witness of Martyrs (2 Maccabees 6–7)

    A. Eleazar (6:24-30)

    B. The mother and her seven martyred sons

        1. Willing to die for God's laws (7:2, 9, 11, 30)

        2. Suffering as a redemptive act

            a. To draw down God's mercy on Israel

            b. Fulfillment in Christ's suffering for the world

            c. Our participation in that suffering

            d. "I'm calling you to a new martyrdom related to chastity and purity"[1]

            e. Mary's participation

VI. The Hasmonean Dynasty (140–37 BC)

VII. Conclusion: The Rise of Rome and Preparation for the Messiah

    A. Pompey captures Jerusalem (63 BC)

    B. Roman Republic
        1. First Triumvirate: Pompey, Julius Caesar, Crassus
            a. Caesar assassinated by Cassius, Brutus

    C. Second Triumvirate (43–33 BC): Mark Antony, Octavian, Marcus Lepidus

    D. Two battles end the republic
        1. Battle of Philippi (42 BC)
            a. Mark Antony and Octovian defeat Cassius, Brutus

        2. Battle of Actium (31 BC)
            a. Octavian defeats Mark Antony and Cleopatra

    E. Beginning of the Roman Empire
        1. Octavian returns unchallenged (29 BC)

        2. Octavian named Augustus ("exalted one") by senate (27 BC)

        3. Caesar worship

        4. Caesar Augustus (formerly Octavian) rules 27 BC–AD 14
            a. Proclaimed "the son of god"
            b. Ushered in Peace of Rome *(Pax Romana)*
            c. Birthday proclaimed the *euangelion* ("Good News," "gospel") for the Roman Empire

---

[1]   St. John Paul II to youth in Rome, 2007.

A. Establish the Context

Home at last after years of exile, the Jews found their very identity threatened by the forced implementation of hellenization under a new ruler, Antiochus Epiphanes. The Temple became home to sexual revels and pagan sacrifices. People who openly practiced their faith, whether by observing the Sabbath or a Jewish feast, circumcising their sons, or even calling themselves Jews, risked torture and death. Soon, a rebellion began under a faithful Jew named Mattathias and his five sons. They fought against enormous odds, but in just three years, they pushed back their enemies and were able to purify the Temple. This victory is commemorated today as the Feast of Lights, or Hanukkah. The fire in the lamps that were lit during the rededication (described in 2 Maccabees 10) gives us the color—orange—for the period of Maccabean Revolt.

The story of this struggle for independence is told in 1 and 2 Maccabees. The books are not merely historical accounts, however. Their greater purpose is to showcase the providence and protection of God and the importance of staying true to the covenant even to death. This victory seems a fitting close to the final historical book of the Old Testament. Israel has been restored; the people are following God; all that is needed to fulfill the ancient prophecies is a king from David's line.

To fill in some additional historical details: Simon, son of Mattathias, came to power as the first in a line of high priests who also governed the people during the Hasmonean rule. (You will notice this name in a triangle in the Maccabean Revolt period on your *Timeline* Chart.) Under their rule, a movement grew that favored hellenization (the Sadducees). Tensions between the Sadducees and the Jews who were zealous in upholding observation of the *Torah* (Pharisees) eventually erupted into civil war. Pompey intervened in 63 BC, killing the priests at their duties in the Temple and entering the Holy of Holies. He established Hyrcanus II as high priest but made Judah a protectorate. This start to Roman rule would not soon be forgotten.

Hasmonean rule ended in 37 BC when pro-Roman Herod the Great was made king of the Jews. The next time period finds Rome as the dominant world power, the Emperors Augustus and Tiberius on the throne, and Herod the Great's son, Herod Antipas, serving as Tetrarch of Galilee. The Jews may be home, but in a sense they are still "slaves" (subject to foreign empires) and spiritual "exiles." They wait in longing for the coming of the Messiah and for the promised Jubilee. Humanly speaking, things do not look good for Israel. But during this time, God has been quietly preparing the world for the next stage in his plan. A common language (Greek) and road system (thanks to the Greeks and Romans) as well as the availability of the Old Testament in that common language will greatly facilitate the spread of the gospel. The 490 years of extended exile prophesied by Daniel are approaching their end. And when Israel looks to be at its weakest, God will change everything.

The period of Messianic Fulfillment is represented by the color gold, which can be remembered by the gift of gold given by the Magi to the Christ child. The story of this time period is told in the book of Luke and also in the "supplemental" books for this period, the Gospels of Matthew, Mark, and John. Luke is the narrative book of this time period not because it is better or more important than the others (it is not), but because Luke also wrote the Acts of the Apostles, and together, these books form a seamless narrative of the two New Testament periods.

B. Read the Story

Read **Luke 1:1–9:50** to prepare for the first part of Messianic Fulfillment, which will focus on who this new Messiah is, on his early life, and on the launch of his ministry. Any questions? Jot them down.

Going Deeper (optional): To get a full picture of this time period before you begin, read the entire Gospel of **Luke**.

As always, pray before you read.

C. Take a Deeper Look

Answering these questions will draw you into the heart of the story. If you do not understand something, make a note of it to bring up in the discussion.

1. In Luke's Gospel, we finally meet the "woman and her seed" announced in Genesis 3:15. Is there anything in the account of the Annunciation (Luke 1:26-38) that makes you think that here, at last, is a "new Eve"—a woman who will do what Eve failed to do so many years before?

Hail Mary, "Full of Grace"

The angel Gabriel addresses Mary with an unusual greeting: "Hail, O favored one, the Lord is with you!" The Greek word translated as "favored one" is *kecharitomene,* "full of grace." This is the first time since Eve that we meet a woman filled with the divine life. Mary is "from the first moment of her conception, by a singular grace and privilege of almighty God and by virtue of the merits of Jesus Christ, Savior of the human race, preserved immune from all stain of original sin" (CCC 491).[1]

---

2. Who is Jesus?

    a. Review the details of Jesus' early life found in **Luke 1–2.** What is his background? What kind of upbringing has he had? What is he like? Record everything you can find out about the boy born to save the world.

    b. What do the following witnesses from Luke's Gospel tell us about who Jesus is and why he has come?

        God through the angel Gabriel (1:26-38) and with his own voice (3:21-22):

        Simeon (2:25-35):

---

[1]   Pius IX, *Ineffabilis Deus* [1854]: DS 2803.

John the Baptist (3:15-17):

Demons (4:33-34, 41 and 8:26-31):

The centurion (7:1-9):

c. What does Jesus say about himself? (For help with this question, see **Luke 4:16-21, 4:43, 5:24, 5:32, 6:5, and 9:22, 44, and 48.**)

d. How would you describe Jesus to someone who asked you about him?

3. **Think About It:** After his baptism, Jesus is tempted by the devil in the desert (Luke 4). Read the story. Are there any similarities or contrasts between this and the Serpent's temptation of Adam and Eve in the Garden (see **Genesis 3**) or between this and the temptations Israel faced in the desert? (See **Exodus 17:1-7** and **Deuteronomy 6 and 8.**) Choose one of these parallel stories, and discuss how Jesus does what previous children of God failed to do and becomes both a "new Adam" and a "New Israel."

4. In **Luke 4:16-30,** Jesus launches his public ministry by standing up in the synagogue and quoting a passage from Isaiah. Read what he says. What does he mean by, "Today this Scripture has been fulfilled in your hearing"? (Review Session 15 for help with this question.)

    Note on Luke 4:16-30: *When Jesus quotes from Isaiah 61, he replaces "the day of vengeance of our God" with something from Isaiah 58:6: "to set at liberty those who are oppressed." As he makes clear in his references to the time of Elijah and Elisha, the Jubilee he is announcing is not one that includes vengeance on the other nations, but one that includes release even for the Gentiles. It is this that makes those who are listening so angry that they try to kill him.*

5. **Think About It:** Luke's "Sermon on the Plain" (6:17-45) parallels the Sermon on the Mount and the Beatitudes in Matthew 5–6. Both show Jesus as a "new Moses" giving God's law to his people. The original Law taught the freed slaves how to live as the free children of God. In Christ, people are free not just externally from slavery, but internally from sin. How does Jesus' teaching illuminate the inner reality and meaning of the Ten Commandments? (See **Exodus 20.**)

Optional Reading: If you are interested in learning more, the *Catechism* discusses the Beatitudes in **CCC 1716–1729** and the Ten Commandments beginning with **CCC 2052.**

6. Luke tells of Jesus feeding five thousand men with five loaves and two fish in **Luke 9:10-17.** Read that, and then read **John 6.** What added insight does John bring to the significance of this event? (See also **CCC 1384.**)

7. a. The question, "Who is Jesus?" comes to the fore in Luke 8–9. Read the following verses, and record who asks the question, and why.

    Luke 8:22-25:

    Luke 9:7-9:

    b. Now read **Luke 9:18-22,** in which Jesus poses the same question twice. The second time, it is not a rhetorical question. Who answers, and what do they say?

    c   **Think About It:** What event does Luke place between Herod's question in **9:9** and Peter's answer in **9:20?** What difference, if any, does this make in the way you read **verses 18-22?**

8. Read **Luke 9:28-35.** What more is revealed here about who Jesus is?

D. Application

These questions will help you apply one of the key themes of the session to your life. After meditating on them, respond to God with a brief written prayer if you choose.

Put yourself in the story: If you were living when Jesus came to earth, and he came through your town, what would you ask? Would your encounter with him be like any of those you read in Luke's Gospel? What would your dialogue with him be like?

Dear Lord …

Session 18 Talk Notes

Messianic Fulfillment – Part 1

I. Introduction to Messianic Fulfillment – Part 1

II. Jesus Fulfills the Story

    A. Galatians 4:4-7 – "when the time had fully come"

    B. Ephesians 1:9-10 – "the mystery of his will"

    C. "Recapitulation" – Jesus reliving, fulfilling the Old Testament

    D. The geographic story

    E. Exile and return as keys to understanding his mission

III. The Coming of the Messiah

    A. John the Baptist (Luke 1:5-25)

        1. Barrenness (Elizabeth and Zechariah)

        2. In the spirit and power of Elijah (Luke 1:17)

            a. Malachi 4:5

    B. Mary (Luke 1:26-38)

        1. Gabriel's message

        2. "Jesus" ("the salvation of God") will assume the throne of David

        3. The new Ark of the Covenant

            a. "The power of the Most High will overshadow you" (Luke 1:35; Exodus 40:34-35)

            b. The Visitation (verse 36ff)

                i. "Let it be done to me according to your word"

                ii. Parallels with Old Testament language regarding the Ark

The Ark (2 Samuel 6)	Mary (Luke 1)
Carried the Ten Commandments, manna, Aaron's budded rod	Carried the Word made flesh, Bread of heaven, the Great High Priest
Verse 9 – "How can the Ark of the LORD come to me?"	Verse 43 – "Why is this granted me, that the mother of my Lord should come to me?"
Verses 14-16 – David leaping and dancing before the Ark	Verse 41 – John leaping in Elizabeth's womb before Mary
Verse 11 – The Ark stayed in the house of Obed-Edom three months.	Verse 56 – Mary stays with Elizabeth for three months.

    C. The Birth of Jesus (Luke 2)

        1. Hypostatic union (fully human and fully God; CCC 464)

             a. Nestorian heresy: unity of two natures denied

             b. Third Council of Constantinople (680–681 BC): Jesus has two wills as well as two natures (divine and human)

IV. Jesus the Man (1 Timothy 2:5: "The Man Christ Jesus")

    A. Jewish

    B. Rabbi

    C. Simeon found in him "the consolation of Israel" (Luke 2:25-32)

        1. Isaiah 40–55: the "Book of Consolation"

V. Announcement of the Messiah (Luke 3)

    A. Proclamation of John the Baptist (from Isaiah 40ff): "Prepare the way of the Lord"

        1. The beginning of the consolation, restoration

        2. Importance of the Jordan: recapitulation

        3. Echoes of Elijah (clothing, food)

        4. Elijah last seen at the Jordan (2 Kings 2:11)

             a. A new Elijah and Elisha

    B. Baptism of Jesus

VI. Temptation of Jesus (Luke 4:1-13)

    A. Parallels to Israel's forty years in the desert – failure to trust God

        1. Jesus answers temptations from Deuteronomy 6, 8

        2. Jesus relives the history of Israel – but trusts God

VII. Nazareth: Jesus Proclaims the Jubilee (Luke 4:14-21)

    A. Release, liberty, "the acceptable year of the Lord"

    B. Inclusion of the Gentiles (verses 25-28)

VIII. Jesus Calls His Disciples (Luke 5)

    A. They will be "catching men"

IX. Miracles Reveal Kingdom: New Wine in Old Wineskins (Luke 5)

    A. Challenges from the "old model" (Chapter 6)

X. Message of the Kingdom: A New Law (Luke 6; see also Matthew 5–7)

A. Jesus: the new Moses giving the new law

B. Beatitudes: the "inside" of the law

C. "Release" to extend through disciples: forgiveness

XI. Jesus: Fully Man and Fully God

A. Feeding of the five thousand (Luke 9) – Jesus the Bread of Life

    1. See also John 6, Matthew 14

B. "Who do you say that I am?"

    1. Peter's confession (Luke 9:18-22)

    2. Matthew 16: keys to the kingdom; "prime minister," *al ha-bayit*

C. The Transfiguration

    1. They see his glory (9:28-36)

    2. "His exodus" (verse 31)

    3. "He set his face to go to Jerusalem" (verse 51)

Palestine at the Time of Christ

A. Review the Context

Part 1 of Messianic Fulfillment began with the announcement that the time had come for the fulfillment of God's promises and the answer to Israel's pent-up hope and longing. Freedom and the restoration of David's throne were on the horizon. The new king was heralded by the angel Gabriel himself, who said he would be called "Son of the Most High." The Son of God himself would come to rule over the house of David. Who could have imagined it?

Jesus launched his public ministry by announcing the Year of Jubilee and freedom to captives. Then he went out to proclaim and bring about that freedom by seeking the lost, healing disease, and forgiving people's sins. His early teaching focused on the need for repentance and turned upside-down the accepted ideas of who would attain beatitude (eternal happiness with God). Whether in prayer or following the law, heart attitude was all-important. Jesus called his disciples to follow him in the law of love.

Part 2 follows Jesus' ministry in Judea and looks at how he establishes the kingdom of God on earth. The first verse of the reading sets the stage for this section: "When the days drew near for [Jesus] to be received up, he set his face to go to Jerusalem." As he discussed with Moses and Elijah on the Mount of Transfiguration, Jesus is preparing for his departure—his "exodus," whereby he will pass through a sea of suffering and lead his people through death to sin and to a new life in him. Keep this mission in mind as you read. Everything Jesus says and does during his journey to Jerusalem—which you will read about in this session—is said and done in light of that mission.

Note: A map of Palestine at the time of Christ can be found on page 130.

B. Read the Story

Read **Luke 9:51–19:27** to become familiar with the main characters and events of the second part of Messianic Fulfillment, in which Jesus trains his disciples and announces the coming of his kingdom. Read it in one sitting if you can. It is packed full of detail, but do not feel you need to absorb it all. You have a lifetime to do that. (If you are familiar with Luke's Gospel already and do not have much time, skim the reading to refresh your memory and then move on to the questions.) After reading, trace the action in the center section of your *Bible Timeline* Chart. Identify the main characters, and notice the flow of key events and where they take place. Any questions? Jot them down.

Going Deeper (optional): To get a full picture of this time period before you continue, read all of the Gospel of **Luke.**

As always, pray before you read.

C. Take a Deeper Look

Answering these questions will draw you into the heart of the story. If you do not understand something, make a note of it to bring up in the discussion.

Jesus Trains His Disciples

1. Jesus is always attracting followers, but they do not always stay with him as disciples. What does Jesus say it will cost his disciples to follow him? (See **Luke 9:57-62 and 14:25-34.**)

2. Read **Luke 11:1-13,** in which a disciple asks Jesus to teach them to pray.

    a. In light of Israel's history, do you find anything interesting in the fact that Jesus asks his disciples to begin their prayer, "Our Father"? (Read also **Galatians 3:26–4:7.**)

    b. Read **CCC 2762–2766 and 2803–2806.** How would you summarize what Jesus teaches about how we should pray?

    c. What attitude does Jesus urge his disciples to take in prayer, and why? (See **Luke 11:5-13.**)

3. Knowing he will be leaving them, Jesus prepares for his absence by training his apostles to carry on after he is gone and by investing them with authority to rule in his place. By appointing twelve apostles to lead the twelve tribes of Israel, he reconstructs the kingdom around himself. Read the following passages, and note the kind of authority Jesus invests in the apostles (some passages are taken from other Gospels to round out the picture).

    a. **Matthew 18:18-20** and **CCC 553:**

    b. **John 20:21-23:**

c.   **Luke 10:18-20** (Think back to Genesis 3:15. How are the disciples sharing in Christ's mission?):

d.   **Matthew 16:13-20** (This account gives more details of Peter's confession than Luke does in 9:20. What does Matthew add?):

Jesus Proclaims the Kingdom

4.   **Think About It:** The kingdom of God is a frequent topic in Jesus' parables and teaching. Think about what you have learned regarding the kingdom of David and Israel's history since the Divided Kingdom. What kind of kingdom do you think people are expecting?

5.   Read the following passages that deal with the kingdom of God (one is from Matthew's Gospel, which deals extensively with the kingdom): **Luke 13:22-30, 14:15-24, 17:20-21** and **Matthew 25:31-46.**

a.   Where is the kingdom?

b.   Who is invited?

c.   Who will get in?

d.   How does this image square with the one you described in your answer to question 4?

6. Read the three parables Jesus tells in **Luke 15** and the event described in **Luke 19:1-10.**

    a. What is their common message?

    b. Jesus tells these particular stories in answer to the Pharisees' displeasure that he has received tax collectors and sinners and has eaten with them. The Pharisees themselves are fastidious in their avoidance and condemnation of anything "unclean" for fear of contamination. What different perspective do the stories provide? (Read **CCC 588–589** for help with this question.)

    Note: The designation "unclean" was given to dead animals, sick people, Gentiles, certain foods, and social outcasts like tax collectors and sinners. It was a physical—as opposed to moral—state of being that disqualified people from participating in public worship.

Jesus Prepares His Disciples

7. As Jesus and his disciples draw near Jerusalem, he prepares them to understand that his coming throne will not be in Jerusalem but in heaven. Read the parable he tells them in **Luke 19:11-27,** in which Jesus is the man of noble birth who leaves to become king. What does he expect of his disciples in his absence?

8. Read **Luke 18:31-34.** This is the third time Jesus has explained to his disciples that he must die and in what manner he will die. However obvious this may seem to us in hindsight, the disciples do not understand it. Why do you think that is?

D. Application

This question will help you apply one of the key themes of the session to your life. After meditating on it, respond to God with a brief written prayer if you choose.

In Jesus' parable of the Prodigal Son (Luke 15:11-32), the younger son sets off for a distant country and squanders his wealth. This is a picture of Israel in exile, squandering its inheritance. Re-read the parable, and put yourself in the position of that son. Describe the inheritance you have in Christ (things like the richness of the Eucharist, for example, or Mary as your Mother). Is there any sense in which you are squandering your inheritance?

Dear Lord …

Session 19 Talk Notes

Messianic Fulfillment – Part 2

I. Introduction to Messianic Fulfillment – Part 2

II. The Journey: Jesus "Sets His Face" Toward Jerusalem (Luke 9:51)

A. Themes

    1. Messianic coming and expectation
    2. Discipleship
    3. "Coming"
    4. "New wine"

B. Jesus involves others in his mission (Luke 10)

    1. The meaning and cost of discipleship

    2. Jesus commissions the seventy
       a. We are witnesses through confirmation
       b. Christ lives in us (see Galatians 2:20)
       c. The seventy sent out, given power over Satan (verses 17-18)
          i. *Protoevangelium* (Genesis 3:15)

III. The Message: Jesus Redefines Holiness

A. Example: the Good Samaritan (10:25-37)

    1. What shall I do to inherit eternal life?
       a. Love the Lord; love your neighbor
       b. Relationship between vertical and horizontal relationship

    2. What makes a person holy?

       a. Pharisees' view: separation defines holiness
          i. "Pharisee" from Hebrew, *perushim,* "the separated ones," from *parash,* "to separate"
          ii. Pharisees cannot help the "unclean" (see Numbers 19:11)

    3. The good neighbor is the one who showed mercy

    4. My neighbor? The unclean; outsiders; the hurting

    5. New wine needs new wineskins (see Luke 5:37)

    6. How do you define holiness?

B. The attractiveness of holiness

    1. Example: Blessed Teresa of Calcutta (Mother Teresa)

    2. Christ's example: importance of prayer to true holiness

      a. CCC 1693

      b. CCC 2602: "His words and work are the visible manifestation of his prayer in secret"

    3. "Teach us to pray" – the Lord's Prayer (Luke 11:1-13)

      a. Order of petitions is important
        i. First and second petitions: directed toward God
        ii. Third to tenth petitions: directed toward our needs and relationships

      b. "Thy kingdom come" = "Thy will be done" (see Matthew 6:10)

      c. Give us our daily bread (food and Eucharist)

      d. Importance of forgiveness (release)

  C. Example: Jonah as a "good Samaritan" (Luke 11:29)
    1. The "sign of Jonah" – forty days

    2. Being a good neighbor by warning Assyria

IV. Missionary Instructions: Do Not Be Anxious (Luke 12:22ff)

V. Parables of the Kingdom

  A. Entry by the narrow door (13:22-30)

  B. Parables of the great banquet, wedding feast (14:7-24)
    1. Behavior (take the lowest place)

    2. Inviting the outcasts

VI. The Cost of Discipleship (14:25ff)

  A. Pick up your cross daily

  B. What Jesus means by "hate"

  C. Suffering: a participation in Christ's mission (see Colossians 1:24)

    1. What could be lacking in Christ's suffering?[1]

VII. Seeking the Lost

  A. The Prodigal Son (Luke 15:11-32) – understanding the Father's love

  B. The "lost" Zacchaeus restored (Luke 19:1-27)

VIII. Conclusion

---

[1] Jeff Cavins quotes from St. John Paul II's *Salvifici Doloris*, "On the Christian Meaning of Human Suffering."

A. Review the Context

In Messianic Fulfillment – Part 1, we finally met the "woman" and her "seed" promised way back in the first chapters of Genesis—the long-awaited Messiah. His many titles hearken back through the history of Israel: Son of David, Son of Abraham, God with us, Horn of Salvation, Chosen One, Messiah, the Son of God. We saw his early ministry, including his baptism and temptation in the desert, in which he was revealed as a kind of new Adam and a New Israel. We listened to his message as he preached the Good News of the kingdom, proclaiming liberty to captives and forgiveness of sins. He also delivered a new law of the Spirit as he taught his followers to obey from the heart.

In Part 2, Jesus "set his face to go to Jerusalem," where he knew he would face his own "exodus." He trained his disciples and appointed them to announce the coming of the kingdom. He also established that kingdom in their midst, on the foundation of Peter and the other apostles. By choosing the Twelve, he reconstituted the twelve tribes of Israel around himself. He gave them authority over the devil, the power to bind and to loose, and the power to forgive sins. He taught them to pray to his Father and began to prepare them for the cost of discipleship. Jesus also prepared the way for the kingdom by showing and explaining in parables that his kingdom is not earthly or interested in military power for Israel, but is a kingdom that is open to all, that holds out welcoming arms to repentant sinners, and whose members extend the loving mercy of God to everyone.

Finally, Jesus prepared his disciples for his death. Recall that in Matthew 16, when Jesus told Peter he must go to Jerusalem to suffer, be killed, and then be raised again, Peter rebuked him. His words, "God forbid, Lord! This shall never happen to you," echo Satan's, "You shall not die!" in the Garden. No surprise that Jesus answered boldly: "Get behind me, Satan! You are a hindrance to me; for you are not on the side of God, but of men." What temptation did Peter's rebuke hold out to Jesus? Think about this. We do not want Jesus to suffer, either. Yet he came for that very purpose. This session's reading shows him resolutely heading for the Cross. Watch to see how Jesus does what Adam failed to do.

B. Read the Story

Read **Luke 19:28–24:53** to become familiar with the main characters and events of Messianic Fulfillment – Part 3, which covers Christ's passion, death, and resurrection—the answer for Adam and for all of us. Read the entire assignment in one setting because the questions will skip through and highlight only the passages important for understanding the period. Trace the action in the center section of your *Bible Timeline* Chart. Identify the main characters, and notice the flow of key events and where they take place. Any questions? Jot them down.

Going Deeper (optional): To get a full picture of this time period, read all of the Gospel of **Luke.** Even if you read it for one of the previous sessions, it will help bring the larger context of the Gospel to mind.

As always, pray before you read.

C. Take a Deeper Look

Answering these questions will draw you into the heart of the story. If you do not understand something, make a note of it to bring up in the discussion.

The Approach to Jerusalem

1. Jesus' approach to Jerusalem is made along a road that goes down from the Mount of Olives and then up to Jerusalem. Read **Luke 19:28-44.** Jesus rides on a donkey just as the first son of David, Solomon, rode a donkey to his coronation years before (see **1 Kings 1:33**). "Blessed is the king who comes in the name of the Lord!" (Luke 19:38) the people shout in praise—a quote from Psalm 118, which is a psalm of praise written in celebration of a Davidic king's victory over his enemies. Jesus is approaching Jerusalem in triumph as the Son of David, heir to the throne. Why, then, does he weep as he approaches the city?

The Last Supper

2. **Luke 22:7-20** tells of the Last Supper—the final meal Jesus has with his disciples. It is a Passover meal. Read **Exodus 12,** and find the Passover in the Egypt and Exodus period on your *Timeline* Chart.

    a. What is the Passover, and why is it still celebrated more than thirteen hundred years later? (**Optional:** Read **Isaiah 52.**)

    b. Read **1 Corinthians 5:7; 1 Peter 1:18-20;** and **Revelation 5:6-14.** How does Jesus fulfill the Passover? (For help with this question, read also **CCC 613–614 and 1340.**)

3. Read **Luke 22:31-34, 54-62.** Peter, "the rock," appears to have failed in spite of Jesus' prayer. Now read **John 21:1-19,** which deals with an event that occurs after Jesus' resurrection.

    a. In Luke 22, does it seem to bother Jesus that Peter will deny him? What kind of man has Jesus chosen to be the foundation of his Church?

    b. What does this say to you about the failures in your own life and God's ultimate plan for you?

The Passion

4. **Think About It:** Christ's passion begins in a garden on the Mount of Olives in an olive grove called Gethsemane. Read **Luke 22:39-46,** paying particular attention to Jesus' words.

   a. Describe the struggle Jesus is going through.

   b. In what sense is Jesus' struggle here similar to that faced by Adam and Eve in the Garden of Eden? (See **Genesis 3.**)

   c. What does Jesus do that our first parents failed to do?

5. How does God fulfill the curse on Satan that he made in Genesis 3:15—"I will put enmity between you and the woman, and between your seed and her seed; he shall bruise your head, and you shall bruise his heel"—and deliver his children from Satan's power? (Read also **Hebrews 2:14-18.**)

6. **Think About It:** If all Jesus has to do is die, couldn't it be in some easier way? Why does Jesus have to suffer? Read **Isaiah 53** and **Galatians 3:13.** (Hint: How does Jesus' death on the Cross solve these two problems: (1) the curse on Adam and (2) Israel's broken covenant with God?)

7. Even with the penalty paid for sin, a problem remains for humanity: the broken nature, the loss of grace, and the tendency to sin (concupiscence) that all inherit from Adam. Jesus' mission is not complete without his resurrection. Read **Romans 6:1-14. (Optional:** Read **CCC 1213–1216 and 1227–1228.)**

a.   When we unite ourselves to Christ in baptism, what happens to our old nature?

b.   Of what does the Resurrection assure us? (See also **Romans 6:5.**)

8.   How does Jesus make sure the good news of his death and resurrection will spread beyond Jerusalem? (See **Luke 24:36-53.**)

D. Application

These questions will help you apply one of the key themes of the session to your life. After meditating on them, respond to God with a brief written prayer if you choose.

From the beginning of this study, we have seen how person after person faced a test: "Can you trust God?" Based on what you know now, can you trust the Father? Why? On what do you base that trust?

Dear Lord …

E. Wrap-Up

Conclude your study of the Messianic Fulfillment period, and fix it in your mind by doing the following:

1.   Recall the color of this time period, gold, and think of it in terms of your reading to help you remember it.

2.   Quickly review Sessions 18-20. Write a brief summary of what the period of Messianic Fulfillment is about or its significance as part of the "big picture."

Session 20 Talk Notes

Messianic Fulfillment – Part 3

I. Introduction to Messianic Fulfillment – Part 3

A. Kingship theme fulfilled

1. God's plan to restore his rule (Genesis 3:15; promise to Abraham)[1]
2. God rules through the earthly throne of David
3. Fulfillment in Christ

B. Lamb theme fulfilled

1. Genesis 22:8 – God will provide a lamb
2. Exodus 12:3 – the Passover lamb
3. John 1:29 – Behold, the Lamb of God

C. The Suffering Servant, the way of peace

II. Jesus Enters Jerusalem

A. The triumphal entry (Luke 19:28-40; Matthew 21)

1. Jesus enters like a king
   a. 1 Kings 1:38-39 (new king rides in on a mule)
   b. 2 Kings 9:13 (garments are spread before the new king)

2. "Blessed is he who comes in the name of the Lord"
   a. Psalm 118, a *Hallel* psalm

3. Jesus weeps over Jerusalem (Luke 19:41-44)
   a. See also Luke 13:31-35; Matthew 23:37-39: "You will not see me until you say, 'Blessed is he who comes in the name of the Lord'"

B. When do we experience his coming or presence?

C. "Would that even today you knew the things that make for peace!" (Luke 19:42)

III. The Passover and the Last Supper

A. Preparations for the Passover (Luke 22:7-13)

1. Jesus as a new David

   a. 2 Samuel 6 – David takes Ark to Jerusalem, offers bread and wine[2]

   b. 1 Chronicles 16:4 – David appoints Levites to give perpetual praise and thanks

---

[1] *Protoevangelium* = "first good news."
[2] RSV-CE: "cake of raisins." The Hebrew word is uncertain. Some scholars translate it "flagon of wine."

         c. When the Messiah comes, all sacrifices will cease except for the thank offering[3]

    B. The Last Supper (Luke 22:14-20)

        1. "Do this in remembrance of me" (verse 19)

           a. Sacramental participation in the Mass: a mystery
           b. "To remember" = *zachar; todah* = "thanksgiving"

        2. The Old Covenant fulfilled in the New Covenant

IV. Christ's Passion

    A. The Garden of Gethsemane ("olive press") (Luke 22:39-46)

        1. Parallels with the first Garden (Genesis 3)

        2. The hour has come

        3. Not my will, but yours, be done

    B. Accusations against Jesus (Luke 22:54–23:25)

        1. "Forbidding us to give tribute to Caesar" (23:2)

        2. Jesus versus Barabbas: the way of peace versus the way of rebellion

           a. Barabbas = "son of the father"
           b. Jesus took his place

    C. The crown of thorns (Matthew 27:29): taking on the curse of Adam

V. The Death and Burial of Jesus (Luke 23:26-56)

    A. The Crucifixion
        1. Simon the Cyrene helps carry the Cross
        2. Galatians 3:13-14, third promise to Abraham fulfilled

    B. Jesus is buried
        1. Joseph of Arimathea (Luke 23:53) – echoes Luke 2:7

VI. The Resurrection (Luke 24)

    A. The empty tomb (verses 1-12)

    B. Jesus appears to his disciples

        1. The road to Emmaus (verses 13-35)
           a. The Old Testament points to Jesus
           b. The structure of the Mass: Liturgies of Word and Eucharist

VII. Conclusion: Why Did Jesus Die?

---

[3] *Pesiqta Rabbati* as quoted in Hartmut Gese, *Essays On Biblical Theology* (Minneapolis: Augsburg Publishing House, 1981), 133.

THE BIBLE
TIMELINE
The Story of Salvation

A. Establish the Context

Messianic Fulfillment – Part 3 was the pinnacle of our journey, the climax toward which the entire story has pointed. Who would have guessed that God himself would come to earth as a man and suffer and die so that the demands of the covenant would be met and all his scattered children could be reunited through his Son? Who would have guessed that Satan's fiercest weapons—suffering and death—would be transformed into the very door to eternal life? It is hard to fathom the depths of God's love for us.

It would seem that the story was over. The promises were fulfilled, the problems solved. And yet something very important remained. The disciples Jesus left on earth, and all those who were to follow were invited to become part of the story, to enter the new kingdom that Jesus founded here and that will reach its own perfect fulfillment in heaven at the end of time. How will they do that? What will the new kingdom look like?

The last stage of *The Bible Timeline: The Story of Salvation* is The Church, which is the earthly embodiment of God's kingdom. It is the stage in which God's "family plan" is realized. This story began with Adam and Eve, continued with Noah and his family, the tribe of Abraham, a nation under Moses, and, finally, a kingdom under David. Now, this plan is realized in One, Holy, Catholic, and Apostolic Church: the worldwide family of God.

The Church began in AD 33 and continues today, although the events recorded in Acts and the other New Testament books span less than one hundred years. The color by which we remember this time period is white for the spotless bride of Christ. It also can be remembered as the culmination of the entire story: In the same way that white light from the sun is made up of all the colors of the rainbow, in the white light of the Church we find all the colors of the preceding periods. Shine the Church's light through the prism of Christ, and you will see the turquoise of the Early World and man created in God's image, lost, and redeemed; the burgundy of the Patriarchs and God's rich covenant promises fulfilled in Jesus; the red of Egypt and Exodus that anticipated Jesus' own exodus and the new freedom of the children of God; the tan of Desert Wanderings and our own pilgrimage toward heaven. … *All* of the New Testament lies hidden in the Old Testament, and the Old Testament is unveiled in the New Testament, as St. Augustine wrote long ago.[1]

Take out your *Bible Timeline* Chart and follow the red genealogy line that begins in the Early World with Adam and continues through the ups and downs of Israel's history until it ends in Jesus Christ. In the period of the Church, it explodes outward until it permeates the entire world. The Blood of Christ that we drink in the Eucharist connects us not just to one another, but to all those who led up to Christ and followed after him. This is our family history as well. It is the family history of the Church.

B. Read the Story

Acts 1:8 gives us the theme and the outline of Luke's Gospel: "But you shall receive power when the Holy Spirit has come upon you; and you shall be my witnesses in Jerusalem and in all Judea and Samaria and to the end of the earth." There will be three sessions covering the Acts of the Apostles, divided along the three "waves of witness" described in that verse (take note of these divisions on the *Timeline* Chart). This session will cover the first wave: the witness in Jerusalem. Read **Acts 1:1–8:4;** then trace the action in the

---

[1]   *Quaest. in Hept.* 2, 73: PL 34, 623.

center section of The Church on your *Bible Timeline* Chart. Identify the main characters, and notice the flow of key events and where they take place. Any questions? Jot them down.

Going Deeper (optional): To get the entire story of this period, read the entire book of the **Acts of the Apostles** now.

As always, pray before you read.

C. Take a Deeper Look

Answering these questions will draw you into the heart of the story. If you do not understand something, make a note of it to bring up in the discussion.

Pentecost and the Holy Spirit (Acts 1:1–2:42)

1. Jesus appears to his apostles over a period of forty days following his resurrection. Along with **Acts 1:1-8,** read **Matthew 28:16-20; Mark 16:14-18; Luke 24:13-49;** and **John 20:19-23 and 21:15-19.** Based on the things Jesus says to the apostles, what seems to be his chief purpose or desire during this time before his ascension?

2. Read **Acts 2:1-42,** which describes the outpouring of the Holy Spirit at Pentecost.

    a. Compare and contrast this to **Genesis 11:1-9.** What parallels do you find between the two events, and what is their significance? (See also **CCC 761.**)

    b. Read **CCC 767–768.** Why does God send the Holy Spirit?

The Early Christian Community (Acts 2:42–8:4)

3. Describe the early Christian community based on **Acts 2:42-47 and 4:32-34.**

4.   Read **CCC 765 and 771.**

   a.   What do you learn in these paragraphs about the visible Church?

   b.   What "seeds," or early indications of this visible structure, can you see in the reading for this session, even at the very beginnings of the Church? (Take note especially of **Acts 1:12-26 and 6:1-7.**)

5.   Read **Acts 6:1-7** together with **1 Timothy 3:8-13.** Why are deacons needed, and what kind of people are supposed to be? (The Greek word used to describe the responsibility of "the Seven," which means "server" or "one who waits on," is the same verb from which the word "deacon" comes.)

6.   One deacon, a man named Stephen, "full of grace and power, [does] great wonders and signs among the people" (Acts 6:8). Nonetheless, he soon attracts opposition from among various groups of people. Read **Acts 6:8–7:60.**

   a.   What charge is made against Stephen?

   b.   How does Stephen answer his accusers?

7. Notice the role that the "young man named Saul" plays in Stephen's martyrdom.

    a. What effect does Stephen's witness and death have on Saul? (See **Acts 8:1-3.**)

    b. Why might Saul react this way instead of like the "devout men" of 8:2 who "buried Stephen, and made great lamentation over him"?

8. **Think About It:** In the days after Jesus' death, his disciples are fearful, sad, and hiding from the authorities. The picture painted of them later in **Acts 1–8** is remarkably different. Find examples of the way the disciples face opposition and suffering. How do you account for the change?

D. Application

These questions will help you apply one of the key themes of the session to your life. After meditating on them, respond to God with a brief written prayer if you choose.

Stephen is the first New Testament example of someone who looks at Jesus' actions and his resurrection and faces death without fear. Are there things in our world or society that cause you fear? Is your faith challenged at work or by your neighbors? Can you find anything in these chapters to strengthen you so you can proclaim the truth without fear?

Dear Lord …

Session 21 Talk Notes

The Church – Part 1

I. Introduction to The Church – Part 1

    A. There are three divisions to this period based on Acts 1:8

        1. 1:1–8:4: "You shall be my witnesses in Jerusalem"

        2. 8:5–15:35: "and in all Judea and Samaria"

        3. 15:36–28:31: "and to the end of the earth"

    B. "You are witnesses" (Luke 24:48-49)

        1. "power" = *dunamis*

        2. "As the Father has sent me, even so I send you" (John 20:21)

        3. The Church reliving the life of Jesus

        4. Promises of Abraham coming to the Gentiles (Galatians 3:13-14)

II. Waiting for the Promised Holy Spirit (Acts 1)

    A. Jesus appears, teaches for forty days after Resurrection

        1. *Mystagogy* (forty days after Easter: Scripture readings from Acts)

    B. Before Ascension: "You shall be my witnesses"

    C. Judas is replaced by Matthias

        1. Casting lots (parallel: 1 Chronicles 24:3-19)

III. Pentecost and the Holy Spirit (Acts 2)

    A. Parallels between Mount Sinai and Pentecost

        1. Jewish Pentecost: Feast of Weeks *(Shavuot)*

        2. Association with the giving of the Law on Mount Sinai

3. Giving of the Law on Mount Sinai marked by sound, fire, speech

4. Law written on stones versus hearts (see Jeremiah 31:31-33)

B. Pentecost

1. Languages understood: a reversal of Babel

2. "Every nation" (2:5)

    a. Reconstituting Israel

    b. Bringing in the Gentiles (Isaiah 11:11-12)

3. Sign of "the last days" (2:17ff; see Joel 2:28-32)

4. The plan of God (2:23 – *oikonomia* = "economy," plan)

5. Three thousand converts (2:37-42): power to be witnesses (1:8)

    a. "Witness" = *martus*

C. What does Pentecost mean to us? – confirmation

1. CCC 1285

    a. Necessary for completion of baptismal grace

    b. Strength to spread and defend the Faith (in word and deed)

2. CCC 1288

    a. Perpetuates the grace of Pentecost in the Church

3. CCC 1302–1303: effects of confirmation

    a. Roots more firmly in filial relationship with God

    b. Unites more firmly to Christ

    c. Increases the Gifts of the Holy Spirit

  d. Perfects our bond with the Church

  e. Special strength to confess the name of Christ boldly

 4. CCC 1304–1305

  a. An indelible mark

  b. Power to profess faith publicly, officially

IV. The Early Christian Community

A. Community life (2:42)

 1. "They devoted themselves …"

 2. "… to the apostles' teaching …"

  a. The Tradition passed on from Jesus

  b. Interpretation, application of Old Testament Scriptures

 3. "… and fellowship …"

 4. "… to the breaking of bread and the prayers"

 5. Galatians 2:20 – "I have been crucified with Christ"

 6. CCC 949–953

B. Living the life of Christ

 1. Parallels between Jesus and the Church (apostles)

	Jesus	**The Church**
Anointing by the Holy Spirit	Luke 3:21-22	Acts 2:1-4
Preaching to the Jews	Luke 4:14-21	Acts 2:14-39 (Peter), 13:16-41 (Paul)
The sick brought to be healed	Luke 4:40	Acts 28:9
Healing of a paralytic	Luke 5:17-26	Acts 3:1-10 (Peter), 14:8-11 (Paul)

2. Acts 3:1-10: Peter heals a lame beggar

C. A new boldness (Acts 4)

   1. Confrontation by the Council

   2. Response to persecution

D. Shared possessions (Acts 5)

   1. Ananias and Sapphira

E. Casting "shadows" (5:14-15)

F. Rejoicing in suffering (5:17-41)

G. Delegating authority: choosing deacons (Acts 6)

V. Stephen's Witness and Martyrdom (Acts 7)

A. Stephen's witness: recap of salvation history

B. Saul as witness

C. Stoning and forgiveness – reflection of Christ

VI. Persecution Leads to Evangelization (Acts 8)

A. Review the Context

The kingdom God established through his Son, Jesus Christ, is the sixth and final development in God's family plan, which will come to its fulfillment one day in heaven. Unlike its forerunner, the Davidic kingdom, this kingdom is comprised in the body of believers and takes form in the Church. As was seen in The Church – Part 1, it began on the foundation of the twelve apostles and grew through their Spirit-inspired witness.

At Pentecost, when the Holy Spirit descended in power on the disciples, about three thousand people were added to the company of those who believed in Jesus Christ. The early Church held all things in common, and Christians lived and worshiped together in peace. It grew in an orderly fashion, with people appointed to positions of responsibility as the needs and numbers of the community grew.

The radical change effected in the disciples by the Holy Spirit can be seen in Stephen, the first martyr. No longer frightened or worried, they preached boldly and suffered willingly for Christ and his message. Stephen's witness triggered the first persecution of the Church and the scattering of Christians, who fled for their lives. Part 2 of The Church opens with the apostles spreading throughout the area of Judea and Samaria and the beginning of gospel witness in those regions. (The witness up to this point has been centered in Jerusalem, which is located just west of the top of the Dead Sea. The second wave of expansion essentially covers the rest of the old kingdom of Israel. Judea is the area formerly known as Judah to the south of Jerusalem. Samaria is the north central area of Palestine to the west of the Jordan.)

B. Read the Story

This session covers the second wave of witness (the witness in Judea and Samaria, which ends with Acts 12) as well as Paul's first missionary journey and the Council of Jerusalem, which belong to the third wave but which are linked to the preceding chapters thematically. Read **Acts 8:5–15:35** (even if you have already read these passages as suggested in "Going Deeper" in Session 21); then trace the action in the center section of your *Bible Timeline* Chart. Identify the main characters, and notice the flow of key events and where they take place. Any questions? Jot them down.

Going Deeper (optional): You can read more about the Holy Spirit in the *Catechism* beginning with **CCC 683.**

As always, pray before you read.

C. Take a Deeper Look

Answering these questions will draw you into the heart of the story. If you do not understand something, make a note of it to bring up in the discussion.

The Gospel Begins to Spread (Acts 8:5-40)

1.   Philip, like Stephen, is one of the seven deacons appointed in Acts 6. He is one of the believers scattered throughout Judea and Samaria by the persecution that follows Stephen's death. Describe his witness and ministry as recorded in Acts 8.

Saul's Conversion (Acts 9)

2.   Acts 9 reintroduces us to the young man Saul, who stood by and assented to Stephen's death.

a.   Why is he on the road to Damascus, and what happens to him there?

b.   Why is temporary blindness a particularly apt result of this experience?

3.   Years later, in his first letter to Timothy, Paul (Saul) reflects on God's mercy. Read **1 Timothy 1:12-17.** How does Paul's example give us hope?

Peter's Vision (Acts 10–11)

Note: The Pharisees interpreted the laws rigidly and even fanatically—it was not just eating certain foods, but even coming into contact with a Gentile, that would render one unclean and unfit for public worship.

4.   One day, Peter falls into a trance while he is praying and waiting to eat.

a.   Read **Acts 10,** and describe the vision he has.

b.   What does it mean?

c.   Read **Matthew 15:11 and Chapters 19–20.** How does Jesus prepare the way for this revolutionary thought?

d.   How does Peter respond to the vision?

5. How do the believers in Jerusalem react to this news (Acts 11), and what is Peter's defense?

6. As the Good News spreads and takes root in other cities, what is the response of the apostles (who remain in Jerusalem and anchor the expanding Church)? See **Acts 8:9-25, 11:19-26, and 14:21-23.**

Peter's Escape from Prison (Acts 12)

About this time, King Herod begins to persecute the apostles. (Previously, they were persecuted primarily by the Jewish leaders and against the other Christian believers.) Herod arrests Peter during the Feast of Unleavened Bread, intending to bring him to trial after the Passover.

7. What happens to Peter when he is imprisoned for preaching the gospel, and how does Herod fare?

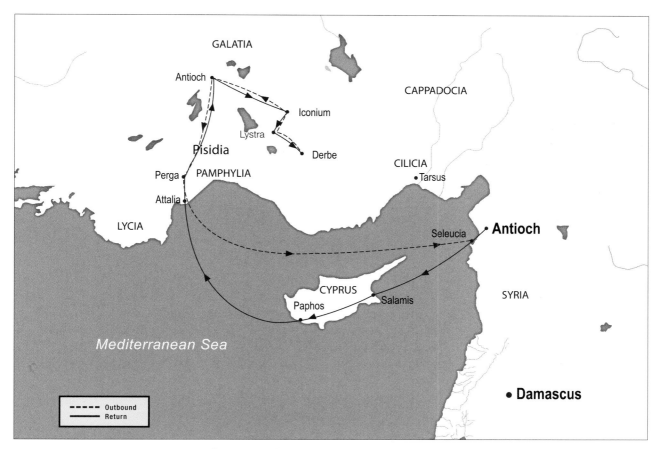

Paul's First Missionary Journey (Acts 13–14)

Paul's First Missionary Journey (Acts 13–14)

8. a. From this point on in the Acts of the Apostles, Saul is called by his Roman name, Paul. Chapters 13–14 describe Paul's first missionary journey into Galatia, where he establishes a number of churches. At each stop, he and Barnabas speak first in the Jewish synagogue. What kind of reception do they get from the Jews? From the Gentiles?

    b. What part of God's original promise to Abraham (Genesis 12:1-3) is finally being fulfilled?

The Council of Jerusalem (Acts 15)

9. The conversion of Gentiles leads to a serious dispute among the believers. Read **Acts 15.**

    a. What is the nature of the problem?

    b. How is it settled?

10. **Think About It:** Read **CCC 880–892** regarding the Church's hierarchy today and its teaching office. How does this structure safeguard the unity of the Church and the truth of its teachings?

D. Application

These questions will help you apply one of the key themes of the session to your life. After meditating on them, respond to God with a brief written prayer if you choose.

Are there teachings of the Church today that you do not accept or understand? According to the pattern set by Christ's apostles, what would be the best way of coming to a conclusion about these?

Dear Lord …

Session 22 Talk Notes

The Church – Part 2

I. Introduction to The Church – Part 2

II. The Gospel Spreads to Judea and Samaria

A. Persecution leads to scattering (Acts 8:1-6)

B. Philip's witness and ministry

1. Simon the magician (Acts 8:17-24)

2. The Ethiopian eunuch (Acts 8:26-36)

   a. Hearing the voice of the Lord

   b. Do you know what you are reading? (Isaiah 53) Isaiah 56: "To the eunuchs who … hold fast my covenant, I will give … an everlasting name"

   c. The need to be taught

      i. CCC 85–86: role of the Magisterium

         • The living, teaching office of the Church

         • Bishops in union with the Holy Father

      ii. CCC 890

III. Saul's Conversion (Acts 9)

A. Saul's background

1. Tribe of Benjamin

2. Pharisee, zealous

3. Taught by Gamaliel

4. Roman Jew from Tarsus

B. On the road to Damascus: "I am Jesus, whom you are persecuting" (9:5)

C. Ananais' vision

D. Saul's eyes are opened: a recognition that Christ fulfilled the Law

IV. The Gospel Spreads to the Gentiles (Acts 10–11)

A. Cornelius, "God-fearer"[1] (Acts 10) – vision at the time of the evening sacrifice

B. Peter's vision of the sheet

---

[1] A "God-fearer" was a Gentile who engaged in the Jewish religion to varying degrees but without actually becoming Jewish.

    C. Cornelius is baptized: "God shows no partiality" (10:34)

        1. Peter's report to the Jerusalem church (Acts 11)

        2. A church forms at Antioch (here first wording "Christians")

V. The Gospel Spreads to Rome (Acts 12–14)

    A. Herod's persecution (12:1-5)

        1. "During the days of Unleavened Bread" – Passover

    B. Peter's escape from prison (12:6-10)

        1. Language reflects Exodus and first Passover

VI. Paul's First Missionary Journey: Paul (Saul) and Barnabas Go to Cyprus (Acts 13–14)

VII. The Council of Jerusalem (Acts 15)

    A. The question: How do Gentiles get saved?

        1. Circumcision party: They must first adhere to Jewish Law

    B. Solution sought at first council

        1. Peter testifies (verses 7-12); assembly keeps silence

        2. James – pastor in Jerusalem – makes a biblical argument for the decision (Amos 9:11-12; Hosea 3:4-5; Jeremiah 12:15-16)

    C. Directive circulated to the churches

    D. Councils of the Catholic Church (examples)

        1. Nicaea (325) – the Creed

        2. Ephesus (431) – Mary, Mother of God

        3. Chalcedon (451) – two natures, divine and human

        4. Third Council of Constantinople (680–681) – two wills in Christ, human and divine

        5. Second Council of Nicaea (787) – veneration of holy images

        6. Council of Trent (1545–1563) – many dogmatic and reformatory decrees

        7. Second Vatican Council (1962–1965)

            a. How to be people of God in the modern world (*Gaudium et Spes*)

            b. Call for a New Evangelization

VIII. Conclusion: The *Al Ha-Bayit*, "Prime Minister," "Papa," "A Peg in a Sure Place"[2]

---

[2]   Isaiah 22:15-24 speaks of the role of steward of the kingdom of David, the *al ha-bayit*.

A. Review the Context

In Part 2 of The Church, the gospel spread into Judea and Samaria as some of the Jews reacted with hostility to the message and began to push the messengers out of Jerusalem. While the apostles stayed in Jerusalem to anchor the growing Church, others moved out to preach. A dramatic encounter with God transformed a young man named Saul (later called Paul) from a zealous persecutor of the new believers into a powerful evangelist for Christ. He witnessed fearlessly by the power of the Holy Spirit, and despite continued opposition, made many disciples in cities throughout the region.

When Paul and the others disciples entered a city, they spoke first in the synagogues. But their message attracted Gentiles as well, and soon people from outside the fold of the people of Israel were making up the bulk of the Church. God gave Peter a vision to reassure them that this was of God's doing: Gentiles were no longer to be shunned as "unclean" but were to be welcomed into the kingdom. The subsequent debate over whether Gentile believers should be required to adhere to the Law of Moses and be circumcised prompted the first official Church council, the Council of Jerusalem. There, the apostles determined that Gentiles should not be required to follow all the rituals of Judaism, although they would have to make a clean break from pagan practices linked to idolatry. Circumcision would not be required. Entry into God's kingdom was based on God's grace and faith in Christ and would not depend on strict observance of the Law. Having settled this key question, the Church was ripe for expansion.

B. Read the Story

The Church – Part 3 looks at the launch of the third wave of gospel witness, the witness to the end of the earth, with Paul's second and third missionary journeys. As you read **Acts 15:36–28:31,** follow along on the maps on pages 158-159. Trace the action in the center section of your *Bible Timeline* Chart. Identify the main characters, and notice the flow of key events and where they take place. Any questions? Jot them down.

Going Deeper (optional): The Church has its roots here in the Acts of the Apostles. You can read what the *Catechism* has to say about this, starting at **CCC 748.**

As always, pray before you read.

C. Take a Deeper Look

Answering these questions will draw you into the heart of the story. If you do not understand something, make a note of it to bring up in the discussion.

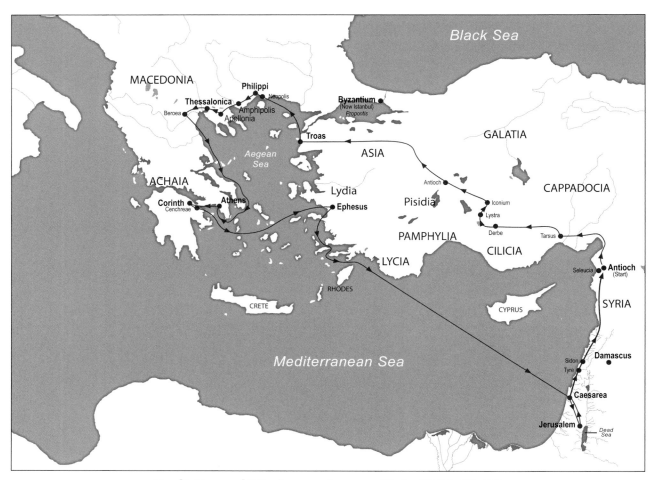

Paul's Second Missionary Journey (Acts 15:36–18:22)

Paul sets out on a second journey in AD 50–52 through Asia Minor and Greece. Accompanied by Silas and Timothy, he visits the places where he has preached the gospel previously. In each place, they deliver the decision reached at the Jerusalem Council and work to strengthen the young churches in the Faith.

1.   What is Paul's experience in Thessalonica? (See **Acts 17:1-15.**)

2.   a.   Now read **1 Thessalonians 2–4,** part of a letter Paul writes to the Thessalonian church soon after these events while he is in Corinth (Acts 18). How does Paul continue to strengthen the Thessalonian believers even in his absence?

     b.   What kind of lives does he urge them to lead?

3. Paul stays a year and a half in Corinth, where he lives with fellow tent makers Aquila and Priscilla. How do things come to a head in that city (**Acts 18:1-18**), and how does God reassure Paul?

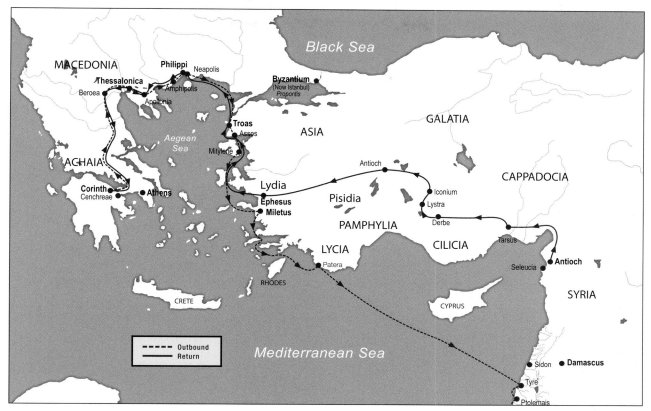

Paul's Third Missionary Journey (Acts 18:23–21:16)

Paul's third missionary journey, which takes five years, begins in the spring of AD 53.

4. During his two-year stay in Ephesus, Paul writes to the church in Corinth to instruct and correct them and answer some questions they have about matters of faith and morality. This letter is preserved as 1 Corinthians, a supplemental book for this time period.

   a. Read the following passages, and note some of the problems the young Church faces:

      1 Corinthians 1:10-17:

      1 Corinthians 5:1-2, 6:12-20:

      1 Corinthians 8:

      1 Corinthians 11:17-34:

b. In some of the most beautiful words recorded in Scripture, Paul also writes to the Corinthians about love. Read **1 Corinthians 13.** Although he is speaking here in the context of his teaching about spiritual gifts, how does what he says in this chapter pertain to the problems you listed in your answer to question 4a?

c. **Living Tradition:** The first problem mentioned in question 4a, that of factions and divisions in the Church, remains a problem today. Read **CCC 817–819,** "Wounds to Unity," which discusses the serious rifts that resulted in some churches separating from full communion with the Catholic Church. How does the Church view these other churches and Christians?

Paul's Arrest and Imprisonment (Acts 21:17–28:31)

5. Back in Jerusalem after his travels, Paul faces violent opposition from the Jews and is arrested. Before entering the barracks, Paul asks for permission to speak to the crowd. What in Paul's testimony in **Acts 22** most arouses the Jews' anger?

6. In **Acts 23:** On trial before the Sanhedrin (the highest court of the Jews), how does Paul turn a disagreement between the Pharisees and Sadducees to his own advantage?

7. In **Acts 24,** the commander, who has been warned of threats on Paul's life, transfers him to Caesarea to appear before Governor Felix. What charge does Tertullus bring against Paul on behalf of the Jewish leaders, and what is Paul's defense?

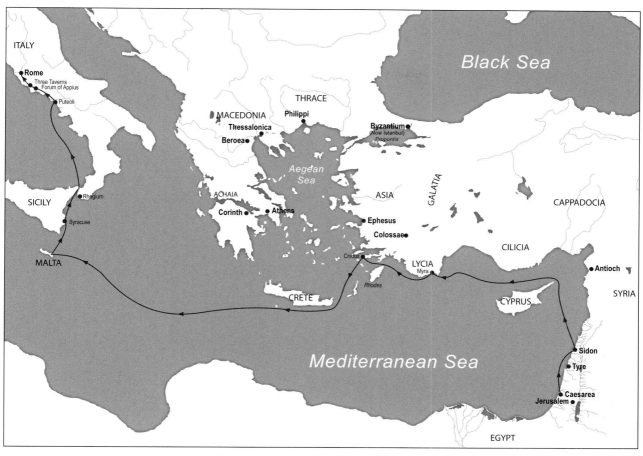

Paul's Voyage to Rome (Acts 21:17–28:31)

The rest of the Acts of the Apostles has to do with Paul's arrest and imprisonment in Caesarea and the trials that lead to his journey to Rome and ministry there.

8.   Paul appeals to Caesar and is eventually taken to Rome. He remains there for two years under house arrest but freely preaching the kingdom of God. Why, ultimately, do the Jews not understand the message Paul brings to them? (See **Acts 28:17-28.**)

9.   What good does God bring out of the persecution Paul faces? (For help, read **Philippians 1:12-18.**)

10. **Old Testament Connection:** Paul tells Herod Agrippa that he is "on trial for hope in the promise made by God to our fathers, to which our twelve tribes hope to attain, as they earnestly worship night and day. And for this hope I am accused by Jews, O king! Why is it thought incredible by any of you that God raises the dead?" (Acts 26:6-8). In what promise do the twelve tribes hope, and what does that promise have to do with the hope and truth of resurrection? (For help with this question, read **Ezekiel 37.** Ezekiel prophesied during the Babylonian exile. His message was one of judgment—Jerusalem would fall and the Temple would be destroyed—and of future restoration.)

The Apostlic Mission Continues to This Day

"And [Paul] lived there two whole years at his own expense, and welcomed all who came to him, preaching the kingdom of God and teaching about the Lord Jesus Christ quite openly and unhindered" (Acts 28:30-31).

The Acts of the Apostles closes without recording the outcome of Paul's Roman trial. Was this intentional, to show that the Church's mission was just beginning to bring the Good News of Jesus Christ and his kingdom to the world? Whatever the answer, it is true that the Church's mission continues to this day. The drama that began with a rupture in God's family has found its solution in God's Son. Where are you in the story as it continues today?

D. Application

These questions will help you apply one of the key themes of the session to your life. After meditating on them, respond to God with a brief written prayer if you choose.

The Acts of the Apostles gives us a chance to take an objective look at the effectiveness of the message of Christ. Is there any difference between the family of God before Christ and the family of God after? How do the lives of the apostles and early believers give witness to the new life they have in Christ? What is the reason? Is this new life evident in you?

Dear Lord …

E. Wrap-Up

Conclude your study of The Church, and fix it in your mind by doing the following:

1. Recall the color of this time period, white, and think of it in terms of your reading to help you remember it.

2. Quickly review Sessions 21-23. Write a brief summary of what the period of The Church is about or its significance as part of the "big picture."

Session 23 Talk Notes

The Church – Part 3

I.   Introduction to The Church – Part 3

II.   Paul's First Missionary Journey (Acts 13:2–14:28)

A.   Saul (Paul) and Barnabus commissioned

B.   Hub: Antioch

C.   Purpose: to spread the gospel, start new churches

III.   Paul's Second Missionary Journey (Acts 15:36–18:22)

A.   The journey starts after the Council at Jerusalem

   1.   Paul and Barnabas separate

      a.   Barnabus takes Mark, sails for Cyprus

      b.   Paul takes Silas, heads through Syria and Cilicia

   2.   Purpose

      a.   Visit churches already established (15:36)

      b.   Deliver decision of Jerusalem Council (16:4-5)

   3.   Timothy joins Paul in Lystra

   4.   Paul's vision of a Macedonian (16:9-10)

      a.   Spread of the gospel to Europe

B.   Philippi (16:11-40)

   1.   Conversion of Lydia – first European convert

   2.   Paul exorcises the demon from the slave-girl, soothsayer

   3.   Paul and Silas are imprisoned and freed

C.   Thessalonica (17:1-9)

   1.   Paul teaches first in the synagogue

   2.   "These men who have turned the world upside down" (verse 6)

D.   Beroea (17:10-15)

E.   Athens (17:16-34) – Paul teaches at the Areopagus (Mars Hill)

   1.   Marketplace of ideas

   2.   An altar "to an unknown god" (verse 23)

   3.   Paul's method

    4. Means of revelation (CCC 31–50)

  F. Corinth (18:1-17)

    1. Paul stays with Priscilla and Aquila

      a. They disciple Apollos

    2. "From now on I will go to the Gentiles" (verse 6)

    3. Problems at Corinth

IV. Paul's Third Missionary Journey (Acts 18:23–21:16)

  A. Destination: Asia Minor

  B. Ephesus (Chapter 19)

    1. Three years teaching, healing

    2. Spiritual conflict (the occult)

    3. Revelation: letter to Church in Ephesus – you have lost your first love

  C. Miletus: Paul's farewell to the elders of Ephesus (20:17-38)

V. Paul's Journey to Jerusalem (Acts 21)

  A. Prophecy of Agabus

  B. Arrest during Pentecost (correlation between Peter and Paul)

VI. Paul on Trial

  A. Arrest and imprisonment

    1. Paul's defense (Chapter 22) – a summary of salvation history

    2. Appearance before various rulers; appeal to Caesar

VII. Voyage to Rome (Acts 27–28)

  A. Shipwreck on Malta – remains faithful

  B. Under guard in Rome; preaches two years

  C. Significance of Rome (see Daniel 2)

  D. How Paul accomplishes his mission

    1. 2 Corinthians 12:10: "When I am weak, then I am strong"

VIII. Conclusion

  A. Witness of the apostles: They give their lives, knowing death is not the end

  B. The baton has been passed to you

By now you should be familiar with the story of salvation history and ready to continue on your own. But first, review what you have learned. Look at *The Bible Timeline* Chart and see if you remember the major features of each period. Then review the "Outline of Bible Periods" on page 168, and trace the narrative books through the periods. Look at the rise and fall of the major world powers, and think of ways in which they impacted the story. Are there any areas you would like to learn more about?

If you have not yet read all the way through the fourteen narrative books that tell the story of salvation history, do so now while this study is fresh in your mind. On page 167 is a ninety-day plan for reading the Bible that you can use to track your progress. *The Bible Timeline Guided Journal* is also available. This resource will help you follow the ninety-day plan by providing summaries of the time periods, clarification of difficult terms and passages, and space to record your observations, questions, and prayers of response.

At some point, you will want to begin reading the supplemental books. Are you particularly interested in the time of the Divided Kingdom? Read through some of the prophets that spoke during that time, or see how 2 Chronicles tells the story from a different angle. Have you always wanted to read the Wisdom literature? Brush up on the Royal Kingdom, and then dive into Psalms or Proverbs for a start. Keep your Chart and Bookmark in your Bible so you can keep what you are reading in the context of the big picture.

As you progress in your Scripture reading, consider what the Church has to say about the interpretation of Sacred Scripture and its various "senses." The *Catechism* instructs us to follow three guidelines when interpreting Scripture: (1) Read each piece in light of the whole; (2) consider Scripture within the living Tradition of the Church; and (3) pay attention to the way the truths of faith are coherent among themselves and within God's plan (see CCC 111–114). We have attempted to demonstrate this in this study. On the way, we have focused for the most part on what is called the "literal sense" of Scripture as a foundation for understanding the "spiritual senses." The literal sense takes such things as the type of literature and figures of speech of the time into account to determine the meaning of the words: the message the author intended for the audience.

The three spiritual senses are based on the literal, and they open up the many layers of meaning in Scripture. They are: (1) the allegorical sense (the sense in which many events find their significance in Jesus Christ); (2) the moral sense (the sense in which they direct us to put what we read into practice); and (3) the anagogical sense (the way in which many of the events and earthly truths found in Scripture are signs of heavenly realities). You can read more about the senses of Scripture in CCC 115–119 or in the book, *Making Senses Out of Scripture: Reading the Bible as the First Christians Did,* by Mark Shea. We urge you to continue to read the Bible and to study and meditate on God's Word. Listen prayerfully to the Scripture readings while you are at Mass, and ask God to speak to you through them. Finally, do not keep it to yourself. The *Catechism* says, "Those who with God's help have welcomed Christ's call and freely responded to it are urged on by love of Christ to proclaim the Good News everywhere in the world. ... All Christ's faithful are called to hand [this deposit] on from generation to generation, by professing the faith, by living it in fraternal sharing, and by celebrating it in liturgy and prayer" (CCC 3).

That includes you and me. Go out and pass on what you have learned. May God richly bless you.

What's Next?

Two additional studies from *The Great Adventure* build on *The Bible Timeline: The Story of Salvation* and can help you build a firm foundation for a lifetime of Scripture reading and study. *Matthew: The King and His Kingdom* shows how Jesus builds on the foundation laid in the Old Testament to inaugurate the kingdom of heaven on earth and explains that Jesus is the fulfillment of all that the Old Testament pointed to. *Acts: The Spread of the Kingdom* rounds out the Foundational Series by showing how Christ's kingdom began to spread in the earliest days of the Church. It also shows how Christ's work continues through you and me in the Church today. Here is where you "find yourself in the story" that you learned in *The Bible Timeline: The Story of Salvation.* To find out more, visit BibleStudyForCatholics.com or AscensionPress.com.

We Would Like to Hear from You

Was this study helpful to you? Did it deliver what it promised? What was your experience with the study questions and responses? Were the video presentations informative? Please take time to share your experience of *The Bible Timeline: The Story of Salvation.* Email comments to info@BibleStudyForCatholics.com, or mail them to *The Great Adventure,* P.O. Box 1990, West Chester, PA 19380.

Reading Through the Bible Historically
Ninety-Day Reading Plan

Month #1

Early World
__ 1. Genesis 1–4
__ 2. Genesis 5–8
__ 3. Genesis 9–11

Patriarchs
__4. Genesis 12–16
__5. Genesis 17–20
__6. Genesis 21–24
__7. Genesis 25–28
__8. Genesis 29–32

__ 9. Genesis 33–36
__10. Genesis 37–40
__11. Genesis 41–45
__12. Genesis 46–50

Egypt and Exodus
__13. Exodus 1–4
__14. Exodus 5–8
__15. Exodus 9–12
__16. Exodus 13–16
__17. Exodus 17–20

__18. Exodus 21–24
__19. Exodus 25–28
__20. Exodus 29–32
__21. Exodus 33–36
__22. Exodus 37–40

Desert Wanderings
__23. Numbers 1–4
__24. Numbers 5–8
__25. Numbers 9–12
__26. Numbers 13–16

__27. Numbers 17–20
__28. Numbers 21–24
__29. Numbers 25–28
__30. Numbers 29–32
__31. Numbers 33–36

Month #2

Conquest and Judges
__32. Joshua 1–4
__33. Joshua 5–8
__34. Joshua 9–12
__35. Joshua 13–16
__36. Joshua 17–20
__37. Joshua 21–24
__38. Judges 1–4
__39. Judges 5–8
__40. Judges 9–12
__41. Judges 13–16

__42. Judges 17–21
__43. 1 Samuel 1–4
__44. 1 Samuel 5–8

Royal Kingdom
__45. 1 Samuel 9–12
__46. 1 Samuel 13–16
__47. 1 Samuel 17–20
__48. 1 Samuel 21–24
__49. 1 Samuel 25–28
__50. 1 Samuel 29–31

__51. 2 Samuel 1–4
__52. 2 Samuel 5–8
__53. 2 Samuel 9–12
__54. 2 Samuel 13–16
__55. 2 Samuel 17–20
__56. 2 Samuel 21–24
__57. 1 Kings 1–4
__58. 1 Kings 5–8
__59. 1 Kings 9–11

Month #3

Divided Kingdom
__60. 1 Kings 12–15
__61. 1 Kings 16–19
__62. 1 Kings 20–22
__63. 2 Kings 1–4
__64. 2 Kings 5–8
__65. 2 Kings 9–12
__66. 2 Kings 13–16

Exile
__67. 2 Kings 17–20
__68. 2 Kings 21–25

Return
__69. Ezra 1–5

__70. Ezra 6–10
__71. Nehemiah 1–4
__72. Nehemiah 5–8
__73. Nehemiah 9–13

Maccabean Revolt
__74. 1 Maccabees 1–4
__75. 1 Maccabees 5–8
__76. 1 Maccabees 9–12
__77. 1 Maccabees 13–16

Messianic Fulfillment
__78. Luke 1–4
__79. Luke 5–8
__80. Luke 9–12

__81. Luke 13–16
__82. Luke 17–20
__83. Luke 21–24

The Church
__84. Acts 1–4
__85. Acts 5–8
__86. Acts 9–12
__87. Acts 13–16
__88. Acts 17–20
__89. Acts 21–24
__90. Acts 25–28

The Bible Timeline Guided Journal is available from Ascension Press to help you journey through this reading plan in light of the story you have learned through *The Bible Timeline: The Story of Salvation.*

Outline of Bible Periods

Each numbered event corresponds to a numbered event on *The Bible Timeline* Chart.

Early World (Turquoise) Creation to 2000 BC
1. Creation . . . . .Genesis 1:1–2:24
2. Fall . . . . .Genesis 3:1-24
3. Curse and promise *(protoevangelium)*. . . . . .Genesis 3:8-24
4. Flood. . . . . .Genesis 6:1–9:17
5. People scattered at Babel . . . . .Genesis 11:1-9

Patriarchs (Burgundy) 2000–1700 BC
6. God calls Abram out of Ur . . . . .Genesis 12:1
7. Melchizedek blesses Abraham. . . . . .Genesis 14:18-20
8. Sodom and Gomorrah . . . . .Genesis 18:16–19:38
9. Binding of Isaac. . . . . .Genesis 22
10. Covenant with Abraham
    Three-fold promise . . . . .Genesis 12:1-9
    First covenant (Land Promise) . . . . .Genesis 15:1-21
    Second covenant (Kingdom Promise). . . . . .Genesis 17:1-11
    Third covenant (Promise of Worldwide Blessing) . . . . .Genesis 22:1-19
11. Jacob steals blessing and flees . . . . .Genesis 27:1-46
12. Jacob wrestles with God . . . . .Genesis 32:22-31
13. Joseph sold into slavery. . . . . .Genesis 37:12-36
14. Jacob's family moves to Egypt. . . . . .Genesis 46

Egypt and Exodus (Red) 1700–1280 BC
15. Four hundred years of slavery . . . . .Exodus 1:1-22
16. The burning bush. . . . . .Exodus 3:1–6:30
17. Ten plagues . . . . .Exodus 7:1–11:10
18. Exodus and first Passover (1280 BC). . . . . .Exodus 12:1–14:31
19. Red Sea . . . . .Exodus 13:17–15:21
20. Manna . . . . .Exodus 16
21. Covenant with Moses (Mount Sinai) . . . . .Exodus 19:1–31:18
22. Golden calf . . . . .Exodus 32:1-35
23. Levitical priesthood. . . . . .Exodus 32:27-29; Numbers 3
24. Tabernacle. . . . . .Exodus 25–27, 36–38

Desert Wanderings (Tan) 1280–1240 BC
25. Twelve spies sent out . . . . .Numbers 13:1-33
26. Aaron's rod . . . . .Numbers 17
27. Moses strikes the rock . . . . .Numbers 20:1-13
28. Bronze serpent . . . . .Numbers 21:4-9
29. Covenant in Moab . . . . .Deuteronomy 29:1-29

Conquest and Judges (Green) 1240–1050 BC
30. Israel crosses the Jordan . . . . .Joshua 1–4
31. Fall of Jericho. . . . . .Joshua 5:13–6:27
32. Covenant renewal . . . . .Joshua 8:30-35
33. Southern campaign. . . . . .Joshua 9–10
34. Northern campaign. . . . . .Joshua 11
35. Tribal allotment. . . . . .Joshua 13–21
36. Israel asks for a king. . . . . .I Samuel 8:1-22

Royal Kingdom (Purple) 1050–930 BC

37. David kills Goliath . . . . .1 Samuel 17:1-31
38. Covenant with David . . . . .2 Samuel 7:1-29
39. Ark moved to Jerusalem . . . . .2 Samuel 6
40. First Temple built (961 BC) . . . . .1 Kings 5:1–8:66

Divided Kingdom (Black) 930–722 BC

41. The kingdom divides. . . . . .1 Kings 12:16-20
42. Jezebel fights Israel . . . . .1 Kings 18–21; 2 Kings 9
43. Hosea marries a prostitute . . . . .Hosea 1–3

Exile (Baby Blue) 722–538 BC

44. Israel falls to Assyria (722 BC) . . . . .2 Kings 17:1-41
45. Foreign possession of Samaria . . . . .2 Kings 17
46. Image of the five kingdoms . . . . .Daniel 2
47. Judah falls to Babylon (587 BC) . . . . .2 Kings 25:1-30
48. First Temple destroyed (587 BC). . . . . .2 Kings 25:8-17

Return (Yellow) 538–167 BC

49. Zerubbabel rebuilds Temple (537 BC) . . . . .Ezra 3:1–6:22
50. Ezra returns and teaches (458 BC). . . . . .Ezra 7:1–8:36
51. Esther saves her people . . . . .Esther 1:1–10:3
52. Nehemiah returns and rebuilds Jerusalem walls (444 BC) . . . . . . .Nehemiah 3:1–4:23

Maccabean Revolt (Orange) 167 BC–AD 1

53. Antiochus desecrates the Temple (167 BC) . . . . .1 Maccabees 4:43
54. Purification of the Temple (Hanukkah – 164 BC) . . . . .1 Maccabees 4:36-61

Messianic Fulfillment (Gold) AD 1– AD 33

55. Annunciation. . . . . .Luke 1:26-38
56. Baptism of Jesus (AD 29) . . . . .Luke 3:21-22
57. Sermon on the Mount . . . . .Luke 6:20-49
58. Wedding at Cana . . . . .John 2:1-12
59. Keys to Peter . . . . .Matthew 16:13-20
60. Last Supper . . . . .Luke 22:1-38
61. Passion (AD 33) . . . . .Luke 22–23
62. Jesus gives his mother to the Church . . . . .John 19:25-27
63. Resurrection (AD 33) . . . . .Luke 24:1-12
64. Ascension . . . . .Luke 24:44-53

The Church (White) AD 33–

65. Witness in Jerusalem (AD 33–35). . . . . .Acts 1:1–8:4
   • Pentecost (AD 33) . . . . .Acts 2:1-13
   • Choosing of the seven (diaconate) . . . . .Acts 6:1-7
   • Stephen martyred . . . . .Acts 6:8–7:60
66. Witness in Judea and Samaria (AD 33–45) . . . . .Acts 8:5–13:1
   • Saul's conversion (AD 33/34) . . . . .Acts 9
   • Peter's vision . . . . .Acts 10
   • Peter's arrest and deliverance . . . . .Acts 12
67. Witness to the ends of the earth (AD 45–68) . . . . .Acts 13:1–28:31
   • Paul's three missionary journeys (AD 45–58). . . . .–
      First journey . . . . .Acts 13:1–14:28
      Second journey . . . . .Acts 15:36–18:22
      Third journey . . . . .Acts 18:23–21:16
   • Council of Jerusalem (AD 49) . . . . .Acts 15
   • John's Apocalypse (AD 68). . . . . .Revelation
68. Destruction of the Jerusalem Temple (AD 70). . . . .–

THE BIBLE TIMELINE
The Story of Salvation

Responses to the Study Questions

How to Use These Responses

After completing the home preparation, discussing the questions, and viewing the video presentation, the final step is to review the responses to the questions. These responses summarize the main points from the session and help you continue your Bible study in the next session.

Although it can be tempting to read these responses ahead of time, please wait until after you have completed the questions for each session and engaged in the small-group discussion. It is not necessary to have the "right" answers before going to the small-group discussion. In fact, one purpose of the discussion is for participants to learn by sharing their insights and questions with each other and, through that discussion, coming to a better understanding of the Scripture passages. This makes for a better Bible study experience for everyone.

For best results, follow these steps in order:

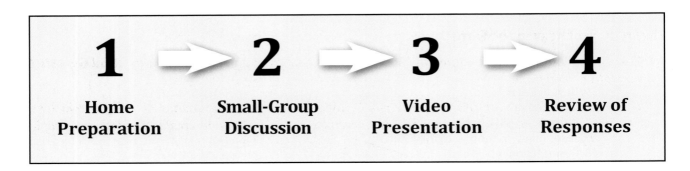

1	2	3	4
Home Preparation	Small-Group Discussion	Video Presentation	Review of Responses

Session 2 – Responses
Early World – Part 1

THE BIBLE
TIMELINE
The Story of Salvation

Facilitators: *Read these recommended responses to the questions ahead of time to help you prepare to lead the small-group discussion.*

Participants: *Reinforce what you have learned by reviewing these recommended responses after the small-group discussion and before you go on to the next session.*

A. Establish the Context

Facilitators: Before you begin, make sure anyone who missed the Introduction has all needed materials. Have participants look at *The Bible Timeline* Chart and identify the Early World period along with its color and narrative book. Have them point out the key people and events. The purpose of this is to gain familiarity with the Chart.

B. Read the Story

Facilitators: If there is time, have someone read each passage aloud before it is discussed.

C. Take a Deeper Look

The Creation of Heaven and Earth

1. *There are two accounts of Creation in Genesis 1 and 2, told from different viewpoints. Read **Genesis 1** carefully several times.*

   a. *What does this account tell you about God? Think about the way God creates; the order in which he forms and fills the earth; the way he blesses; even the simple fact that he creates the earth and people at all.*

   Answers will vary. Encourage discussion. The fact that God created the heavens and the earth tells us that God wanted it all to exist. He also wants us—those he has created in his very image and likeness—to exist. The manner in which he calls everything into existence shows the awesome power of his Word. He acts deliberately, demonstrating his love for order, beauty, and goodness. The way he blesses and provides for those he creates shows his fatherly love.

   b. *What does Genesis 1 tell you about the nature and purpose of the world and the things around us?*

   The Creation account is worded in such a way so as to communicate the inherent goodness and beauty of everything God has created. Everything is interdependent, and there is a hierarchy built into the system in which mankind is given stewardship of creation. The world and all it contains has been fashioned as a dwelling place, tailored for our work and enjoyment.

The Creation of Mankind

2. *The creation of mankind is told twice, in **Genesis 1:26-31 and 2:4-25**. Read both accounts, paying close attention to **Genesis 1:27**.*

   a. *What does it mean to be created in God's image? Read also **CCC 356–357 and 364**.*

   Created in God's image and likeness, we occupy a unique place in creation. As the *Catechism* explains, only mankind has the dignity of being *someone* and not *something;* only mankind can know God and love him and share in his life (see CCC 356–357). Every person is animated by a soul and created to be, in Christ, the temple of the Holy Spirit (see CCC 364). We are like him in that we are rational beings, capable of love and wisdom and possessing a free will. We are also like him in the things we do: We procreate, make things beautiful, bless and work, rest, and exercise dominion.

   b. *What does "male and female he created them" add to your understanding of the image in which we are created? For help with this question, read **CCC 369–373**.*

   Individually, in our masculinity or femininity, we possess the dignity of God's image and reflect his goodness and wisdom (see CCC 369). But male and female are also created *together* and are meant *for* one another, complementary in physical makeup and each a helpmate for the other. In the communion of male and female that becomes "one flesh" in marriage (Genesis 2:24) and in the way that new life springs from that love in procreation, we see reflected the image of a God who is One and who at the same time, is a communion of three persons, existing in an eternal exchange of love.

3. **Think About It:** *Genesis 2:1-3 tells us that after completing his work of Creation, God rested on the seventh day, blessed it, and made it holy. Years later, the children of Israel will be commanded to refrain from work on the seventh day in imitation of God. If we are created in his image, is there any sense in which we stifle the image of God in ourselves when we ignore this command? Or, to put it another way: In what way does this command enable us to more fully live in God's image? For further reading about the Sabbath, see **CCC 345–349**.*

   God creates and he rests. When we intentionally set aside one day free from work, we empty it of our own pursuits and agendas—not in order to be idle, but to be free from self and from life's demands and to turn our attention to God and our hearts to worship. "Creation was fashioned with a view to the Sabbath and therefore for the worship and adoration of God," says the *Catechism*. "Worship is inscribed in the order of creation" (CCC 347; cf. Genesis 1:14).

   God builds this period of rest and worship into the rhythm of our lives not because he needs it but because we do. Created in his image, we are free to create and to rest from creating; to work and to lay down our work; to exercise our dominion and care for our needs and the needs of those around us and to do "the work of God—that is, solemn worship" (CCC 347).[1]

Fall and Promise

4. *"Behind the disobedient choice of our first parents lurks a seductive voice, opposed to God" (CCC 391). That is the voice of Satan, the devil, who is pictured in Genesis 3 as a serpent. Review the command God gives to Adam in **Genesis 2:16-17;** then read the exchange between the Serpent and the woman in **Genesis 3:1-4.***

   a. *What is the Serpent trying to accomplish?*

---

[1] St. Benedict, *Regula* 43, 3: PL 66, 675–676.

The Serpent, who is Satan, attacks God by tempting those God loves to rebel against him. Rebellion is more complete when it is intended rather than forced, so Satan begins by planting seeds of doubt in the woman's mind—doubt as to God's intent, his motivation, and the quality of his love.

b.   *What strategy does he use?*

The Serpent starts by questioning the intention behind God's command, suggesting that he is withholding good from Adam and Eve: "Did God say, 'You shall not eat of any tree of the garden'?" (3:1). Having put Eve on the defensive, Satan zeroes in and tells an outright lie to plant the possibility of disobedience in her mind. "You will not die. For God knows that when you eat of it your eyes will be opened, and you will be like God, knowing good and evil" (3:5). Eve takes the bait.

5.   *In **Genesis 3:4,** the Serpent calls God a liar—"You will not die," he says—and proceeds to tell the woman why it will be to her benefit to disobey God.*

a.   *What are these "benefits"?*

Satan proposes three "benefits" of eating the fruit: (1) Their eyes will be opened; (2) they will be like God; and (3) they will know good and evil. This is the first test. Do Adam and Eve trust in God's love and goodness? Will they submit to their Creator or abuse their freedom and follow their own wills instead?

b.   *Do these benefits offer Eve anything she does not already have? What do they offer?*

There is great irony in the choice the Serpent proposes. His offer is a tragic, hollow imitation of what the man and woman already have in God's friendship. Their eyes are opened to God's goodness and love, to the beauty of all he has given them. Satan wants to open their eyes to their shame. They are already like God in the way no other created being is like him, including the angels and Satan himself—they bear his image and likeness in their very beings. Satan suggests that they can be like God, but without God and in some way other than the way God intends. They know good and evil as God has revealed it to them. Enjoy creation, he has told them; it is all good. But do not eat of the fruit of this one tree, or you will die. Satan's counterfeit is for them to determine good and evil according to their own desires.

6.   *What immediate effects do Adam and Eve's disobedience have on their behavior, which show the consequences of their sin?*

The consequences of choosing self over God are immediately evident: Adam and Eve realize they are naked, and they are so ashamed, that they hide from each other. They no longer live together in harmony. Next, they realize they have sinned, and they hide from God because they are afraid. Their image of him is distorted. They do not see him as a loving Father to run to, but as a punishing judge from whom to hide. They no longer live in harmony with God. Unable or unwilling to take responsibility for their actions, they begin blaming one another, excusing themselves. Sin now has dominion over them.

These "natural consequences" are carried a logical step forward by the sentence God pronounces upon them. The fractured relationship between man and woman will continue in tension, lust, and the desire to dominate. The way in which they reflect God through procreation and work will be fraught with pain. The earth will become alien and hostile. All creation will be subject to bondage and decay. Death has entered the world.

7.   *Read God's curse on the Serpent and on Adam and Eve in **Genesis 3:14-19.***

a. *Does God abandon his disobedient children? What ray of hope do you see?*

Far from abandoning his wayward children, God announces a resolution to the problem. The first glimmer of hope can be found in his condemnation of the Serpent. The battle between the Serpent and the "woman" will continue through their offspring, but one day the seed of the woman will prevail. (Imagine the insult. The very humans through whom Satan sought to attack God, who folded without a whimper against his first onslaught, will crush the Serpent's head.) This pronouncement in Genesis 3:15 of ultimate victory is known as the *protoevangelium*—"first gospel."

b. *Is there anything about their punishment that might help mankind learn the lesson Adam and Eve so sadly failed?*

The judgment God pronounces is profoundly remedial. The woman will have pain in childbearing, and the man will toil in his labor, fighting against thorns and thistles and eating by the sweat of his brow. Why?

God's children are unwilling to deny themselves their desire for the forbidden fruit. They do not trust God and are unwilling to obey him when it means facing the frightening and possibly deadly Serpent (see Revelation 12:3-9 for a vivid description). And yet, at the heart of love, is the willingness to suffer and even die for the one loved. What better way to learn this than to suffer for love, for work, and for food—to suffer and learn that out of giving oneself comes new life.

As for the final pronouncement, the verdict of death and the exile from Eden: God in his mercy will not allow mankind access to the Tree of Life through which they might live forever in their fallen condition. A more permanent and glorious solution is in the works.

8. **New Testament Connection:** *The apostle John borrows language and imagery from the Creation story to begin his Gospel. Read **John 1:1-14**. What new creation is he describing?*

John describes the new creation, the dawn of the kingdom of God on earth, in terms reminiscent of the story of Creation in Genesis. "In the beginning … all things were made," John writes in 1:1-3. The Word of God that spoke all into being at Creation is revealed in the Gospel to be Christ, the light that "shines in the darkness, and the darkness has not overcome it" (1:5-6). Christ offers the children of Adam, fallen from their original relationship with God, "power to become children of God … And the Word became flesh and dwelt among us, full of grace and truth" (1:12-14). God once again is walking with his people in harmony. What was lost in the Garden of Eden is restored in the kingdom of God.

D. Application

Facilitators: If time allows, have group members share their responses to the following application questions.

What are some ways we hide from the presence of God? How does sin drive us further from his presence?

Close with the Responsive Prayer found on the inside front cover of this Study Set Workbook. Pray through the Early World period.

After the small-group discussion, watch Jeff Cavins' video presentation on *Session 2 – Early World: Part 1*.

Facilitators: Read these recommended responses to the questions ahead of time to help you prepare to lead the small-group discussion.

Participants: Reinforce what you have learned by reviewing these recommended responses after the small-group discussion and before you go on to the next session.

A. Review the Context

Facilitators: Take a moment to review the context and what was learned in the previous session. If you like, use the following question to encourage discussion:

- *What is the most important thing you learned about God in Genesis 1–3?*

B. Read the Story

Facilitators: If there is time, have someone read each passage aloud before it is discussed.

C. Take a Deeper Look

Cain and Abel (Genesis 4:1-16)

1. *With the births of Cain and Abel, we see the first offspring of the woman, Eve. Is there any chance one of these might be the promised "seed" who will defeat Satan? Do they look like it to you? Explain.*

    Whatever hopes we (or Eve) might have that either of her sons is the promised seed are dashed when Cain kills Abel. Cain appears more like a candidate for seed of the Serpent: selfish, murderous, more interested in himself than in God, and cast out from God's presence to a place "east of Eden."

2. *What is wrong with Cain's offering as compared with Abel's?*

    The problem with Cain's offering is not *what* he brings (produce as opposed to meat), but what he gives *of himself.* Abel seeks out the best of his flock, the firstborn, and brings the choice fat portions to God. He gives the best he has and gives from his heart. In contrast, Cain seems to simply grab some grain or vegetables on the way to the altar. All sacrifice is important, not for what it is (what use does God have for a sacrificed animal or burnt handful of grain?), but for what it represents: a recognition that all good things come from God and a heart turned to God in gratitude, giving back to God from one's bounty.

The Family Grows (Genesis 4:17–5:32)

3. *Compare and contrast the two family lines. Why do you think the author focuses on Seth's descendants rather than on those of Cain in Adam's "official" genealogy?*

    Cain builds a city named after his son. His descendants play music, raise livestock, and forge tools and weapons. They also are polygamous, violent, and vengeful like their forefather. The picture is one of a civilization bent on self-sufficiency, on pleasing itself, and on conquering others.

Seth's line stands in sharp contrast to the self-determination and violence of his brother's line. Seth's descendants are described not by their accomplishments, but by their characters: Enoch "[walks] with God" and is taken by God before he dies. Lamech predicts that his son, Noah, will bring relief from the toil brought on by the Fall. One of these men avoids death altogether, and another brings relief from the curse. Surely, this is a group of people whose faces remain turned toward God, waiting for his promised Deliverer instead of taking the curse as a challenge to rise above. From the first verse of Seth's genealogy, the author notes that this son is "in [Adam's] own likeness, after his image." This is the genealogy line we are meant to follow in our search for the "seed of the woman."

The Flood and God's Covenant with Noah (Genesis 6–10)

4. *Lamech names his son "Noah," which means "rest," saying, "Out of the ground which the LORD has cursed this one shall bring us relief from our work and from the toil of our hands" (Genesis 5:29). Taking this together with **Genesis 6**, what other relief is needed on the earth?*

    Relief from wickedness, that is "great in the earth," is needed. "Every imagination of the thoughts of [man's] heart was only evil continually" (Genesis 6:5). Cain-style civilizations has evidently become the rule. The earth is corrupt and full of violence.

5. *What is God's solution to the problem?*

    God's solution is to send a great flood to destroy the earth and all the wicked people on it. Rather than starting fresh with a new Adam and Eve and new creatures, he saves one righteous man (Noah) and his family, along with two of every unclean animal (Genesis 6:19) and seven pairs of every bird and clean animal (Genesis 7:2-3).

6. ***New Testament Connection:*** *The Church has long seen that God's actions in the Old Testament prefigure what he will do one day through his Son, Jesus Christ. The Old Testament figures are called "types" of the New Testament. Think for a moment about the Ark: A great vessel rides above the deathly waves of a flood and carries the righteous to safety. Can you think of a New Testament parallel of which the Ark is a type? Read **1 Peter 3:18-22** along with **CCC 845 and 1219–1220**. What do the Ark and the Flood signify? Explain.*

    The Ark signifies both the Church—which bears Christians above the waters of sin and saves them—and baptism—whose waters bring both the death of the old (sinful) life and the birth of new life. Noah is saved because of his faithful obedience—the same saving "obedience of faith" that St. Paul calls people to in Romans 1:5.

7. *Read **Genesis 8:20–9:17**.*

    a. *What solemn promise does God make to Noah, and with what sign does he seal that covenant?*

    God makes a covenant with the family of Noah and with all living creatures to never again destroy all life on earth as he did with the Flood. He seals his covenant promise with the rainbow, which will be a perpetual reminder of the promise.

    b. *As is typical with covenants, this covenant makes demands on Noah and his sons as well. What are they?*

    For their part, Noah and his sons are to be fruitful and multiply, to fill the earth and rule over creation. These are things God commanded Adam and Eve also, but this time (possibly mindful of Cain's sin and the sins of all those destroyed in the Flood), God adds these stipulations: The people must not eat meat that still has blood in it, and they must not kill. Anyone, whether man or beast, who kills a person will be killed himself. Mankind is made in God's image, and, therefore, every person is precious.

The Tower of Babel (Genesis 11)

8. *a.* *Review the events following the Flood and God's covenant with Noah (see* **Genesis 9:18–11:9***). Do you see any change in man's behavior? What is the new civilization like? Did the "Flood solution" to evil work?*

    Getting rid of the "bad guys" does not seem to have gotten rid of the bad. Almost immediately, Noah gets drunk, and his son takes advantage of him. Great cities are built, and mighty hunters rule. There is no record of people walking with God or calling on his name. Instead, they strive together to make a name for *themselves* by building a tower to the heavens, a challenge God meets by confusing their languages and scattering the people throughout the earth. If the Flood was meant to make a permanent change, it does not appear to have worked.

    b. **Think About It:** *Have you ever wondered why God does not just reach down and "wipe out the bad guys"? He did this once and promised never to do it again. Why not? Why was that not the solution? What is it about baptism and the Church that is more effective than the Flood that prefigured them? For help with this question, read* **CCC 1213ff.**

    What does the fact that the Flood seemingly fails in its intent mean about God? This is worth pondering. We have seen already in Genesis 3 that God's first punishment of man's disobedience is *remedial*. God is not intent on vengeance, as we tend to be. We must look for a deeper lesson in the Flood. How often have you heard someone ask, "Why doesn't God just wipe out all the bad guys?" Guess what—he already did. The aftermath of the Flood shows clearly that the problem lies deep within human nature and affects all of us. Good behavior is not enough. Whatever change in man's nature that occurred at the Fall persists even in the offspring of the righteous Noah.

    Full restoration will require a far different solution. Under the New Covenant in Jesus Christ, the Church and baptism will do, in fact, what the Ark and the Flood only pointed to. They will drown the sinful nature itself *within* people, purify them and restore them to new life in Jesus Christ, and place them in the family of God, which is the Church.

    Having this new nature does not mean that every baptized person is automatically forever without sin. The temporal consequences of the Fall—suffering, death, and what is called "concupiscence" (the inclination to sin)—remain and must be wrestled with by the help of God's grace. For a deeper understanding of baptism and its effects, read **CCC 1213** and the section following.

9. *In* **Genesis 11,** *men build "a tower with its top in the heavens." What might this tower express about their relationship with God?*

    The people who build the Tower of Babel intend to make a name for themselves. They are proud, building as if they want to get on a level with God by reaching the heavens. They have seemingly lost their identity as the created in relationship to their Creator.

10. **New Testament Connection:** *God's response to mankind's self-exaltation and determination to rely on themselves instead of on God is to confuse their languages and to divide and scatter the people across the earth. In the New Testament, something happens that is, in effect, a reversal of the Babel event. Read* **Acts 2:1-13.** *What happens?*

    At Pentecost, when the Spirit of God descends on Jesus' disciples, they begin speaking in other languages so that people from every corner of the earth are able to understand them. This is the opposite of the Tower of Babel incident. It represents the bringing together of all that has been scattered. In the Church, as was demonstrated at Pentecost, God is gathering his lost children from every corner of the globe—from every nation of the earth—into a relationship with him.

D. Application

Facilitators: If time allows, have group members share their responses to the following application questions.

What enables Enoch and Noah to stand alone and remain righteous amid great wickedness? Are you the same kind of light, or is it too easy to succumb to the influence of others? How can you keep your own light bright against the darkness?

E. Wrap-Up

1. Remember the Early World by its color, turquoise: the color of the earth as seen from space.

2. Answers will vary. Here is one possible reply: In the Early World period, God creates the world for man to live in and then creates mankind in his image. Adam and Eve disobey and fall from God's grace, but God promises that one day, a "seed of the woman" will be victorious over the Serpent's seed.

Close with the Responsive Prayer found on the inside front cover of this Study Set Workbook. Pray through the Early World period.

After the small-group discussion, watch Jeff Cavins' video presentation on *Session 3 – Early World: Part 2*.

Facilitators: Read these recommended responses to the questions ahead of time to help you prepare to lead the small-group discussion.

Participants: Reinforce what you have learned by reviewing these recommended responses after the small-group discussion and before you go on to the next session.

A. Establish the Context

Facilitators: Take a moment to review what was learned in the previous session and to establish the context for the Patriarchs. If you like, use the following question to encourage discussion:

- *Think about the contrasting qualities of the descendants of Cain and Seth. Are there parallels between them and people today? What have you learned?*

B. Read the Story

Facilitators: If there is time, have someone read each passage aloud before it is discussed.

C. Take a Deeper Look

God's Promise to Abram (Genesis 12:1-9)

1. *Read **Genesis 12:1-3**. What three-part promise does God make to Abram? (Hint: The promise is simplified in the "Abrahamic Covenant" box in the Patriarchs section of your* Bible Timeline *Chart.)*

   God promises: (1) to make Abram into a great nation and to bless him, (2) to make his name great so that he can be a blessing, and (3) to bless those who bless him, curse those who curse him, and bless all the families of the earth through him. In essence, it is a three-part promise to give his descendants land and a kingdom and to make them a source of worldwide blessing.

   "Bless" is repeated so often that it is easy to miss the rest of the promise. It brings to mind God's benediction over creation in the early chapters of Genesis and after the Flood and, in contrast, the curses that follow mankind's disobedience. This sounds as though God's original blessing will be restored through this man, Abram.

From Promise to Covenant (Genesis 15 and 17)

2. *Review **Genesis 15 and 17**. Which of the original promises do these covenants strengthen, and what new information does each one add? (See the chart on page 30 for help.)*

   The covenant in Genesis 15 strengthens the first promise: that God will make Abram into a great nation. For that to be possible, Abram will need many descendants and the means and place for them to live. So, God promises him offspring as numerous as the stars, great possessions for these people when they return from being slaves in a strange country, and the entire land of Canaan, from the Wadi of Egypt to the Euphrates in the north.

In Genesis 17, God turns to his second promise: to make Abram's name great, which, in essence, means that his descendants will be raised to political power in the new land. Because the covenant stresses the royal nature of his descendants and the everlasting nature of the covenant, this can be looked at as a promise of a future dynastic kingdom. In anticipation of this, the first thing God does is change Abram's name from "Abram" ("exalted father") to "Abraham" ("father of many") and Sarai's name to "Sarah." Both "Sarai" and "Sarah" mean princess, but the change seems to be something closer to "queen mother," signifying that she will be the mother of kings.

3.   a.   *Read **Genesis 15:2-6**, in which Abram's faith is counted as righteousness. How might trying to count the stars in the sky help Abram to trust in God's promise, and how is this a profound example of what faith requires? (Hint: What seems to be the time of day, and why does that matter?)*

God takes Abram outside and says, "'Look toward heaven, and number the stars, if you are able to number them … So shall your descendants be.' And he believed the LORD …" What about a sky full of stars would convince Abram of anything other than that God means to give him more descendants than he can imagine? How would it help him believe God?

The answer is instantly clear if you consider that it might be day when God shows Abram the stars. And, indeed, it may be day. Just six verses later, the sun sets and darkness falls. Imagine a clear afternoon sky and God asking, "Look toward heaven, and number the stars, if you are able to number them." The task of numbering the stars changes from difficult to impossible. They are not there, as far as the eye can see. But do you doubt their existence? Faith is like that. God asks us to believe based on what we know to be true about him—not based on the evidence available to our senses. Abram is able to believe God will give him offspring as numerous as the stars—even though he and his wife are childless and past the age of having children. Like the stars, he cannot see them. But he also does not doubt their existence any more than he doubts the existence of the stars. No wonder God reckons that faith to Abram as righteousness.

b.   *In **Genesis 15:8-21**, why is it significant that God (represented by smoke and fire) passes between the pieces of animal, and how would that reassure Abram? (Read also **Jeremiah 34:17-20**.)*

Jeremiah 34 sheds light on the practice that was common in those days of cutting an animal in two and walking between the halves when making a covenant oath. In doing this, the parties to the covenant were saying, "May this be done to me if I fail to keep this covenant." Imagine what it must mean to Abram to see the presence of God passing between the pieces of meat. It is astonishing that God pronounces such an oath, but it underscores that his promise will be carried out; it will not be broken. (Note: It is the blood of this covenant that gives the Patriarchs period its color, burgundy.)

4.   *Read **Genesis 17:1-23**.*

a.   *What is to be the significance of circumcision to Abram's family? To what does it bind them?*

This time, it is not just God who is promising. He makes clear what Abram's part of the bargain will be: to keep God's covenant and be circumcised. Circumcision represents in the flesh what will be required in later iterations of the covenant: a complete commitment to God and a cutting off from other masters. As St. Paul will say many years later in Romans 2:29, "He is a Jew who is one inwardly, and real circumcision is a matter of the heart, spiritual and not literal." By circumcision, Abram and his descendants will carry in their flesh the kind of sign that Abram witnesses in Chapter 15: If they fail in loyalty and obedience to God, they and their offspring will be cut off from God as the foreskin has been cut. It will also be a permanent reminder of their special covenant relationship with God.

b. **New Testament Connection:** *Under the New Covenant, the Old Covenant sign of circumcision is replaced by a sacrament, which is a tangible sign that brings into reality (i.e., it "effects") what it signifies. Read* **Colossians 2:11-12.** *What is that sacrament, and how does it relate to circumcision?*

The Old Covenant sign of circumcision is replaced in the New Covenant by baptism, in which people die to, or are cut off from, their sinful nature (and allegiance to other "masters") and rise to new life with Christ as children of God. It is truly a circumcision of the heart.

An Impossible Child (Genesis 16–18)

5. *Frustrated and probably bewildered at their childlessness in the face of God's promise, Abram and Sarai (newly named Abraham and Sarah) take things into their own hands. In* **Genesis 16,** *they produce an heir (Ishmael) for Abraham through his servant Hagar. What astonishing promise does God give them in* **Genesis 17:15-22 and 18:1-15,** *and what will be the role of the promised child (Isaac) in relationship to God's covenant promises?*

God promises Abraham and Sarah that they will have a son in a year's time, that his name will be Isaac, and that this will happen in spite of their advanced age (Abraham is one hundred and Sarah is ninety). God's covenant blessing and promises will continue through Isaac. "Isaac" means "laughter," and he will be a perpetual reminder that God can be trusted even when the situation seems laughable. Isaac will also foreshadow another "impossible child," born of faith to a Virgin.

The Ultimate Sacrifice (Genesis 22)

6. *By Genesis 22, the promised son has been born and has become a young man. All the hopes of God's covenant rest on Isaac. Read this chapter carefully.*

a. *At the beginning of this chapter, the author says that God tests Abraham. What kind of test is it? Is there any way in which this test is similar to the test of Adam and Eve?*

This test of Abraham is almost unimaginable. "Take your son, your only son Isaac, whom you love, and go to the land of Moriah, and offer him there as a burnt offering" (Genesis 22:2). Isaac is the only son of the promise, the impossible son of Abraham and Sarah's old age, the one God has insisted on using instead of Ishmael to make Abraham the father of a multitude. This test demands complete and absolute faith on Abraham's part that God is not capricious; that he knows what he is doing; that he is able to raise Isaac from the dead if need be to accomplish his promises.

The first time we saw God test humanity was when he told Adam not to eat of the Tree of the Knowledge of Good and Evil. Both tests ask the question, "Do you trust God?" Did Adam and Eve trust that God was a loving Father with their best interests at heart, or did they suspect him of withholding good from them? Would they submit to God's will as created beings and obey him, or would they go their own way? Does Abraham trust that God is a loving father who has his best interests at heart and who keeps his promises, or does he suspect God of trying to take away the only thing Abraham sees that will lead to their fulfillment? Will Abraham submit to God's will and obey him, or will he balk and protect his son?

Do you trust God? That is the question.

b. *Does Abraham pass the test? What is the result?*

Abraham obeys God without hesitation, rising early the next morning and heading for Moriah. Verse 8 provides a beautiful demonstration of his faith when he replies to Isaac's question with: "God will provide himself the lamb for a burnt offering, my son." God responds to Abraham's obedient faith by providing a ram for the offering. And then Abraham's obedience becomes the occasion for God swearing a solemn oath—"by myself I have sworn," he says in verse 16—in a final confirmation of the promises he made in Genesis 12. Because Abraham is willing to give up his only, promised son, all nations will receive God's blessing.

c. ***Living Tradition:*** *In Genesis 15, Abraham's faith in God's promise to give him descendants as numerous as the stars was exhibited in his belief. Now, he is being asked to prove that belief by acting on it. Read **CCC 143–147 and 154–155** as well as **James 2:14-23**. What is the relationship between obedience and faith?*

Faith and obedience, which is to submit to or act according to God's Word, cannot be separated. In fact, according to James 2:17, "Faith by itself, if it has no works, is dead." Faith is an action word. Hebrews 11, which is quoted in this section of the *Catechism,* describes faith using several examples from Abraham's life. He obeys God and moves to Canaan, showing that he believes God's promise to make him great there. He obeys and stays there even though he remains childless and a nomad. He obeys and offers his only son, showing that he believes God will give him descendants through Isaac. The reason Abraham is held up as a model of faith is not that he believes much, but that he acts on his belief.

7. ***New Testament Connection:*** *It is in giving up his son that Abraham becomes the father of the nation that will bless the world. In doing so, he is able to "share in the power of God's love that saves the multitude" (CCC 2572). What does Abraham's act foreshadow, which God will ultimately do? Give as many parallels as you can between the two events.*

Abraham's act of obedience foreshadows God's ultimate sacrifice of his Son. Many parallels can be drawn between the two events. Here are some: Abraham is asked to offer his only and beloved son; God gives his only and beloved Son. Abraham is asked to offer Isaac on Mount Moriah; the crucifixion is on one of the hills of Moriah. Isaac walks obediently up the hill carrying the wood of the offering; Jesus walks obediently up the hill carrying his cross. God tells Abraham he himself will provide the lamb for the offering; while he does provide a ram on that day, one day he will provide the Lamb of God, his Son, for the sacrifice. Abraham's obedience becomes the source of blessing for all the nations of the earth; that blessing is ultimately made possible through the obedient sacrifice of Jesus Christ on the Cross.

D. Application

Facilitators: If time allows, have group members share their responses to the following application questions.

God proclaims to Abraham and Sarah that he will give them a son. When they hear this, Sarah laughs with unbelief (Genesis 18:12). Are there issues in your life at which you laugh in response to God's promises? What from Abraham's life can you take on your faith journey?

Close with the Responsive Prayer found on the inside front cover of this Study Set Workbook. Pray through the Patriarchs period.

After the small-group discussion, watch Jeff Cavins' video presentation on *Session 4* – Patriarchs: Part 1.

Facilitators: Read these recommended responses to the questions ahead of time to help you prepare to lead the small-group discussion.

Participants: Reinforce what you have learned by reviewing these recommended responses after the small-group discussion and before you go on to the next session.

A. Review the Context

Facilitators: Take a moment to review the context and what was learned in the previous session. If you like, use the following question to encourage discussion:

- *Did anything in Abraham's story stand out to you? What about his faith journey can help you in yours?*

B. Read the Story

Facilitators: If there is time, have someone read each passage aloud before it is discussed.

C. Take a Deeper Look

Jacob (Genesis 25–36)

1. Read **Genesis 25.**

    a. *The lives of these early people often exhibit what will be true of the nations that come from them. In Genesis 25, God tells Rebekah that the twins jostling in her womb will become two struggling nations, and that the nation that springs from the elder will be weaker and will serve the nation that comes from the younger. How is this demonstrated in the lives of Jacob and Esau far before they give rise to nations?*

    "Jacob" means "he grasps the heel" or, figuratively, "he deceives." And from the moment of Jacob's birth, he is grasping at what belongs to his older brother: first his heel, then his birthright, and finally their father's blessing. Esau is no match for Jacob's cunning. He is more interested in satisfying his immediate physical needs than in hanging on to his birthright, and Jacob is able to wrest it from him for a pot of stew. Later, he and Rebekah trick Isaac into giving him the blessing as well. The boys struggle from day one, and the younger comes out on top.

    b. *In choosing which son of Isaac to bless, God goes against ancient laws that give the eldest son leadership in the family. Does God choose Jacob because of his own merit? How do you know?*

    God chooses Jacob not because of his faithfulness or his behavior—not because of anything he has done, either good or bad. He chooses Jacob while Jacob is still in his mother's womb.

    c. *Why do you think God does this? (Read also **Romans 9:10-13** and **CCC 218**.)*

    God chooses Jacob before he has a chance to do anything good or bad to show that God's people do not rise "naturally" or according to worldly skill or wisdom but because of his initiative. They are not chosen because they are better than others but simply out of what the *Catechism* calls God's "sheer gratuitous love" (CCC 218).

2. **Think About It:** *The "ladder" in Jacob's dream (Genesis 28) is likely the stepped sides of a tall, sloping tower known as a ziggurat. Think back to the last time you saw such a tower, in Genesis 11. Compare and contrast this event with the previous one. What does the comparison tell you about what God desires for and from his people?*

> In Genesis 11, the Tower of Babel is built by men trying to make a name for themselves, to consolidate power, and to keep themselves from being scattered over the earth. In contrast, in Jacob's dream, the tower becomes the means by which God reaches down to Jacob to bless him. While God "scatters" the people across the earth from Babel, he tells Jacob that his descendants will "spread abroad" to the four corners of the earth and be a source of blessing to all those previously scattered families. Jacob responds in worship. The contrast seems to emphasize God's desire to bless and to draw all people back into a relationship with himself. It also seems to show that unlike other nations, which are focused inward toward themselves and their own interests, God's people look outward to worship God and bless others.

> **Facilitators:** There is no set answer for this question, and not everyone will have one. That is OK. Use the discussion time to find out what people see when comparing the two stories. Many biblical images from these passages are drawn on in later books of the Bible, and this is just one of thousands of connections that can enrich our understanding. Encourage people to get in the habit of noticing these connections, even if they do not understand them. After a while, a pattern may emerge.

> Here is a later passage that draws on imagery from Jacob's dream: In the New Testament, Jesus says Nathanael will "see heaven opened, and the angels of God ascending and descending upon the Son of man" (John 1:51). If you are familiar with Genesis 28, this should bring Jacob's dream to mind—God personally confirming his blessing on Jacob as the one chosen to bear his blessing to the world—a shadowy picture of the One who will ultimately fulfill that blessing.

3. *Read* **Genesis 29.** *Fleeing Esau's wrath, Jacob goes north to Haran to live with his mother's family. (This movement out of Canaan is represented by the names of Jacob's sons in the "12 Sons of Israel" box in the Patriarchs section of your* Bible Timeline *Chart.) How does Jacob get back what he dished out to his brother?*

> Jacob falls in love with Rachel and works seven years to earn her as his bride. Laban pulls a fast one on him, switching his older daughter, Leah, for Rachel on the wedding night. Jacob accuses him of deceit, and there is rich irony in Laban's reply: "It is not so done in our country, to give the younger before the firstborn" (Genesis 29:26). Jacob, who once deceived his own brother and father to take the rights of the firstborn, is deceived himself into taking the firstborn. He must work another seven years for Rachel.

4. *Jacob's years in Haran are arduous, and Jacob continues to wrestle with Laban and a contentious home life. Nevertheless, God blesses him with twelve sons and a daughter and increases his flocks and herds. After a time, and in obedience to God's call, he sets out for home.*

   a. *Read* **Genesis 32.** *What does Jacob learn about God in his midnight wrestling match?*

   > Jacob learns that it is *God* with whom he must "wrestle" for blessing, not his father, brother, uncle, or any other person. He also learns—via a permanent reminder in his hip—that, ultimately, God is in control.

   b. *To name something in ancient times meant you had dominion over that thing. When God renames Abraham, the new name marks him as God's servant and also indicates the role he will play as patriarch. What is the significance of Jacob's new, God-given name?*

God marks his servant with a new name that signifies the role the servant will play in the nation God is building. "Jacob"—meaning "deceiver" or "he grasps"—will now be "Israel"—"he struggles with God." The one who grasped with his own power for birthright and blessing has learned to struggle with God and be blessed. Unlike Abraham, who was never again called Abram, this patriarch is called alternately "Jacob" and "Israel." The nation that bears his name will exhibit the characteristics of both.

Joseph (Genesis 37–50)

5. *Jacob (Israel) is now the father of twelve sons from whom will come the twelve tribes of Israel. Read* **Genesis 37–50.** *This "account of Jacob" focuses on Joseph, who is his eleventh son and the firstborn son of his beloved wife, Rachel. As were those before him, Joseph is tested. In spite of dreams indicating that he will rule over his brothers, circumstances are against him for years. The question is still, "Will you trust God?" How does he fare?*

    In spite of mistreatment by his brothers—being sold as a slave, enduring unjust accusations, and languishing forgotten in prison—Joseph never loses faith in God. He is honest, hardworking, thoughtful, and courageous. He is humble and gives all credit to God rather than trying to advance himself in the eyes of others. He does not grasp what has been promised but waits patiently for it, trusting that God will do as he has said. Consequently, he rises to the chief position of leadership under Pharaoh and is able to bless not only Egypt, but the surrounding countries as well.

6. *Taken together, Genesis 38 and 39 present a curious juxtaposition of events in the lives of Joseph and his older brother, Judah. How would you compare and contrast the two men based on these chapters?*

    Judah leaves home to marry, live among Canaanites, and seek his fortune. His sons are so wicked that God kills them. He denies Tamar her legal right to bear children through the next of kin and then eventually sleeps with her, thinking she is a prostitute. In contrast, Joseph is the picture of moral strength. He leaves home unintentionally, under force. He works hard to increase Potiphar's fortunes and not his own. Finally, he resists the advances of his master's wife, refusing to hurt Potiphar or sin against God. Clearly, he values obedience to God above all else.

7. *Follow Jesus' genealogy line (the red line) on your* Bible Timeline *Chart through the Patriarchs period. Which son of Jacob does it go through, and which grandson? Do you notice anything unusual?*

    Jesus' genealogy extends from Jacob through Judah (who is Jesus' ancestor) to Perez—Judah's son by his daughter-in-law, Tamar. Curious that it should go through a man who was the fruit of such an unsavory relationship. In the genealogy of Jesus Christ in Matthew 1, attention is drawn to Tamar and three other women: the harlot Rahab, the Moabitess Ruth, and "the wife of Uriah" with whom David committed adultery. Does that seem strange? Remember that our God is a God of mercy. He does not discard people because of their sin; he works to restore them. Jesus is a man, descended from ordinary humans with the same foibles we all possess. Anyone of Matthew's day who was inclined to speak ill of the circumstances of Jesus' birth would be silenced when faced with this evidence from the royal line.

8. *After Jacob's death, his brothers ask forgiveness and offer themselves to Joseph as slaves. Read Joseph's reply in* **Genesis 50:19-20.** *What can Joseph see that his brothers do not? What gives him this perspective?*

    If you learn just one verse from Genesis, make it this one: "As for you, you meant evil against me; but God meant it for good" (Genesis 50:20). Joseph has learned through years of patient waiting and through tribulation that God has his hand in our affairs—that whatever things looks like on the outside, God is working them for good. Joseph's faith gives him eyes to take this eternal perspective on events, while his brothers' lack of faith and guilt fixes their eyes on temporal things.

9. **Think About It:** *Genesis closes with the reconciliation of a father and his sons, even as it began with a shattered relationship. Thinking back over Joseph's life, can you see how he is a "forerunner" of Jesus? List as many parallels as you can find between the two.*

   Answers will vary, and there are many parallels. In the small-group discussion, look for similarities in character, in circumstances, and in what they accomplish. Here are a few:

   Both Joseph and Jesus:
   - are humble, forgiving, and strong in the face of temptation
   - are beloved sons of their fathers
   - see beyond the appearance of things and trust in God
   - are betrayed and sold for silver
   - are wrongly accused
   - are brought out of captivity and death to life and glory
   - reconcile their brethren to their father
   - save the world
   - become the source of food and life

10. *By the end of Genesis, what progress has been made toward the fulfillment of God's promises to Abraham?*

    The end of Genesis lists the family of Jacob as seventy strong (seventy being the number of completeness). Where there once was only a couple, there is now a tribe of twelve family units well on their way to becoming tribes. This is the seedbed of what will be the nation (and later the kingdom) of Israel. They are away from the promised land of Canaan but have been planted in fertile land, where they can prosper and grow under Joseph's protection and away from foreign influence (shepherds were a despised class, and the Egyptians would not have intermarried with them). Finally, they have already begun to bless the world thanks to Joseph's leadership and management of the famine. Another stage in the growth of God's family has been completed.

D. Application

Facilitators: If time allows, have group members share their responses to the following application questions.

Do circumstances in your life threaten to pull your eyes off God and away from his promises? Do you feel helpless or abandoned by God? Is guilt enslaving you? What can you learn from the story of Joseph that will help you?

E. Wrap-Up

1. Remember Patriarchs by its color, burgundy: the color of the blood sacrifice that marks God's covenant with Abraham.

2. Answers will vary. One possible reply: The Patriarchs time period chronicles the foundation of God's covenant family on the patriarchs Abraham, Isaac, and Jacob and lays the framework for God's solution to the problem of sin and the fractured relationship with his family. It then gives a picture that anticipates that solution in the story of Joseph in Egypt.

Close with the Responsive Prayer found on the inside front cover of this Study Set Workbook. Pray through the Patriarchs period.

After the small-group discussion, watch Jeff Cavins' video presentation on *Session 5 – Patriarchs: Part 2*.

Facilitators: Read these recommended responses to the questions ahead of time to help you prepare to lead the small-group discussion.

Participants: Reinforce what you have learned by reviewing these recommended responses after the small-group discussion and before you go on to the next session.

A. Establish the Context

Facilitators: Take a moment to review what was learned in the previous session and to establish the context for Egypt and Exodus. If you like, use the following question to encourage discussion:

- *What did you learn about God's faithfulness in the stories of Jacob and Joseph?*

B. Read the Story

Facilitators: If there is time, have someone read each passage aloud before it is discussed.

C. Take a Deeper Look

God Reveals Himself (Exodus 1–4)

1. a. Read **Exodus 3.** *What might Moses have learned about God in this encounter, particularly in the revelation of God's name? List as many things as you can think of. (To read what the* Catechism *says about God's name, see CCC 206.)*

   Answers will vary. Draw out personal responses before going on to those listed here.

   Moses' encounter with God at the burning bush is the most profound, direct revelation that God has made of himself up to this point. He walked with Adam and Eve in the Garden of Eden, and he spoke on occasion to the patriarchs and made promises to them, but he has never yet revealed his name. His first revelation to Moses is visual: a fire that burns but does not consume. God is holiness itself and must be approached with fear and reverence. Their early conversation reveals more: God is personal ("the God of your father"); he is faithful ("the God of Abraham, the God of Isaac, and the God of Jacob"—the God of the promises); he is ready to intervene on their behalf ("I have come down to deliver"); he does not work alone to accomplish his will. He works through people ("Come, I will send you"); and he desires the worship of his people. But in his name, God also reveals his character: "I am. I will be what I will be. I am all-sufficient and all-powerful. I am being itself. I will be with you."

   b. *When Pharaoh responds to Moses by increasing the people's work, and they blame Moses, he crawls back to God in despair. God repeats his name and expands on his earlier revelation. Read* **Exodus 6:1-8.** *What extension of his name does God proclaim in using the words "I am" and "I will"? List them. What effect should knowing these have on Moses and the people?*

God tells Moses in just three verses, "I am the Lord. (Note: Whenever you see the word "Lord" entirely in capital letters in the Bible, it is a translation of the word "yhwh," "I am.") "I will bring you out from Egypt. I will deliver you from bondage. I will redeem you. I will take you for my people. I will be your God. I am the Lord your God. I will bring you into the land. I will give it to you for a possession. I am the Lord."

God seems to tell Moses that the question is not, "Why," but "I." Knowing *who* God is guarantees God *will do* as he says. "I will redeem you" is particularly strong when you understand that the *goel*, or "redeemer," referred to the obligation of the next of kin to deliver or redeem his kinsman from his losses. The amazing thing here is that God is saying he is the next of kin of the people of Israel and takes seriously the obligation to redeem them. It is an awesome assurance.

2. Read **Exodus 3:18 and 4:21-23.** *What message does God send to Pharaoh, and what does it say about Israel's relationship to God and to the other nations?*

    The message is simple: "yhwh, God of the Hebrews, has met with us. Let us go for three days into the wilderness to sacrifice to him." When Pharaoh refuses, Moses gives an ultimatum from God: "If you do not let my firstborn son serve me, then I will kill your firstborn son." This says that God does not see Israel as just another oppressed group of people, but as his children. Israel is his firstborn, born with the right and the responsibility to lead and act as high priest for the world.

3. *"Let my son go (halak) that he may serve (obed) me," says God in Exodus 4:23. "Go (halak) now, and work (obed)," replies Pharaoh (Exodus 5:18). Who is this battle between, and what are the stakes?*

    The battle is between God and Pharaoh, who sees himself as a god. By claiming Israel as his firstborn, God stakes his claim on Israel. Pharaoh counters that the people are his slaves. The stakes are high: Whose people are they? Who is boss? Whom will they serve?

God Delivers Israel (Exodus 5–15)

4. a. *God sends Egypt signs and plagues to display his power and to convince Pharaoh to let his children go. Read* **Exodus 7:8-13.** *What should be clear to Pharaoh in this initial sign from God? (Note: The snake was the emblem of divine majesty in Egypt and could be seen in the image of a cobra on Pharaoh's crown. Wadjet, the cobra goddess, was protector of the pharaoh.) The Hebrew used here,* tannin, *can also be translated "crocodile" or "dragon," and the pharaohs identified themselves with the strength and power of the crocodile god,* Sobek.

    God's opening salvo—turning Aaron's rod into a snake—is a declaration of supreme power. When Aaron's snake swallows the magician's snakes, it demonstrates God's sovereignty over Egypt, Pharaoh, and the magic they rely on.

    b. *Ancient Egyptians worshiped many gods. Hapi, representing the spirit and essence of the Nile, was one of several associated with the river considered to be the sacred lifeline of Egypt, its source and sustainer. The frog-headed goddess, Heqt, goddess of fertility, was believed to assist women in childbirth and control the frog population. The greatest of gods was the sun, called Aton or Amon-Ra, who ruled and protected by day, but was thought to sleep when he disappeared at night. What message do you think God sends with the plagues?*

    These and the other plagues send powerful messages about the relative strength of the Egyptian gods (who represent forces of nature) and of the Lord, the Creator of all things. By turning the Nile to blood, God attacks the lifeblood of Egypt, the god Egypt credits for its existence. By sending a plague of frogs, he demonstrates Heqt's impotence—an impotence felt by the people, who find themselves surrounded by sacred frogs they cannot step on or dispose of. Other plagues attack other gods or expose the inability of Pharaoh (who himself is considered a god) to care for his people. The final, abrupt plunging into darkness must be horrifying, because it leaves the unprepared Egyptians at the mercy of the night, unprotected by Aton. It is easy to imagine them riveted by the light that remains upon Goshen, which is obviously blessed by the protection of the LORD.

5. a. *The tenth plague, the death of the firstborn, brings about the Passover. It calls for extensive preparation, each element signifying some aspect of the people's redemption (bitter herbs for the bitterness of slavery, for example). Read **Exodus 12**. Israel is to obey God's instructions and "keep this service" (observe this rite) as a lasting ordinance. This word, "service," is the same word used in Chapter 1 for slavery. Explain how this new "service" to God will differ from service to Pharaoh.*

Israel is to serve God not as they served Pharaoh, with unceasing, back-breaking work, but by carrying the remembrance of God's redemption with them, re-presenting it each year, and teaching it to their children. Each new generation is to be formed by the Passover. It becomes part of the identity of the people. They are the Chosen People, redeemed by God from darkness and slavery to worship him.

b. **New Testament Connection:** *Today, we show our "service" to God through the liturgy, which literally is "the work of the people." We eat bread and drink wine (in reality, the Body and Blood of Christ) as a memorial of Christ's sacrifice, similar to the way Israel, at Passover, ate lamb as a memorial of the Passover sacrifice. Read **John 1:29; Matthew 26:27-28; 1 Peter 1:17-19; and 1 Corinthians 5:7-8**. Describe the correlation between the Passover lamb and Jesus.*

As John the Baptist says in John's Gospel, Jesus *is* "the Lamb of God, who takes away the sin of the world." What the Passover lamb pointed to, Jesus is. Jesus introduces his disciples to this correlation on the first day of the Feast of Unleavened Bread, on the day it was customary to sacrifice the Passover lamb. At the Passover table in Matthew's Gospel, instead of lamb, Jesus has his disciples share his "Body" and the "Blood of the covenant, which is poured out for many for the forgiveness of sins." Peter tells us that Christ is "a lamb without blemish or defect"—qualifications for the Passover lamb. Paul comes right out and says that, "Christ, our Paschal Lamb, has been sacrificed," and then goes on to encourage the Corinthians to keep the feast ("celebrate the festival") with the "unleavened bread of sincerity and truth"—deliberate references to the Passover.

6. **Think About It:** *The story of Israel's deliverance from Egypt, including the Passover and the crossing of the Red Sea, was used in the early Church for catechesis in preparing adults to be baptized. How does it help you understand what it means to be saved from sin and born again as God's child?*

Answers will vary. The Exodus is a grand example of the way the Church reads the Old and New Testaments in light of each other to gain greater insight into God's plan of salvation (for more on typology, see CCC 128–130). Egypt is analogous to the state of sin and separation from God that enslaves all descendants of Adam and Eve. Pharaoh appears as a "seed of the Serpent" in the garden of Goshen, biting at the heels of God's children and epitomizing the lures of the devil to serve someone or something other than God. In the Passover, we can see the necessity of a redeemer and something of the cost of redemption as well as the Lamb that will substitute for the firstborn. The Red Sea dramatizes the drowning of the old master—sin—in the waves and the birth to a new life as a child of God on the other side. (And, as subsequent lessons will show, Israel's journey to the Promised Land foreshadows the journey of the baptized to heaven. Just what it means to be and to act like a child of God can be gleaned from the lessons God gives the people along the way.)

The Journey to Sinai (Exodus 16–18)

7. a. Read **Exodus 16.** *When God tells Moses he will send bread from heaven (manna) every day, he says he will do it to prove or test the people, to see whether they will follow his Law. What are the rules governing the gathering of manna, and what are they meant to teach?*

God tells the people to gather just enough food for each day (and no more) and to gather a double portion on the sixth day for the Sabbath. Obedience to the letter is important. Those who are greedy or lazy and gather extra food during the week find it breeding worms in the morning. Those who fail to gather more on the sixth day go hungry the next. These are like first steps for infants. God's children are learning to walk. They must learn that God is a faithful provider, and they must trust God to provide for them each day without worrying about the next day. At the close of each week, they must actively prepare to set aside the Sabbath for rest and worship—a rule which shows them the Sabbath is a gift God wants them to take seriously. They are no longer slaves who can never stop working, but sons who do the work they have been created to do and then rest and worship as they have been created to do—all in the image of God. The Sabbath gives them the opportunity for worship that was denied them in Egypt and helps them remember that they are free children of God.

b. Read **John 6,** *and describe the relationship between the manna of Exodus and the "bread from heaven" in John.*

Jesus draws a parallel between himself and manna three times in John 6. He speaks of that earlier bread as something that, while it came from heaven and sustained physical life, was merely a picture or sign pointing to him. He is the *true* bread from heaven, who, when eaten (in the Eucharist), gives eternal life.

8. Read **1 Corinthians 10:1-4.** *How does St. Paul understand the water from the rock described in Exodus 17?*

Paul understands that the water is spiritual drink, just as the manna was spiritual food. And he sees the rock, from which that drink came, to be Christ. The experience of Israel getting water in the desert is just a picture of what will be true in Jesus. Recall John 4:14, where Jesus tells the Samaritan woman: "Whoever drinks of the water that I shall give him will never thirst; the water that I shall give him will become in him a spring of water welling up to eternal life."

D. Application

Facilitators: If time allows, have group members share their responses to the following application questions.

*Do you know God by name? Meditate on "*YHWH*" and what it means. Jesus also is "*I AM.*" In John 8:58, he says, "Before Abraham was born, I am!" At other times, he says "I am": the good shepherd; the bread of life; the light of the world; the Way, the Truth, and the Life. He is all of these things. What difference does that make to you?*

Close with the Responsive Prayer found on the inside front cover of this Study Set Workbook. Pray through the Egypt and Exodus period.

After the small-group discussion, watch Jeff Cavins' video presentation on *Session 6* – Egypt and Exodus: Part 1.

Facilitators: Read these recommended responses to the questions ahead of time to help you prepare to lead the small-group discussion.

Participants: Reinforce what you have learned by reviewing these recommended responses after the small-group discussion and before you go on to the next session.

A. Review the Context

Facilitators: Take a moment to review the context and what was learned in the previous session. If you like, use the following question to encourage discussion:

- *One way of looking at the Exodus is that Israel was freed from the tyranny of work without time to worship God and develop a relationship with him. How does this speak to your own life?*

B. Read the Story

Facilitators: If there is time, have someone read each passage aloud before it is discussed.

C. Take a Deeper Look

Rules to Live By (Exodus 19–24)

1. *Previously, God promised to make of Israel a nation and a kingdom. In Exodus 19:1-6, what kind of nation and kingdom does he say they will be if they obey him and keep his covenant? What impact does he plan for his "firstborn son," Israel, to have on the world?*

   God says that Israel will be three things: "my own possession among all peoples," "a kingdom of priests," and "a holy nation." The first speaks of God's great love for the people. Other translations say they will be a "treasure" to God. As a kingdom of priests, they will represent other nations before God and make God known to other peoples. "Holy" does not mean "perfect," but "set apart"—set apart in the same sense that we set apart good dishes or wedding gowns for special purposes. God has chosen, or "set apart," Israel for a special role among the nations. All of this elaborates on what was said earlier, that Israel was the "firstborn" among nations.

2. a. *How do the commandments in **Exodus 20:2-11** summarize the lessons of Israel's delivery from Egypt?*

   The whole story of the Exodus can be summed up in the first three commandments. Israel has been saved out of a culture steeped in polytheism that does not know or recognize God and that keeps the people's attention bound twenty-four hours a day as slaves to Pharaoh. In liberating them, God reveals his Name and demonstrates his supremacy over creation and all other gods. Not surprisingly, the first commandment directs the people to worship God alone. Put God first; do not make idols of created things, and do not reduce the Creator to an image. This protects them not only against falling back into the patterns they learned in Egypt; it protects them from the fault of Adam and Eve, which was to seek to become gods themselves.

The second commandment, following on the precious gift they received of God's Name, tells them to revere it and not take it in vain. This does not just mean they should not use it as a "curse word." A name represents the person, and invoking God's name thoughtlessly is tantamount to saying his being is worthless.

Finally, God delivers his people so that they can rest and worship him. The third commandment reminds them to remember the Sabbath day and to keep it holy. Their identity as his people, created in his image, requires them to worship him on the sabbath.

b. *How do the rest of the commandments follow on or relate to the first set?*

The first three commandments have to do with establishing a right relationship with God. The remaining commandments, which establish boundaries defining right relationship with others, grow out of the first commandment. They are rules describing the way redeemed people live, to keep them from falling back into bondage. Observed, they provide stability, sanctity of life, and a proper balance between work, rest, and worship. The vacuum left by their absence when they are broken is bondage to self, hatred, greed, and falsehood: to the false gods of this world.

3. *Read* **Exodus 23,** *which emphasizes the importance of worshiping God alone, keeping the prescribed feasts, and obeying and serving God. What does it say will be the benefit to Israel of doing this?*

The benefits to Israel of worshiping and obeying God are many: God will be an enemy to their enemies; he will send his angel to bring them into the Promised Land; they will prosper, have long lives, and enjoy good health. God will establish the borders of their new nation. In effect, he will carry out the promises he made long before to Abraham.

4. **New Testament Connection:** *The Israelites tend to be anxious about what they will eat and drink and how they will fare against their enemies. After years of slavery, they look first for human solutions to their needs. But now, as God's people, they must learn that if they put God first in their lives, he will watch over them.*

    Read **Luke 12:16-31.** *How is this concept of giving priority to God preserved in the New Covenant?*

Enslaved by sin and self, our human tendency is still to seek human solutions to our needs and problems first and to look to God second, if at all. But as the people of God, we must learn to make seeking God and his kingdom the first priority in our lives and to trust him to care for our needs.

Rules for Worship (Exodus 25–31)

5. *At the top of Mount Sinai, God gives Moses explicit directions for building a portable tent of meeting called a "tabernacle" (literally, "dwelling place") and its furnishings.*

    a. *Read* **Exodus 29:42-46.** *What is the purpose of the Tabernacle, which will distinguish Israel from all nations on earth? (See also* **Exodus 33:14-16.***)*

The Tabernacle is a portable "tent of meeting" where God dwells among his people and meets with and speaks to them. God had come down to meet with individuals on occasion previously, but not since the Garden of Eden has there been a place for them to dwell together. By accompanying them in this way, God is distinguishing Israel from among the nations as his own.

    b. *Exodus 25 describes the most important piece of furniture in the Tabernacle, the Ark of the Covenant, which is given pride of place in the Holy of Holies. This symbolizes the throne of God; it is the place where God will come down and speak. Read* **Exodus 16:33-34 and 25:10-22** *and* **Hebrews 9:4.** *What items are to be placed in the Ark?*

In the Ark of the Covenant are kept a jar of manna, for a permanent remembrance of the bread with which God fed them in the desert, and "the testimony," or the stone tablets bearing the Ten Commandments. Later, God will direct them to add Aaron's rod, representing his high priestly authority (this is recorded in the book of Numbers and will be covered in a future session).

6. *New Testament Connection: Read **Revelation 11:19–12:6.***

   a. *Describe the woman in this passage. Who does she represent, and how do you know?*

   "A woman clothed with the sun, with the moon under her feet, and on her head a crown of twelve stars" appears in the sky. She is pregnant and about to give birth to a male child, "one who is to rule all the nations with a rod of iron" but whom a dragon seeks to devour and who is "caught up to God and to his throne." This is none other than Mary, Queen of Heaven and Mother of the child Jesus, who will rule the nations. (She is often identified with the Church, as well.)

   b. ***Think About It:*** *Revelation 11:19 seems to indicate that this woman can also be seen as the New Testament fulfillment of the Ark of the Covenant. Is there any way in which the contents of the Ark support that idea?*

   The Ark of the Covenant is seen within God's Temple in the sky, and then there suddenly appears a woman who is pregnant with the Messiah. Consider these things:

   • The Ark held manna, which was bread from heaven that sustained Israel during its long trip to the Promised Land. Mary held in her womb the true Bread from heaven, Jesus Christ.

   • The Ark held God's words given to Israel as the Ten Commandments. Mary held in herself the Word of God made flesh.

   • The Ark held Aaron's rod, representing his high priestly authority. Mary held the Great High Priest himself, the very Son of God.

   The holy Ark of the Covenant, where God came down to dwell with Israel, provided a graphic image of the day when God would come to earth and live among his people as a man, Emmanuel ("God with us").

A New Priesthood (Exodus 32–40)

7. *Forty days after pledging to be God's people forever, the people get impatient and construct a golden calf to worship. God intends to consume them **(Exodus 32).** Read this chapter, and then review **Exodus 5:22–6:8,** about a time when Moses believed God had "done evil" to the people (when Moses had asked Pharaoh to let the people go and worship, and instead, he earned impossible work for the people and a no-confidence vote for himself).*

   Think About It: *What does the golden calf incident draw out from Moses that he lacked in Exodus 5, and on what basis does he appeal for God's mercy?*

   Moses has learned a lot since his early days of leading Israel to follow God. In Exodus 5, when his pleas to Pharaoh seemingly backfired and brought more work on the people, Moses blamed God and accused him of not fulfilling his promises. He did not seem to remember the things God had told him. His faith wavered. In Exodus 32, Moses intercedes boldly and fearlessly on behalf of the people. The crisis draws out of him a powerful demonstration of faith. Whereas God previously had to remind Moses of his might, his actions, and his purposes and had to promise again to deliver the people so they would know he was God, Moses now knows that for himself. He appeals to God not on the basis of the worthiness of the people, their weakness, or because they are sorry, but on the basis of three things that are true about God:

- God loves Israel. They are God's people, not Moses' people, chosen and brought out of Egypt by God for himself.

- God has a name to uphold. What would it say about God if he destroyed Israel right after saving them so Egypt would know who he is?

- God is faithful. He promised to multiply Israel, bring them into the Promised Land, and establish them there forever. For God to destroy Israel now would be inconsistent with who God is. Moses knows without a shadow of doubt that God is the LORD.

8. *Up until this time, the firstborn of each family unit acted as a priest for the family. As a result of the golden calf incident, the tribes are, in a sense, "laicized." No longer will each family have its own priest, but the priests will come from the tribe of Levi. What attributes do you see in the Levites that qualify them to be priests?*

When Moses asks, "Who is on the LORD's side?" the men of Levi demonstrate their complete devotion and fidelity to God by their immediate, united response. They gather by Moses' side and, without debate, carry out his order to slay those who have betrayed God and worshiped the calf. By standing up for God against even their relatives, they ordain themselves for God's service.

9. **New Testament Connection:** *The end of Exodus describes what happens when work is completed on the Tabernacle: "The cloud covered the tent of meeting, and the glory of the LORD filled the tabernacle" (Exodus 40:34). From that time on, the cloud and fire lead them on their journeys, a visible affirmation of the presence of God. This is not the first time God's presence has been shown by fire or cloud (remember the burning bush in Exodus 3; the cloud and fire on Mount Sinai in Exodus 24; and the cloud that descended to Moses' tent when God spoke with Moses in Exodus 33). Keeping these in mind, read **CCC 696–697**. Who later fulfills these Old Testament figures, and how?*

The *Catechism* tells us that, "in the Holy Spirit, Christ fulfills these figures" (CCC 697). The cloud reveals God while veiling his glory so he can be observed by man. Just as God spoke from the cloud on Mount Sinai to proclaim his Word, God speaks out of a cloud on the Mount of Transfiguration to identify his Son. Just as a cloud revealed God while veiling his glory when speaking to Moses and in the Tabernacle, a cloud carries Jesus away in his ascension and will reveal him when he returns. The Holy Spirit is represented by fire in the New Testament also: As God was present in fire on Mount Sinai at the founding of the nation of Israel, he is present at the founding of his Church on Pentecost, in the person of the Holy Spirit made manifest in tongues of fire on the disciples' heads.

D. Application

Facilitators: If time allows, have group members share their responses to the following application questions.

The incident of the golden calf shows that it is one thing to bring Israel out of Egypt, but it is another to get Egypt out of Israel. God's children will continue to struggle with an attraction to other gods. You might not be tempted to erect a golden calf in your living room, but are there other things, ideas, or people you give credit for God's work in your life? Are there other things you put before him? How can the lessons Israel learned in these early years help you today?

Dear Lord …

E. Wrap-Up

1. Remember Egypt and Exodus by its color, red, which is a reminder of the Red Sea that God brought the children of Israel across and in which he drowned the armies of Pharaoh.

2. Answers will vary. One possible reply: The Egypt and Exodus time period tells how God heard the cries of Jacob's family who had become slaves in Egypt. He came down and revealed his name, delivered them from bondage so they could worship him, and gave them a way to live and worship as a holy nation consecrated to him.

Close with the Responsive Prayer found on the inside front cover of this Study Set Workbook. Pray through the Egypt and Exodus period.

After the small-group discussion, watch Jeff Cavins' video presentation on *Session 7* – Egypt and Exodus: Part 2.

Facilitators: Read these recommended responses to the questions ahead of time to help you prepare to lead the small-group discussion.

Participants: Reinforce what you have learned by reviewing these recommended responses after the small-group discussion and before you go on to the next session.

A. Establish the Context

Facilitators: Take a moment to review what was learned in the previous session and to establish the context for Desert Wanderings. If you like, use the following question to encourage discussion:

- *What about the way God provided for Israel can help you trust God in your own life?*

B. Read the Story

Facilitators: If there is time, have someone read each passage aloud before it is discussed.

C. Take a Deeper Look

Preparing to Leave Sinai (Numbers 1–10)

1. *Israel has been at Mount Sinai for a year. The people have received the Law and the assurance of the presence of God in their midst, enthroned on the Ark of the Covenant. Now, they are preparing to depart for Canaan.*

   a. *Read **Numbers 1–2**. What does God have Moses do before setting out, and for what purpose?*

   Before they leave for Canaan, God has Moses take a census of all men twenty years of age and older who are able to serve in the army and puts them in marching order by tribe. God is mustering the nation for battle.

   b. *One tribe is exempt from this process. Why?*

   The tribe of Levi is not counted in the census. This is the priestly tribe—God has set them apart after the golden calf incident in place of all the firstborn sons of Israel (who were originally set apart by God at the first Passover). Because they are responsible for the care of the Tabernacle, they will not be expected to fight and are not counted.

   (Note: After removing Levi, the total number of twelve tribes is maintained by counting Joseph as two tribes under his sons Ephraim and Manasseh—the double portion of inheritance Jacob blessed Joseph with before he died).

2. *In Chapter 10, the blasts from the silver trumpets lend a decidedly military air to Israel's proceeding. Notice the order of the procession, particularly the way in which the Ark of the Covenant and the Tabernacle are situated in relation to the tribes. Who or what is at the very front, and what does this show? (See verses 33-36.)*

The Ark leads the people as a conquering army. The presence of the Ark and Moses' call to God each time they set out will be a constant reminder that God is establishing this new kingdom (not the people themselves) and that he will lead them and defeat their enemies. If the job ever seems too big for them, this should remind the people that it is not their power that will determine the victory, but God's.

Israel Rebels (Numbers 11–25)

3. *After the people leave Egypt, God tells Moses that he will send manna to "test" the people. Read* **Deuteronomy 8.** *(Deuteronomy, which is the supplemental book for this period, records Moses' final address to the people before they enter Canaan.)*

    a. *Elaborate on God's purpose in giving them manna and on what they are meant to learn from it.*

    God does not want his children to forget him in their prosperity as they are poised to enter Canaan, a land "flowing with milk and honey." The temptation will be great to take credit themselves for their success and to forget that there is more to life than food. The Word of God and obedience to that Word are more important.

    b. *Read* **Numbers 11.** *At the start of their journey, what does Israel's failure to pass God's test say about its relationship with him?*

    In rejecting God's gift of manna, Israel rejects God and his provision. It fails the test of faith. The people do not trust God, and they are not grateful to him. They are looking at his good and bountiful gift and calling it evil, wanting something other than what God knows is good for them. They are acting like Adam and Eve acted before them.

    c. ***New Testament Connection:*** *Read* **Matthew 4:1-4,** *in which Jesus rebuffs Satan using Moses' words from Deuteronomy 8:3. What parallels do you see between these stories?*

    Jesus, God's firstborn Son, is also tempted in the desert, but does not allow Satan to sidetrack him into failing to trust God. Here is a Son of Israel doing what Israel failed to do—he is obedient to God's Word. Obedience to that Word—not bread alone—brings life.

4. *In* **Numbers 12,** *an attack on Moses' authority comes from those closest to him, his siblings Miriam and Aaron. What is the true nature of their complaint and their attitude toward God-given authority?*

    A protest against Moses' Cushite wife cloaks the real reason for Miriam and Aaron's anger, which is Moses' authority and special relationship with God. "Has the Lord indeed spoken only through Moses? Has he not spoken through us also?" they complain. Are they irked by the way God shares his Spirit with the seventy elders, rather than giving them more of a role? The Bible does give the reason. But in verse 14, God compares his rebuke of Miriam to a father's rebuke of a daughter in disgrace. She despises the high position God has given her (Micah 6:4 says God sent Miriam and Aaron along with Moses to lead Israel) and wants more. She is jealous of God's appointed leader, rather than respecting him, which is her duty to God. (See CCC 2234 for our duty to honor those to whom God has given authority.)

5. a. *It looks as though Israel is at last ready to possess the land promised to Abraham. Read* **Numbers 13–14.** *What happens?*

    God tells Moses to send men to explore the Promised Land—a land of exceeding goodness, "a land which flows with milk and honey" (Numbers 14:8). Rather than focusing on the goodness of God's gift to them, the people forget God's promises and well-demonstrated strength and zero in on the one obstacle: the size of the cities and enemies they will need to conquer to obtain the land. Ten of the men come back saying the odds are too great against them. Only two (Joshua and Caleb) trust in God.

b. *Compare and contrast the test Israel faces in spying out the land with the test Adam and Eve faced.*

In the same way that the people of Israel allow the size of the enemy to overshadow their faith in God, Adam and Eve allowed the size of the Serpent and his false promises to obscure their sight of God's blessing and the memory of his Word. Adam and Eve succumbed. In the later incident there is this hope: Two of the twelve men fix their trust in God.

c. *Despite what they know of God and what they have been promised, the people of Israel fail to trust in God. As a consequence, they will wander a year in the desert for each day they have spent spying out the land. What does this setback in Israel's story tell you about the nature of sin and its punishment? Is there a correlation?*

The nature of Israel's sin is such that it reveals the immaturity of their faith. This lack of faith might lead to the very outcome they fear if they are permitted to continue into the land. God's punishment—one year wandering in the desert for each day they explore the land—will mean that those who lack the faith to conquer the land will not enter the land. They will get what they ask for when they say, "Would that we had died in the land of Egypt! Or would that we had died in this wilderness!" (Numbers 14:2). The punishment is not only punitive; it is also remedial. As Moses says in Deuteronomy 8, all the testing Israel goes through in the desert is to teach them the obedience and reliance on God that they lack. This is so that all will go well with them when they enter Canaan.

6. a. *In **Numbers 16–17**, a second attack on Moses' authority comes, this time from the people. What is the charge this time, and to whom is the challenge really made?*

Recall that at the first Passover, God claimed for himself the firstborn male of every family. After the golden calf incident, the Levites—the only ones who stood up for the LORD—were set apart in place of the firstborn sons of the nation. Among the Levite families, Aaron and his sons were given the priesthood. Now, their authority is challenged. Not surprisingly, it comes from the disenfranchised: Korah is a Levite who wants to be a priest. Those who back him in his attack are from the tribe of Reuben, Jacob's firstborn son who challenged his authority and lost the status and rights of the firstborn back in Genesis. What is their charge? *Everyone* is holy because of God in their midst, so they think Moses and Aaron have no right to exalt themselves. They are challenging Moses, but their real challenge is to God and his prerogative to appoint leaders.

b. *How is God's response different this time from his response to Miriam's challenge? What lasting proof does he give that Aaron's authority comes from him?*

God does not just punish the challengers; he kills them and their families and followers. When the people complain, 14,700 more die of a plague. Only Aaron—the rightful priest, offering incense as only he should—is able to atone and stop the plague. In the same way that the Levites camped around the Ark to form a buffer between the people and God, Aaron's sons stand between the people and God to deliver them from judgment.

God's sign that Aaron has God-given priestly authority is unmistakable. Twelve rods representing the twelve tribes are left overnight in the tent of the testimony. The next day, Aaron's rod has not only sprouted and budded, it has blossomed and borne ripe almonds. The people keep this rod before the tablets of the testimony (Numbers 17:10) in the Ark of the Covenant (Hebrews 9:4) as a lasting reminder to all who would rebel against the priestly leadership God has established.

7. *By **Chapter 20**, forty years have passed, and the children of Israel are back at Kadesh. They complain about the lack of water. Moses is instructed to speak to the rock in front of them, but he takes his staff and strikes the rock twice. Consequently, he and Aaron are prohibited from leading the children of Israel into the Promised Land. Does this seem like a harsh punishment? Why do you think they receive such discipline?*

> Moses' fury seems justified: This is the next generation, the people who have had forty years to learn the lessons of manna and God's provision. But they seem to have learned nothing. "Hear now, you rebels," Moses rages. "Shall we bring forth water for you out of this rock?" (verse 10). Who can blame him for striking the rock?
>
> The penalty seems severe. One slip after a lifetime of faithful service, and he and Aaron will not see the fruit of their labor. Why? God says Moses does not trust him enough to honor him as holy. He should believe God will provide with a word, as he has said, and show that to the people. But he takes things into his own hands. "Shall we bring forth water for you out of this rock?" sounds like desperation and anger, not gratitude. Moses begins to sound like a magician at their service rather than the spokesman of God. Moses disobeys, and it is not a small matter. He does not honor God as holy before the people, and they will need that, above all, in a leader as they enter the Promised Land to claim it.

8. *In Numbers 22, Israel has amassed on the Plains of Moab, just east of the Jordan River across from Jericho. God has led them in a number of military victories. The local kings are nervous and hire the powerful prophet, Balaam, to curse Israel. Able to say nothing other than the words God puts in his mouth, however, Balaam blesses them instead. Review the things Balaam says about Israel in **Numbers 22–24**. How do you explain the magnitude of God's blessing following their continual grumbling and lack of faith?*

> The explanation for God's continued blessing of Israel lies in his character, which does not change, and in his faithfulness to his promise (see Numbers 23:19-20). No sorcery or divination can be worked against Israel because God is with them. The blessing comes five times, reiterating and expanding on God's covenant promises and the blessings Jacob gave to his sons. Perhaps this is a reminder to Israel of God's faithful love, as much as it is a rebuke to king Balaak. Individuals might fail and lose out on the promise, but God will still do as he has said.

D. Application

Facilitators: If time allows, have group members share their responses to the following application questions.

The Church's teaching on authority is founded on Scripture—on this and other passages where God appoints leaders to represent him and teaches his people what attitude they should have toward authority. These are timeless principles that do not change. Read CCC 1897–1900, focusing particularly CCC 1899. Have you or anyone you know ever questioned the Church's authority over faith and morals? What problems do you see in today's society that echo the challenges Moses faced from Miriam and Aaron or from Korah, Dathan, and Abiram?

E. Wrap-Up

1. Remember Desert Wanderings by its color, tan, the color of the desert sands.
2. Answers will vary. One possible reply: During the Desert Wanderings, Israel rebelled against God after leaving Egypt and spent forty years wandering in the Sinai for their lack of trust in God.

Close with the Responsive Prayer found on the inside front cover of this Study Set Workbook. Pray through the Desert Wanderings period.

After the small-group discussion, watch Jeff Cavins' video presentation on *Session 8 – Desert Wanderings*.

Facilitators: *Read these recommended responses to the questions ahead of time to help you prepare to lead the small-group discussion.*

Participants: *Reinforce what you have learned by reviewing these recommended responses after the small-group discussion and before you go on to the next session.*

A. Establish the Context

Facilitators: Take a moment to review what was learned in the previous session and to establish the context for Conquest and Judges. If you like, use the following question to encourage discussion:

- *Which of the many lessons Israel learned in the wilderness carries the most personal meaning for you?*

B. Read the Story

Facilitators: If there is time, have someone read each passage aloud before it is discussed.

C. Take a Deeper Look

Preparation and Entry (Joshua 1–5)

1. *As Israel prepares to cross the Jordan into the Promised Land, Joshua takes over the leadership of God's people. According to **Joshua 1:1-9**, what will be the key to his success and theirs?*

   The key to Joshua's success as a leader—and to the success of Israel's campaign to inherit the land of Canaan—will be strength and courage based not on the size or strength of his forces but on his trust in God and his promises. Specifically, he is to meditate constantly on the Word of God and take care to obey it. Devotion to God, expressed both in time spent with God and also in obedience, will result in God's continued presence and support.

2. *In **Joshua 2**, God uses a Canaanite prostitute, Rahab, to help Israel in its mission.*

   a. *Why do you think Rahab is eager to help Israel?*

   Rahab helps Israel in order to save her own skin: Along with everyone else, she has heard about the Red Sea and the fate of Egypt, knows that God has given the land to Israel, and is terrified. But unlike everyone else, she does something about it. She responds to what she heard about God by wanting to be saved and reaching out to help, rather than by cringing in fear or giving the spies over to the authorities.

   b. *According to **Hebrews 11:31** and **James 2:24-26**, how will Rahab be remembered?*

   Rahab will be remembered forever as a woman of faith who acted on what she believed and so was saved. She was not killed along with her disobedient kinsmen "because [by faith] she had given friendly welcome to the spies" (Hebrews 11:31). James lauds her actions as an example of the truth that "a man is justified by works and not by faith alone" (James 2:24). She is "justified by works" (verse

25), by what she does. Interestingly, Rahab presumably leaves her life of prostitution, marries into the nation that saved her, and becomes one of the ancestors of Jesus.

3.   *What is the significance of the twelve stones God has Israel set up at its camp on the far side of the Jordan? (See Joshua 4.)*

The twelve stones, one for each tribe, are taken from the middle of the Jordan and set up as a permanent memorial of their entry into Canaan on dry land. The event is a dramatic demonstration of God's power; it is evidence that he is with them even as he was at the Red Sea and will drive out their enemies before them. It is a sign "so that all the peoples of the earth may know that the hand of the Lord is mighty; that you may fear the Lord your God for ever" (Joshua 4:24).

Conquest (Joshua 6–12)

4.   *Read Joshua 6. Describe the marching order and plan of attack to conquer Jericho. What kind of warfare is this? What spiritual message should this send to Israel?*

The Ark of the Covenant is the central focus of the army, led into battle by seven priests blowing on seven rams' horns announcing the presence of God. These are surrounded in front and behind by armed men and the rear guard. All together and in silence except for the trumpets, they circle the city once a day for six days. On day seven, the drill is the same, except they circle seven times. At the end, a mighty shout causes the walls to come crashing down.

This might be called liturgical warfare. It is structured and orderly. The priests lead the way, and God is given pride of place. Music—not war cries—precedes the charge. Forty years earlier, Israel was too afraid of the Canaanites to enter the land. Now they are being shown how to enter it properly—not in a show of their own strength, but by announcing that Yahweh has come, by putting God first and allowing him to drive the enemy out before them, by obeying his directions to the last detail. And when the walls fall down, they should know without a shadow of a doubt that the Lord is with them.

5.   a.   *Read Joshua 7–8. What happens in the aftermath of Jericho that causes God to withdraw his support so that the Israelites lose their first battle against Ai?*

One man, Achan, has disobeyed the ban God placed on Jericho under which every person living in the city must be killed, and everything that cannot be destroyed must be dedicated to God's house. Achan has kept some treasures for himself with the result that Israel itself becomes "a thing for destruction" (Joshua 7:12).

b.   *How does Achan's failure illustrate what St. John Paul II spoke of as a "communion of sin," whereby one person's sin, no matter how private, affects the rest of the Church?*

Even though only one man has sinned, Israel is routed in its first attack on Ai. The whole community will suffer if that sin is not atoned for. This illustrates that "communion of sin," by which personal sin always has repercussions beyond itself and pulls down the whole community, to a greater or lesser extent, depending on the sin committed.

Note: Achan's theft of a few items must not be considered alone, isolated from the context in which it is done. Almost as the first fruits of a harvest belong to God, or as the firstborn sons were originally to be set apart to God, these first cities and everything in them are to be "devoted to the Lord" (Joshua 6:17) but by destruction. (Because of the great wickedness of these cities, they are under a complete ban, and nothing can be taken for personal use.) In later cities, it will be a different story. Achan is not stealing just any plunder; he is stealing what belongs to God, and at the very outset of their mission. This sin will affect the entire nation and, as such, it is punished accordingly.

Division of the Land (Joshua 13–22)

6.   Read **Joshua 21:43-45.** *Where does Israel stand in seeing the fulfillment of God's promises?*

After dividing the land among the tribes and appointing cities of refuge and towns for the Levites, "the LORD gave to Israel all the land which he swore to give to their fathers; and having taken possession of it, they settled there" (Joshua 21:43). God gives them rest from their enemies; "not one of all the good promises which the LORD had made to the house of Israel had failed; all came to pass" (verse 45). Essentially this marks the fulfillment of the first part of the threefold promise. They are numerous, they have the land, and they have God's Law. Israel is now a nation. It is only a matter of time before they will become a royal kingdom and a blessing to the entire world.

Covenant Renewal (Joshua 23–24)

7.   *Joshua's farewell address is recorded at the close of the book. Read **Joshua 23–24.***

   a.   *What is Joshua's warning to the leaders? (See **Joshua 23**.)*

First Joshua admonishes the leaders to remember that God has fought for them and given them this land, and he will continue to fight for them, driving out the inhabitants before them, so that they can take possession of it. He then warns them that if they turn away from God and intermarry and align themselves with the surviving Canaanites, they will be on their own.

This message is important because, while the land has been conquered, it has not all been occupied. There remain many Canaanites in the land, and it must be cleansed of idolatry. If they get lazy and fail to push out the Canaanites, they will become a thorn in their side. The temptation to worship other gods has plagued them since their days in Egypt; it will be all the more difficult to resist if they live among the others and intermarry. And if they turn away from worshiping and serving the LORD alone, they will lose the good land God has given them.

   b.   *What is the central message of his general address? (See **Joshua 24**.)*

The central message of Joshua's farewell address to the people is the importance of holding fast to God, being careful to love and obey him. "Choose this day whom you will serve," Joshua exhorts them, "whether the gods your fathers served in the region beyond the River, or the gods of the Amorites in whose land you dwell; but as for me and my house, we will serve the LORD" (Joshua 24:15). Only if they do this, will God continue to push out the inhabitants of the land and establish Israel. God will be faithful to his promises, but he also will carry out the curses should they break their part of the covenant.

8.   ***Think About It:*** *Israel's conquest and occupation of the Promised Land anticipates the Church's warfare against the powers of the world and its efforts to establish and spread the kingdom of God on earth. The apostles Paul and Peter encourage the early Christians in this battle. Read the following passages from their letters, and note what they say about the nature of the battle and the weapons God gives us to fight it. Relate them to the book of Joshua if you can.*

   a.   ***2 Corinthians 10:3-4:***

2 Corinthians 10:3-4 tells us that the nature of the war we are carrying on is not worldly. The strongholds we must bring down are not tangible like the fortified walls of Jericho but are spiritual strongholds. Consequently, God gives us spiritual weapons to destroy them. Think of the divine power God made available to Israel to destroy the walls of Jericho: the "weapons" they used were to give God center stage and trumpet his presence, to obey God's instructions to the letter, and to

refrain from fighting with their own power until God brought down the walls. There is much we can learn from their example.

b. ***1 Peter 2:11:***

St. Peter says that the war for our souls is waged by fleshly passions, which we need to resist. Israel may initially have been afraid of the size and strength of the Canaanites, but it will eventually be the lure of their women and other gods that will be hardest to face.

c. ***1 Timothy 6:11-12:***

St. Paul describes the Christian's fight as a fight to take hold of eternal life by shunning other desires and aiming instead at "righteousness, godliness, faith, love, steadfastness, gentleness." He calls it "the good fight of faith"—which is our chief weapon in the battle. Similarly, God tells Joshua—and he in turn tells Israel—that success will be his if he holds fast to God and obeys his Word. Israel is going to have to take hold of the Promised Land by shunning desires to be like the Canaanites and striving instead to fear, love, and obey God.

d. ***Ephesians 6:11-18:***

God tells Joshua four times in Chapter 1 to be strong and courageous, for God will be with him. St. Paul gives the Ephesians the same message. It is God's power that will defeat the enemy and allow us to stand in the end. Our fight is not against other people, but against principalities, powers, "the world rulers of this present darkness … the spiritual hosts of wickedness in the heavenly places" (verse 12). We cannot hope to stand against the devil on our own, but "the whole armor of God" (verse 11) is available to strengthen us. We have only to put it on. What is that armor? Most is defensive: We are to stand clothed in truth, righteousness, and the gospel of peace, wearing the helmet of salvation and carrying the shield of faith to quench any flaming darts the devil sends our way. The offensive weapons offered are "the sword of the Spirit, which is the word of God," and prayer for ourselves and for others.

D. Application

Facilitators: If time allows, have group members share their responses to the following application questions.

Think about what the people of Israel are up against when they set out to conquer Canaan and about the methods and instructions God gives Joshua to guide the people in that task. What strongholds are you up against as you seek to "enter the rest" of God's kingdom on earth? What makes it hard for you to push out the enemy? Are there any basic principles you can apply from this session to the battle in your life?

Close with the Responsive Prayer found on the inside front cover of this Study Set Workbook. Pray through the Conquest and Judges period.

After the small-group discussion, watch Jeff Cavins' video presentation on *Session 9 – Conquest and Judges: Part 1.*

Facilitators: *Read these recommended responses to the questions ahead of time to help you prepare to lead the small-group discussion.*

Participants: *Reinforce what you have learned by reviewing these recommended responses after the small-group discussion and before you go on to the next session.*

A. Review the Context

Facilitators: Take a moment to review the context and what was learned in the previous session. If you like, use the following question to encourage discussion:

- *What in particular about the nature of the battle—or the weapons God gives us to fight it—struck you as it applies to your life?*

B. Read the Story

Facilitators: If there is time, have someone read each passage aloud before it is discussed.

C. Take a Deeper Look

Israel's Occupation of Canaan: Prologue (Judges 1:1–3:6)

1. Read **Judges 1:1–3:6.**

   a. *After the initial victories God gives to Israel on entering the land, it remains Israel's task to fully occupy it by driving the people out and breaking down their altars. Compare the way Judah and Simeon set out to occupy their tribal area in the South with the way the other (Northern) tribes occupy theirs.*

   The men of Judah and Simeon join together to fight against the Canaanites. They fight steadily and methodically and succeed in pushing them out from all but the plains, where their enemies have iron chariots. The remaining tribes are not as zealous. They do not drive out the inhabitants as God has commanded, but subject them to forced labor or live among them.

   b. *What is God's response? (See **Judges 2**.)*

   By failing to drive out the people and cleanse the land of idolatry, Israel has disobeyed God's command. Thus they are subject to the punishment Joshua warned them of before he died: God will allow the pagan nations to stay in the land as thorns in the side of Israel and the pagan gods as a snare to them.

2. *In Moses' final words to the people in **Deuteronomy 11,** he warns them to be careful to teach God's words to their children, and God will drive out the nations before them. Read **Judges 2:10-15.** What is the result of that generation's failure to do this?*

The very next generation does not know the LORD or what he has done for Israel! They abandon God and instead serve the false gods of the pagans they have allowed to remain in the land. Consequently, God fights against them instead of for them, delivering them into the hands of their enemies.

Israel's Occupation of Canaan: Epilogue (Judges 17–21)

3. *The closing chapters of Judges are flanked with this phrase: "In those days there was no king in Israel; every man did what was right in his own eyes" (see Judges 17:6 and 21:25).*

   a. *This might sound like a recipe for freedom, but what is the result in Israel, based on the stories in Judges 17–21?*

   When everyone does what seems right to themselves, the result is chaos and defeat. Ignoring God's instructions and going their own way leads not to freedom, but to the worst kinds of evil and debauchery. The people become idolatrous, violent, selfish, and degenerate. They abuse the priesthood. The tribes fight not just against their enemies, but also against each other. The horrifying incident of the Levite and his concubine ends in the near-loss of the tribe of Benjamin, which they gain back only by more murder and trickery. In short, without God as their leader, they become like the people they were meant to displace.

   b. *The Catechism states that, "There is no true freedom except in the service of what is good and just. The choice to disobey and do evil is an abuse of freedom and leads to 'the slavery of sin'" (CCC 1733; cf. Romans 6:17). How does Israel's history so far illustrate this truth? (For more on what the Church has to say about man's freedom, read all of CCC 1730–1748.)*

   God frees Israel from involuntary bondage in Egypt so they can freely serve him instead. When they move into Canaan, it becomes evident that what was *imposed* by Pharaoh is just as bad when it is *chosen* by them. God creates people to be what you might call "free agents," free to determine their own actions so they can freely seek God and his blessings by following him. For that choice to be real, there must be an option. They are free to choose God or themselves, to choose good or evil. The paradox is that the more one chooses God and good, the freer one becomes. At this point, the people of Israel are choosing their own way over God's way, and they are fast slipping back into slavery. Just as with the first Passover, freedom will depend on God's powerful intervention.

Seven Cycles of Sin and Deliverance (Judges 3:7–16:31)

4. *Choose the story of one judge, and use it to describe the cycle. (Othniel is the simplest and shortest example, but the others are more interesting!)*

   Replies will vary. Discuss them with the aim of learning the cycle. The story of Othniel, the first judge, provides a short summary of its elements:

   • Sin – Each cycle begins with the Israelites doing evil in the sight of God, forsaking him, and serving other gods.

   • Servitude – God punishes them by allowing their enemies a victory over them. In this case, he sells them into servitude to a neighboring king for eight years.

   • Supplication – Crushed, the people cry out to God.

   • Salvation – God raises up a judge (Othniel) to deliver them, filling him with his Spirit so he can lead the people to victory.

- Silence – God gives them peace for the judge's lifetime (in this case, Othniel lives another forty years).

5. *The story of Gideon is in **Judges 6–7.***

   a. *What do these two chapters tell you about the ways of God in the midst of seemingly inevitable defeat?*

   God uses seemingly impossible situations to demonstrate his power and might on behalf of his children. When Gideon wonders why God does not choose someone more suited to the job, God lets him know that what matters is his obedience: that he "go in the strength [he has]" (Judges 6:14, NAB). God condescends to Gideon's weakness by giving him all the signs he needs to bolster his confidence, even having Gideon eavesdrop on the enemy so he will discover that they are afraid of him. Then he strips Gideon's army down from thirty-two thousand men to three hundred so it will be evident that God—not Gideon—is the one who wins the battle. God makes the enemy army turn on each other, and they are routed at night by Gideon's small band. God is not hampered by our weakness; rather, he makes use of it to show his strength.

   b. *Gideon is so successful a deliverer that the Israelites ask him to rule over them. Read **Judges 8:22-23.** How does Gideon's reply focus on one of the main issues of this time?*

   Gideon's reply is emphatic: "I will not rule over you, and my son will not rule over you; the LORD will rule over you" (Judges 8:23). The people want a human power to rule over them and give them stability. This is not necessarily wrong, but their motivation is. They want a human king instead of God, whom they have rejected. (Interestingly, when Gideon's son Abimelech tries to make himself king after Gideon's death, chaos and bloodshed result.)

6. ***Think About It:*** *Human nature is no different today than it was then. We can find ourselves slipping into the same cycle of sin, servitude, supplication, salvation, and silence all too easily. What do we have available to us in the New Covenant that Israel did not have and that will help us break the cycle? (See **John 20:23** and **CCC 1210–1213, 1325, 1426, and 1446** for help.)*

   In brief, we have the sacraments. The New Covenant sacraments achieve, in fact, what was only pointed to in the Old Covenant. For example, crossing the Red Sea saved Israel from slavery to Egypt so they could be free members of God's family. Baptism, which the Red Sea crossing prefigured, actually breaks the power of original sin, gives us God's own life, and makes us his adopted children. We are able to put off "the old man" and put on an entirely new nature that is like God's (Ephesians 4:22-24).

   Similarly, in the Passover, the Israelites were redeemed from physical death by the blood of many lambs. In the New Covenant, Christians are redeemed from eternal, spiritual death by the Blood of Jesus, the Lamb of God.

   Freed from death and slavery in Egypt, Israel still struggled with sin on a daily basis. An elaborate sacrificial system was set up to atone for individual sins. In the New Covenant, we have the sacrament of reconciliation to absolve us from sin and reunite us with the Father and the Church. The Church Fathers likened this sacrament to a "plank" offered to the "shipwrecked"—a way to get back on board after falling into grave sin (see CCC 1446).

7. *All through the book of Judges, we see the influence pagan nations and false gods have on Israel. Read **Psalm 115:1-9** and **CCC 2085–2086 and 2112.** What distinguishes the pagan gods from the One, True God?*

   The One, True God is Creator and LORD of the universe; the pagan gods are created beings. The LORD is living; he watches over his people from heaven, and helps and protects them. The pagan gods cannot speak or move or do anything, because they are made of wood, stone, silver, and gold; they are creations of men. The LORD demonstrates his superiority over the other gods when he brings Israel out of Egypt. He never changes; he is always faithful, just, and good, with no evil in him (unlike the fickle pagan deities).

8. *Judges paints a dark picture of the unfaithfulness and moral and religious decline of this period when, if it were not for God's covenant faithfulness, Israel might be swallowed up by the pagan nations. All is not dark, however. The book of* **Ruth,** *written during this time, provides a welcome counterpoint to the closing chapters of Judges. Read the entire book (it is only four chapters long). How is Ruth's story the opposite of the one told in Judges?*

> The story of Ruth is almost the story of Judges in reverse. She is a woman from a pagan nation whose people are hostile to Israel (it was Moabite women who seduced Israel to worship Baal at Peor, and Moab's king Balak who summoned Baalam to curse Israel back in Numbers 22–25). But Ruth forsakes the gods of Moab to faithfully serve Yahweh. The fact that Chapter 4 recognizes Ruth as an ancestress of David, and that Matthew includes her in the genealogy of Jesus, helps us remember that God's ultimate plan is to include all nations in his family. Ruth is, in many ways, what Israel is called to be.

D. Application

Facilitators: If time allows, have group members share their responses to the following application questions.

What similarities do you see between our time and the time of the Judges? Think about the pressures and influences you face today compared with the pressures Israel faced. Where did the people of Israel go wrong? What have you learned from them that you can use to avoid getting caught up in the same never-ending cycle?

E. Wrap-Up

1. Remember Conquest and Judges by its color, green, which represents the green hills of Canaan.

2. Answers will vary. One possible reply: In Conquest and Judges, Israel triumphantly enters the land of Canaan but does not entirely possess it. The people forget God and settle into a cycle of sin, servitude, supplication, salvation, and silence.

Close with the Responsive Prayer found on the inside front cover of this Study Set Workbook. Pray through the Conquest and Judges period.

After the small-group discussion, watch Jeff Cavins' video presentation on *Session 10 –* **Conquest and Judges: Part 2.**

Facilitators: Read these recommended responses to the questions ahead of time to help you prepare to lead the small-group discussion.

Participants: Reinforce what you have learned by reviewing these recommended responses after the small-group discussion and before you go on to the next session.

A. Establish the Context

Facilitators: Take a moment to review what was learned in the previous session and to establish the context for the Royal Kingdom. If you like, use the following question to encourage discussion:

- *Is there something about the cycle of sin and supplication that spoke to you this week?*

B. Read the Story

Facilitators: If there is time, have someone read each passage aloud before it is discussed.

C. Take a Deeper Look

The Call of Samuel (1 Samuel 1–7)

*1.   a.   Hannah is barren until God blesses her with a son she names Samuel, a child who will become the last and the greatest of all the judges. Can you remember any other great figures in the Bible who were born of women whose bodies were unable to conceive until God intervened? (For help with this question, see **Genesis 21:1-3, 25:21, and 30:22-24; Judges 13:2, 24;** and **Luke 1.**)*

Many of the great figures in the Bible were born by God's miraculous intervention, including most of the patriarchs:

- Sarah and Abraham were well beyond child-bearing age when God gave them Isaac.

- Rebekah was barren for many years before conceiving Esau and Jacob.

- Jacob's wife Rachel gave birth to Joseph only after many years of barrenness and prayer.

- Then in Judges, we saw that Samson was born to Manoah's barren wife after prayer.

- In the New Testament, both John the Baptist and Jesus Christ were born in "impossible" situations, humanly speaking.

b.   Is this coincidence? Why do you think the authors make it a point to describe the circumstances of these men's births?

Coincidence or not, it seems that nearly every time God sets out to advance his plan or save his people, he does it by calling a particular person. And most often, this person is *not* chosen after he shows himself to be worthy, but seems specifically created by God for the purpose. By giving these children to previously barren or very old women (and a virgin!), God's initiative stands out. Without him, these children would be "impossible." But as God says in response to Sarah's laughter, "Is anything too hard for the LORD?" (Genesis 18:14)—a response that foreshadows Gabriel's statement at the Annunciation: "For with God nothing will be impossible" (Luke 1:37).

2. *What in the description of Samuel's early life gives further proof of God's initiative and purpose for Samuel?*

Samuel is raised by the high priest Eli, whose own sons are wicked men with no regard for God. They treat God's offering with contempt, sleep with the women who serve at the tent of meeting, and ignore their father's rebukes. In spite of this corrupt atmosphere, "the boy Samuel continued to grow both in stature and in favor with the LORD and with men" (2:26). God's hand was clearly upon him. According to Chapter 3, it was unusual for people to hear from God directly in those days. Samuel does not yet know God. Yet, God calls Samuel, persisting until he hears and replies. God continues to speak to Samuel and reveal himself to him through his Word. It is instructive to contrast 1 Samuel 3:1 and 4:1. Whereas, formerly the Word of God was rarely heard, now God's Word comes through Samuel to all Israel. The prayers of Hannah have taken deep root and are answered abundantly.

3. a. *In **1 Samuel 4-6**, the people of Israel send for the Ark of the Covenant when the Philistines defeat them. Is this the wrong thing to do? After all, God had them march against Jericho led by the Ark. Why does God deliver them to the Philistines and allow the Ark to be taken?*

In the battle against Jericho, every detail pointed to God leading the battle. The people stood back and let God act and then cooperated with him in defeating Jericho. This time, Israel goes out alone. They seem to think about God and the Ark of the Covenant only after losing. God is an afterthought—and even then, they do not seek his help, but drag the Ark into battle as though it were a magic talisman to do their bidding. Israel is thinking like the other nations and treating the LORD as a (false) god who can be manipulated.

When Israel is routed again, the Ark taken, and the high priest and his sons killed, Israel is chastened. God makes his power and glory manifest to the Philistines through the Ark, so they return it in fear. And those who treat it lightly and dare to look inside are killed. Another generation must learn to treat God's throne with respect and honor—and learn that he is the true source of power and victory.

b. *By Chapter 7, twenty years have passed. The Ark of the Covenant has been returned to Israel, but the people are still oppressed by the Philistines. Samuel calls an assembly at Mizpah and prepares to do battle. How do you account for Israel's victory? How are their actions in this battle different from their actions in the earlier battle described in **1 Samuel 4**?*

Led by Samuel, the people fast and confess their sin. Threatened by the Philistines, they plead for Samuel's intercession that God might rescue them. In answer, God throws the enemy into confusion so that Israel can subdue them. The picture is completely different this time. It is more in line with the way God taught them at Jericho—in which God is in control and fighting their battles.

Israel Asks for a King (1 Samuel 4–8)

4. Read **1 Samuel 8**.

a. *It is the end of the era of the judges, and the people ask for a king. Why do they want a king, and what does this say about their relationship with God?*

Israel wants "a king to govern us like all the nations" (verse 5); they want a human king to lead them and fight their battles. They do not want to be different by serving God—even though he has brought them out of Egypt and has fought their battles and led them faithfully. They want to be like everyone else. As God tells Samuel in verse 7, they have rejected him from being their king (they have not simply rejected Samuel's sons). They have forsaken him and are serving other gods.

b.   *What does God tell Samuel the outcome will be if they have a king?*

Before granting their request, God warns them: A king will take their children into his service. He will take the best part of their fields and produce for his officers and servants. He will take their servants and cattle for himself, and he will make them his slaves. And when they cry out to God because of the king they have asked for, God will not answer. This does not change their minds.

The First King of Israel: Saul (1 Samuel 9–31)

5.   **Think About It:** *In Chapter 9, Samuel anoints a man named Saul of the tribe of Benjamin to be king. Look at the "Twelve Tribes" map on page 65. Think back to what you learned about the tribes in the book of Joshua. Is there anything significant about the location of the tribe of Benjamin that makes it a good place for Israel's first king to be from?*

The tribe of Benjamin is small, but it sits in that same strategic area that Jericho occupied: central to the land and at the dividing line between Judah, the major tribe to the south, and the tribes of Joseph (Ephraim and Manasseh) and the other tribes to the north. In Joshua, we read of the infighting that has gone on between the tribes during the time leading up to this point. A Benjaminite king would be able to play a pivotal role in unifying the tribes into one kingdom.

6.   *Israel now has a king like the other nations. But is its king going to be like those of other nations? Read* **1 Samuel 12:12-15** *(part of Samuel's farewell speech to the nation) and* **Psalm 47 and Psalm 2.** *(Psalms is a supplemental book for this time period, and many psalms were written during the time of the Royal Kingdom.) How will Israel's king be radically different from those of other nations?*

Israel now has a king as the other nations do, but not a king like the others' kings. Here is a king who will be subject to the Great King, God himself, and subject to his instructions (whether those contained in the Law given to Moses or those delivered directly to him through a priest or a prophet such as Samuel). He will be an instrument of God's rule and not a power unto himself. Both he and his people must take care to fear and obey God, who will continue to lead, protect, and establish them.

Psalm 47 is a hymn of praise to the God who is the Great King over all the earth, who subdues nations under the feet of Israel and reigns on his holy throne over the nations, and who owns the kings of the earth. Psalm 2 exults in God, who installed his king on Zion (Jerusalem) to rule the nations of the earth. It warns kings to serve God—as opposed (presumably) to setting themselves up as rival powers as Pharaoh did in Egypt.

7.   *Read* **1 Samuel 13:1-14 and 1 Samuel 15.** *What sins does King Saul commit, and what does he lose because of his serious sin?*

King Saul does not submit to the requirements of kingship in Israel, which are that he submit to God and to his Word as spoken through Samuel. He sins first by offering sacrifices in Samuel's place when Samuel has clearly instructed him to wait (1 Samuel 10:8). Saul is meant to honor Samuel's word as God's. At Gilgal, he takes things into his own hands rather than waiting on God (and Samuel). His impatience costs him the kingdom, which God would have established in his name forever. "But now your kingdom shall not continue; the LORD has sought out a man after his own heart; and the LORD has appointed him to be prince over his people, because you have not kept what the LORD commanded you" (1 Samuel 13:14).

When God sends Saul against the Amalekites, he again disobeys. Rather than destroying everything as God has commanded, he saves the king and the best animals. Not only that—he lies about his intentions to Samuel and then attempts to shift the blame to his men. Only when Samuel challenges Saul with God's Word and tells him that God has rejected him as king, does he admit to his sin. It is too little, too late for King Saul.

8. *Samuel anoints the young David as the next king of Israel, although Saul will remain "acting" king until his death. Soon afterward, Goliath, a mighty champion of the Philistines, taunts Israel (Chapter 17). How do you explain David's confidence that he, a mere boy, can defeat Goliath, especially when the experienced soldiers are all so afraid?*

David has his perspective straight. "Who is this uncircumcised Philistine, that he should defy the armies of the living God?" (17:26), David asks. He knows God; he has experienced his help against wild animals, and he is confident that he will help against Goliath. But most of all, David has his eyes and heart fixed on God. Saul's men are fixated on the size of the enemy. They have forgotten everything God has ever done for them. Because they are relying on their own strength, they are rightly terrified.

9. *Saul has been chosen by God, anointed by Samuel, and divinely equipped for the position of king (see **1 Samuel 10:6**). Even when Saul disobeys God and tries to kill David because he is jealous of him—and even though David knows he himself has also been anointed king—how does David show his respect for Saul, God's anointed one? What does this say about David's relationship with God? (See **Chapters 23–24 and 26**.)*

David's respect for Saul is remarkable, particularly under the circumstances. Forced to flee from Saul for years, he refrains from retaliating and spares the king's life when it is in his power. David will not kill someone who has been anointed by God, however bad the situation seems to be. He refuses to take things into his own hands, but leaves the situation to God. "Who can put forth his hand against the LORD's anointed, and be guiltless?" David says in 1 Samuel 26:9-11. "As the LORD lives, the LORD will strike him; or his day shall come to die; or he shall go down into battle and perish. The LORD forbid that I should put forth my hand against the LORD's anointed."

This shows great strength and closeness in David's relationship with God. He knows God has anointed him to be king, and he is willing to rest in that knowledge and wait for God to achieve his purpose in his own time.

D. Application

Facilitators: If time allows, have group members share their responses to the following application questions.

Israel's request for a king is a refusal of God's kingship and reflects Israel's desire to be "like the other nations." Are you looking to anyone other than God to be king in your life? Do you have trouble trusting in him and so try to take things into your own hands the way Saul did? Look through the psalms, and find one that speaks to your heart. Many of the early psalms, were written by David. They speak strongly and with great beauty of God's kingship. Meditate on one of them, and make it your prayer.

Close with the Responsive Prayer found on the inside front cover of this Study Set Workbook. Pray through the Royal Kingdom period.

After the small-group discussion, watch Jeff Cavins' video presentation on *Session 11 – Royal Kingdom: Part 1*.

Facilitators: Read these recommended responses to the questions ahead of time to help you prepare to lead the small-group discussion.

Participants: Reinforce what you have learned by reviewing these recommended responses after the small-group discussion and before you go on to the next session.

A. Review the Context

Facilitators: Take a moment to review the context and what was learned in the previous session. If you like, use the following question to encourage discussion:

- *What is the most important thing you learned in Session 11?*

B. Read the Story

Facilitators: If there is time, have someone read each passage aloud before it is discussed.

C. Take a Deeper Look

King David (2 Samuel)

1. *After Saul's death, David is anointed king first over Judah in the South and then over all Israel (see **2 Samuel 2, 5**). The first thing he does is to conquer Jerusalem and establish it as his royal city. Jerusalem was on the border of the northern and southern halves of the nation but was controlled by neither, so it was an ideal city to unite the kingdom. After defeating the Philistines, David moves the Ark of the Covenant from its resting place in Kiriath-jearim to Jerusalem with great fanfare (see **Chapter 6**). What is the significance of this first royal action?*

   By bringing the Ark of the Covenant to Jerusalem, David is bringing the earthly throne of God to a place of prominence in the new royal city. This demonstrates that David understands who the true King of Israel is.

2. *A thousand years earlier, in this same place (then called Salem), the priest-king Melchizedek brought out bread and wine and blessed Abram, who paid him a tithe (see **Genesis 14:18-20** and the boxed note on page 27. Here, after the Ark of the Covenant is returned to its place, David blesses the people and gives them meat and cakes of bread and raisins. Read **2 Samuel 6:12-22**. Does anything make you believe David is acting as much like a priest as a king? Why is this significant? (See **Hebrews 7:1-4, 14-17** and **Psalm 110:4**.)*

   David looks very much like a priest in 2 Samuel 6. He dances before the LORD wearing a linen ephod, the type of garment typically worn by the Levites, possibly doing a liturgical dance. He offers burnt offerings and peace offerings and blesses the people in the name of the LORD—all actions normally performed by priests.

   This is significant because God had reserved these actions for the priesthood. In 1 Samuel 13, Saul was rebuked for offering a burnt offering to God. It looks rather as though God's original plan to raise Israel as a kingdom of priests might be coming back into play. Here we have a king ruling not by his own power and might but through priestly service to God. In Psalm 110, David writes that the LORD has sworn about him and his sons, "You are a priest for ever according to the order of Melchizedek." According to the author of Hebrews, this is an order of priesthood higher than that of Aaron and his sons, an exalted priesthood that one day would be exemplified in a particular Son of David, Jesus Christ (see Hebrews 7).

3. *David is a conquering king, and under his rule, Israel is at its strongest in terms of power and size. Read* **2 Samuel 7.** *Once David is given rest from his enemies, he wants to build a permanent dwelling place for the Ark. What is God's response to David, and how does it relate back to his promise to Abraham?*

God uses David's desire to build a house for him as an opportunity to renew and fulfill his earlier promise. God does not need a place to live, but he will give Israel a home of its own and will build a house for David—not a literal house, but a "house" in the sense of dynasty. Not only that, but through David's offspring God will establish a house—and kingdom and throne—that will endure forever. This is the sense behind, "I will make your name great," which God says in 2 Samuel 7:9 and which he promised Abraham. The second part of that three-part covenant is being fulfilled in a covenant with David.

God does not completely reject the idea of a house for himself, however. Once God establishes the kingdom through David's own son, that son will build a house for God's Name, and God will establish his throne forever. And God promises that although he will punish wrongdoing, he will never withdraw his love. David's house, kingdom, and throne will endure forever.

4. *Although David is "a man after God's own heart," he is not without sin. In* **2 Samuel 11,** *we read of his sin with Bathsheba and Uriah. What are the consequences for David and his family? (Nathan's warning is in Chapter 12.)* **Optional:** *See how the consequences play out by reading* **Chapters 12–20.**

God does not remove him as king or take his life, but because David has "despised" God and his Word (12:9, 10), killed Uriah, and taken Bathsheba, calamity falls upon his house and family. As Nathan foretold in 12:10-14, the child conceived by Bathsheba dies, and tragedy haunts David's household. His daughter Tamar is raped by his son Amnon. Absalom, the brother of Tamar, retaliates by killing Amnon. Estranged from his father and believing himself to be heir to the throne, Absalom later leads a revolt against David and takes Jerusalem. He then sleeps with David's concubines on the roof of the palace, where all Israel can see him—a final blow against David that signifies a claim to his power. The battle between them ends in Absalom's death and David's great sorrow.

5. *Even though God punishes David for his sin, he does not withdraw the kingdom. In contrast, when King Saul disobeyed God, he took the kingdom from him (1 Samuel 15). Why the difference? (For David's response to God's rebuke, read* **2 Samuel 12:15-23** *and* **Psalm 51,** *which records his prayer. Read also* **CCC 1847 and 1850.**)

Both kings sinned, but their responses are completely different. David cries out to God. He throws himself on God's mercy and humbly prays for forgiveness. He knows that although he has sinned against Bathsheba and Uriah, ultimately his sin is against God. He also knows that God will "take no delight in sacrifice; were I to give a burnt offering, you would not be pleased. The sacrifice acceptable to God is a broken spirit; a broken and contrite heart, O God, you will not despise" (Psalm 51:16-17).

There is no such contrition in Saul. Caught, he tries to justify his actions and placate God by saying the animals they saved from slaughter were for God. Told he will lose his kingdom, he owns up. But he does not seem to realize the gravity of his choice. Rather than fall on his face before God, Saul begs Samuel to forgive and honor him so he can worship when he returns. He refers to God as "the LORD your God." Does Saul know God? His heart is hard. He does not recognize his sin as disobedience or as an offense against God. And he loses the kingdom. In contrast, David's throne is established forever.

King Solomon (1 Kings 1–11)

6. *Solomon is perhaps twenty years old when he assumes the throne of Israel after his father, David.*

    a. *When God tells him to ask for anything he wants, how does he respond? (See* **1 Kings 3.***)*

    Between his own youth and lack of experience and the volatile political climate, Solomon is well aware of the difficulties he will face. Rather than ask for wealth or a long life, he asks for "an understanding mind to govern … that I may discern between good and evil" (see 1 Kings 3:9).

    b. *What is God's response to Solomon's request?*

    God is pleased and gives Solomon not only wisdom, but also the things he does not ask for: riches and honor. God also promises him a long life if he will follow his commands and walk in his ways.

7. *In 1 Kings, we learn that, "King Solomon excelled all the kings of the earth in riches and in wisdom" (10:23). He wrote thousands of proverbs, many of which are preserved in the book of Proverbs, one of the supplemental books for the Royal Kingdom time period. Read* **Proverbs 1:1-7 and 2:1-11.** *What do these Scripture passages teach us about wisdom?*

    Answers will vary. Proverbs 1 introduces all the proverbs and their purpose: to teach wisdom and understanding, discipline, prudence, and discretion. Verse 7 is important: "The fear of the LORD is the beginning of knowledge; fools despise wisdom and instruction." "Fear" does not mean terror or dread, but a reverence for God that shows itself in obedience to God. The way to wisdom lies on the path of obedience. Those who despise God's instruction and go their own way are fools. Proverbs 2 lauds the benefits of searching for wisdom: you will understand the fear of the LORD and will come to know God. He will protect you and give victory. You will be protected and guided by wisdom and discretion and saved from evil.

8. a. *Once Solomon is given peace on all sides, he builds a magnificent Temple for the Name of God, a permanent place for God to dwell among his people. Read* **CCC 2580–2581.** *What will the king do there, and what is the Temple meant to be for God's people?*

    The king will lift his hands in prayer in the Temple for the daily needs and forgiveness of the people that their hearts might belong to God. It will be a sign to the nations that God is the only God. The Temple will manifest God's holiness and glory and will be the place where the people learn to pray and worship and turn their hearts to God.

    b. ***Think About It:*** *What is the relationship between the Tabernacle, the Temple, Jesus Christ, the Church, and individual believers? (Read also* **Matthew 12:6 and 26:61** *and* **1 Corinthians 3:16 and 6:19.***)*

    God gave the Tabernacle so he could "tabernacle," or live, among his people. Although he was not confined therein, it contained his throne—the Ark of the Covenant—and was where he met with them. The Tabernacle moved with the people, but the Temple was tied to the City of David, Jerusalem, "God's Holy Hill." It manifested the presence of God among his people and anticipated "something greater than the temple" (Matthew 12:6): Jesus Christ. In Christ, God came down to live among his people in a unique way, and after he came, there was no need for a temple building. After his ascension and the giving of the Holy Spirit at Pentecost, his body, the Church, becomes the temple, the place where God is present on earth. That is true today of the Church as a whole and of Christians as individuals: "Do you not know that you are God's temple and that God's Spirit dwells in you?" (1 Corinthians 3:16). "Your body is a temple of the Holy Spirit within you, which you have from God … So glorify God in your body" (1 Corinthians 6:19-20).

9. *God consecrates the Temple Solomon has built for his Name and reminds Solomon of the importance of keeping the covenant in order to continue enjoying its blessings. In* **1 Kings 9:10–11:13,** *we learn about the rest of Solomon's reign. Read Moses' instructions for the king in* **Deuteronomy 17:16-17.** *How does Solomon fare, and what is the result?*

Solomon squanders his blessing and wisdom and breaks the conditions of kingship. He amasses chariots and horses, silver and gold. Perhaps most grievously, he takes hundreds of wives and concubines, many from surrounding nations. And, "when Solomon was old his wives turned away his heart after other gods; and his heart was not wholly true to the Lord his God" (1 Kings 11:4). As a result, God raises up enemies against Solomon and determines to tear the kingdom away from him.

10. *Read* **1 Kings 11:26-43.** *Describe Ahijah's prophecy to Jeroboam, whom Solomon has put in charge of laborers from the Northern tribes on his building projects. What hope is given in this prophecy for the long-term outlook of David's dynasty and the kingdom?*

Ahijah's prophecy dramatizes what God plans to do to Israel due to Solomon's sin and the people's rebellion. He tears his new cloak (representing the kingdom) into twelve pieces, one for each tribe. Ten he gives to Jeroboam; in the same way, he will tear ten tribes away from Solomon's son and give them to Jeroboam. But for the sake of David, "one tribe" will be reserved for Solomon's son. There will always be a "lamp" before God in Jerusalem. In other words, the Davidic dynasty will continue in the city where God has chosen for his Name to dwell. God will humble the descendants of David, "but not forever."

D. Application

Facilitators: If time allows, have group members share their responses to the following application questions.

God gave Solomon "wisdom and understanding beyond measure, and largeness of mind like the sand on the seashore, so that Solomon's wisdom surpassed the wisdom of all the people of the east, and all the wisdom of Egypt" (1 Kings 4:29-30). How could the wisest man in the world fail so miserably? What turned his heart away from God? What does this say about our own vulnerability to error, and how can we avoid Solomon's error? Think about the example of David, who may not have been as wise as his son, but who was called "a man after God's own heart" (1 Samuel 13:14).

E. Wrap-Up

1. Remember the Royal Kingdom by its color, purple, the color of royalty during the time of the monarchy.

2. Answers will vary. One possible reply: During the Royal Kingdom, God gave Israel three kings—Saul, David, and Solomon—who united the nation, expanded its borders, and brought it to its zenith of peace and prosperity. This fulfilled the next stage in God's plan because it brought to pass his second promise to Abraham (the promise of royal dynasty).

Close with the Responsive Prayer found on the inside front cover of this Study Set Workbook. Pray through the Royal Kingdom period.

After the small-group discussion, watch Jeff Cavins' video presentation on *Session 12 – Royal Kingdom:* **Part 2.**

Facilitators: Read these recommended responses to the questions ahead of time to help you prepare to lead the small-group discussion.

Participants: Reinforce what you have learned by reviewing these recommended responses after the small-group discussion and before you go on to the next session.

A. Establish the Context

Facilitators: Take a moment to review what was learned in the previous session and to establish the context for the Divided Kingdom. If you like, use the following question to encourage discussion:

- *What have you learned about God's promises and faithfulness?*

B. Read the Story

Facilitators: If there is time, have someone read each passage aloud before it is discussed.

C. Take a Deeper Look

The Kingdom Divides

1. *Read **1 Kings 12:1–14:20,** which begins with Rehoboam ascending the throne after the death of his father, Solomon. What is the immediate cause of the division of the kingdom?*

   The people of Israel are fed up with the heavy burden imposed on them by Solomon and his building projects and ask for relief. Rehoboam heeds his friends instead of the elders and replies that he will increase their burden, not lessen it. The ten Northern tribes repudiate David's line. "What portion have we in David? We have no inheritance in the son of Jesse. To your tents, O Israel! Look now to your own house, David" (1 Kings 12:16). "Israel"—as the Northern tribes call themselves—rebels, leaving only the tribe of Judah (which has absorbed Simeon) and a portion of the tribe of Benjamin to be ruled over by the house of David.

2. *Jeroboam, king of the Northern Kingdom (Israel), is faced with a major dilemma in that Jerusalem, the center of worship, is in Judah to the south.*

   a. *What is he afraid will happen, and what does he do to solve this problem?*

   Jeroboam is afraid that if the people continue going south to worship at the Temple in Jerusalem, their allegiance will return to Rehoboam and the Davidic line of kings. To forestall this, he makes two golden calves. "You have gone up to Jerusalem long enough," he says. "Behold your gods, O Israel, who brought you up out of the land of Egypt" (1 Kings 12:28). These calves he sets up in Bethel (just north of Jerusalem) and Dan (far up in the North). He then appoints priests from tribes other than Levi and establishes new festivals for worship at those places. In short, he starts a new religion for the North, breaking the command to have no other gods before God and rejecting some of God's biggest gifts to Israel: his presence in the Jerusalem Temple, where the Ark of the Covenant is, and the Levitical priesthood. In effect, the North is back where Israel started before the covenant God made with Moses on Mount Sinai.

b. *What is the result of his disobedience?*

God declares that one day a king named Josiah will sacrifice the false priests on the altar, and also that the altar itself will split apart and the ashes be poured out—which happens immediately. Then God announces through Ahijah that because Jeroboam sinned and made other gods for the people to serve, God will bring disaster on his house. His son will die, and all Israel will be uprooted and scattered and given up due to Jeroboam's sins. (Many warnings and chances to repent have been given, all unheeded, before this actually comes to pass.)

The Kings of Israel

3. *Read **1 Kings 15:25–16:34 and Chapter 21,** which tell about the first eight kings of the Northern Kingdom. (If you have time, read about the others in **2 Kings 15:8-31 and 17:1-2.**)*

a. *The same refrain appears nearly verbatim in the account of each king. What is it? (See **1 Kings 15:34.**)*

The same sad refrain condemns nearly all of the Northern kings: "He did what was evil in the sight of the LORD, and walked in the way of Jeroboam and in his sin which he made Israel to sin." A long succession of kings follows Jeroboam, and not one of them tears down the altars or destroys the calves Jeroboam erected at Dan and Bethel.

b. *What kind of men are these rulers, and what is Israel like under their rule?*

These are not God-fearing men. They fail to turn away from the sins of their predecessors and in some cases increase them. Their sins extend even to drawing the people to the worship of Baal. Under the terms of the covenant, Israel's welfare depends on its obedience, and as they sin, so goes the kingdom. From the beginning, it is wracked with violence and political upheaval. By the end, they are so stubbornly unfaithful to God that exile seems inevitable.

c. *Look at the "Kings of Israel (Northern Kingdom)" chart on page 93. It names every king of the Northern Kingdom and tells when and for how long each reigned, whether he was a bad or good king (B/G), and his relationship to his predecessor. It also includes information on the way he died and where his reign is recorded in Scripture. From Jeroboam I to Hoshea, how many dynasties ruled Israel in the North? (A "dynasty" is a series of rulers from the same family. Do not figure Tibni in your count; he struggled with Omri for control but lost after several years of a split "reign.") What does the way many of these kings died seem to indicate?*

Nine dynasties rule in Israel from Jeroboam I to Hoshea, over what is roughly a two-hundred-year period (Jeroboam begins his reign in 930 BC, and Hoshea is exiled in 722 BC): So many of these kings are killed by their usurpers that it suggests a violent, tumultuous, and unstable time.

Prophets Sent to the Northern Kingdom

4. *One of the greatest prophets during this time was Elijah, whose main ministry was during the reign of Ahab—a man who "did more to provoke the LORD, the God of Israel, to anger than all the kings of Israel who were before him" (1 Kings 16:33). What is God's message to Israel through Elijah, especially as it is dramatized at Mount Carmel? (See **1 Kings 18:16-39;** if you have time, read the entire account of Elijah in **Chapters 17–19.**)*

Elijah presents the people with two options reminiscent of Joshua's earlier "choose this day whom you will serve" (Joshua 24:15) as they prepare to enter Canaan. The people are wavering, trying to serve Baal and God as well. Elijah's test at Mount Carmel displays the contrast between the priests of Baal—who work themselves into a frenzy and cut themselves to try to get Baal's attention—and his simple appeal to God to remember his people and defend his name. The outcome is dramatic: nothing for hours of pleading from Baal versus an immediate conflagration from the LORD. God is reminding his people who is God in Israel and that he is turning their hearts back to himself.

5. *Elijah's mantle—and a double portion of his spirit—falls (literally) on Elisha when the older prophet is taken up to heaven. Read **2 Kings 2, 4, and 5,** which record this and some of the miracles Elisha does in Israel. How do these miracles show God's grace and desire to bless those who follow him?*

   Elisha brings relief from famine and danger; he restores foul water and food that has been poisoned; and for a widow, he multiplies oil and twenty loaves so they feed one hundred. He heals Namaan from leprosy, prays for a barren woman to conceive a child, and then brings the child back to life when it dies. In all these things, he demonstrates God's loving care in a very tangible way.

   Elisha's name means, fittingly, "God saves." It is hard to read about him without thinking of Jesus himself, who would come one day to offer God's salvation to all, and who would heal the sick, restore people to life, and multiply loaves for a multitude.

6. *Read **CCC 2582–2584.** How do Elijah and the other prophets find strength for their often-dangerous missions?*

   Elijah and the other prophets find strength in prayer and in their personal encounters with God. Their faith is strong. They know who God is, and they know him (which is not always the same thing), and they are obedient to his Word.

7. *Under the reign of Jeroboam II (2 Kings 14:23-29), the king is able to restore Israel's northern borders, and Israel enjoys a time of relief from foreign pressure. The people become complacent, worship other gods, and fail to follow God's commands. God sends Amos and Hosea during this time to announce that he will not spare them forever but will send them into exile to Assyria, the new world power to the north. Read **Hosea 1–3.***

   a. *What does God tell Hosea to do at the start of Chapter 1, and why?*

   God has Hosea take a harlot for a wife in order to dramatize to the nation what they are doing to God. God is your husband, is his message, and you are playing the harlot by prostituting yourself with foreign gods. The message is sharp but at the same time tender. God still loves them and is calling them back to their covenant relationship with him.

   b. *List the names of Hosea and Gomer's children along with their meanings. What message does God send Israel through these names?*

   God has Hosea name his first son Jezreel, "God scatters," to proclaim the coming end of the kingdom of Israel in which they will be scattered in exile. He has Hosea name his daughter *Lo-Ruhamah,* "not loved." God will no longer show love to Israel, although he will continue to save Judah. The second son is named *Lo-Ammi,* "not my people." This is a final declaration that breaking the covenant has consequences. If they do not want to be God's people, then he will no longer claim them as his own. In pronouncing this, though, God gives hope of future restoration and a new unity with Judah under a single leader.

c. *How will God treat Israel for its unfaithfulness, as symbolized by the way he tells Hosea to treat Gomer in Chapter 2?*

God will isolate Israel and expose its shame. He will withhold his blessings so Israel will know the true source of those blessings and not attribute them to other gods. But the punishment is remedial. Having done that, God will woo Israel back to peace and safety. The final words of Chapter 2 are a beautiful expression of God's loving plan:

> "And I will betroth you to me for ever; I will betroth you to me in righteousness and in justice, in steadfast love, and in mercy. I will betroth you to me in faithfulness; and you shall know the Lord. And in that day, says the Lord, I will answer the heavens and they shall answer the earth; and the earth shall answer the grain, the wine, and the oil, and they shall answer Jezreel; and I will sow him for myself in the land. And I will have pity on Not pitied, and I will say to Not my people, 'You are my people'; and he shall say 'Thou art my God'" (Hosea 2:19-23).

8. **Optional:** *Around this same time, God calls on the prophet Jonah to bear a message to the Assyrian capital of Nineveh. Read the book of **Jonah** (it has just four chapters). What does this story tell you about God?*

Answers will vary. One of the central messages of Jonah concerns God's love for all humankind, from every nation. The fact that God chose a particular people to be his own treasured possession does not mean that he has abandoned the rest. His fatherly compassion reaches out to all, and Nineveh in this story is in need of his mercy. If Israel has become complacent, thinking themselves the only recipients of God's care, they better think again. They are meant to be not just a royal nation, but a kingdom of priests as well, showing other nations the way to God.

D. Application

Facilitators: If time allows, have group members share their responses to the following application question.

Are there ways you are unfaithful to God? Meditate on God's love for you as expressed in Hosea 11 and 14. Make your confession, and be reconciled to your Father.

Close with the Responsive Prayer found on the inside front cover of this Study Set Workbook. Pray through the Divided Kingdom period.

After the small-group discussion, watch Jeff Cavins' video presentation on *Session 13* – Divided Kingdom: Part 1.

Session 14 – Responses

Divided Kingdom – Part 2

THE BIBLE
TIMELINE
The Story of Salvation

Facilitators: Read these recommended responses to the questions ahead of time to help you prepare to lead the small-group discussion.

Participants: Reinforce what you have learned by reviewing these recommended responses after the small-group group discussion and before you go on to the next session.

A. Review the Context

Facilitators: Take a moment to review the context and what was learned in the previous session. If you like, use the following question to encourage discussion:

- *What in Hosea's life or message spoke particularly to you?*

B. Read the Story

Facilitators: If there is time, have someone read each passage aloud before it is discussed.

C. Take a Deeper Look

Kings of the Southern Kingdom

1. Read *1 Kings 14:21–15:8.*

    a. *What is Judah like under Rehoboam's rule? Read also **2 Chronicles 11:5–12:1.***

    Rehoboam rules from Jerusalem, which the author of 1 Kings is careful to point out is "the city which the LORD had chosen out of all the tribes of Israel, to put his name there" (14:21). He fortifies Judah and Benjamin and makes them strong. Priests and Levites from all over the North, rejected by Jeroboam, move to Jerusalem. Godly people from throughout Israel follow them there to offer sacrifices to the LORD. During this early period, they strengthen Judah and walk in the ways of David. But once the kingdom is well-established, Judah's king, Rehoboam, and the people forsake God's laws and turn to other gods, setting up sacred stones and Asherah poles on the high places and engaging in cult prostitution as had the Canaanites before them.

    b. *What fact is recorded twice in **1 Kings 14:21 and 14:31** that might explain why Judah turns from God? (Make sure to use an RSV-CE or NAB Bible; the wording in other Bible versions may differ.)*

    Rehoboam's mother was an Ammonite (verses 21 and 31) who most likely followed the "detestable" Ammonite god Molech and may have turned Rehoboam's heart away.

2. *In spite of the evil done by kings of Judah, God again promises to maintain a "lamp" for David in Jerusalem forever (the first time he promised this was in **1 Kings 11:34-36**). What does that mean, and why does God do it?*

    Back when Solomon sinned, and Ahijah told Jeroboam that God was going to tear the kingdom from Solomon's son and give it to him, he said that he would leave Rehoboam with one tribe so that David would always have a lamp before God in Jerusalem. This symbolized the permanence of the

Davidic dynasty in the city where God had chosen his name to dwell. To snuff out one's lamp means to take away life, and God promised an everlasting throne to David.

Now, when Rehoboam's son Abijah is not fully devoted to God, he maintains that lamp by raising up a son to succeed him and by making Jerusalem strong against its enemies. Years later when Jehoram follows Israel into evil practices, God is not willing to destroy Judah for David's sake and for the sake of his promise "to give a lamp to him and to his sons for ever" (2 Kings 8:19).

3. Read **2 Kings 8:16-29 and Chapters 11 and 12.** *After sixty-six years of good kings (whose reigns are not included in this session's reading) and peace, an evil king, Jehoram, takes the throne (see **2 Kings 8**).*

   a. *How do you account for the dramatic change?*

   Jehoram marries Athaliah, the daughter of King Ahab of Israel. Through her influence, Jehoram introduces Baal worship to the Southern Kingdom (even as Ahab had done in the North, after marrying Jezebel).

   b. *How tenuous does the situation become in just fifteen years? (See **2 Kings 11–12**.)*

   The relationship to Ahab's family proves deadly. When Athaliah's son is killed, she sets out to kill off all other heirs to the throne and to rule Judah herself. Were it not for the courage of Jehoram's daughter Jehosheba, the line of David would have been completely extinguished. As it was, Athaliah reduced the line to a single boy. Jehosheba took her one-year-old nephew Joash, one of the royal princes, and hid him with a nurse at the Temple.

   Note: The child is called both "Joash" and "Jehoash" in Chapters 11 and 12. Do not confuse him with King Jehoash who reigned over Israel (see 13:10).

   c. *Is Athaliah ultimately successful in her attempt to destroy the royal line? Explain.*

   Athaliah is not successful. Jehoiada the priest leads a conspiracy against Athaliah, crowns Joash, and has Athaliah put to death. Jehoiada destroys the Temple, idols, and altars of Baal and restores the Jerusalem Temple. He also renews the people's covenant with God.

4. **Read 2 Kings 18:1–21:18.** *King Hezekiah (Chapters 18–20) trusts God and does what is right in his eyes. God gives him success during his twenty-nine-year reign. Among other things, Hezekiah removes the high places dedicated to Baal and cuts down the Asherah poles. Sennacherib, king of Assyria, deports people from the Northern Kingdom during Hezekiah's reign and then comes down and marches against Jerusalem.*

   a. *Think back for a moment. What options does God set before the people before they enter the Promised Land? (Read **Deuteronomy 30:15-20**.)*

   God sets before them life and good, death and evil: life and good and blessing in the land God promised to Abraham if they love God and cleave to him and obey his commandments, and death and evil and a curse if they do not.

   b. *Now read **2 Kings 18:28-35**. What options does Sennacherib present to them? How does Sennacherib's "offer" compare or contrast with God's?*

   Sennacherib offers another land, another life, another source of blessing. If they trust and follow him (he from whom no god has been able to deliver), they will prosper. If they stick by the LORD in opposition to him, he will destroy them. Same offer, different source. Whom will they trust?

   c. *Do you hear in Sennacherib's words any echo of the voice of the Serpent to Adam and Eve?*

"Do not listen to your king," Sennacherib says, sounding very much like the Serpent's *"Did* God say?" He frightens them and sheds doubt on God's faithfulness. He offers things God already provides, just as the Serpent offered Adam and Eve a chance to be like God (which they already were), to know good from evil (which they already did). He holds out the "apple" of a good life away from God's provision. He neglects to mention that it is in exile. Such a thing as good apart from God does not exist.

d. *How does Hezekiah respond, and what is the result?*

Hezekiah does not heed the taunts of Sennacherib, but tears his clothes over the insult to God. Bolstered by a report from the prophet Isaiah, Hezekiah spreads out Sennacharib's letter before God and asks him to vindicate his name. That night, an angel of the LORD puts to death 185,000 Assyrian soldiers, and Sennacherib withdraws his army.

5. *Hezekiah's son Manasseh follows him as king. What are the sins of Manasseh, and how does God say he will judge them? (See* **2 Kings 21:1-18.**)

Manasseh undoes all the good of Hezekiah. Not only does he restore the altars of Baal, he worships the stars and builds pagan altars in the Temple. He sacrifices his son to Moloch, practices sorcery, and consults mediums. In 2 Kings 21, we learn that he does more evil than the Ammorites before him, even killing many innocent people, and he leads Judah into sin.

Judah by this time has a long history of swinging in and out of devotion to God. The sins of Manasseh anger God to the point of declaring an end to the kingdom. He will bring disaster upon them, wipe his hands of them, and toss them to their enemies. He will "cast off the remnant of [his] heritage" (verse 14)—not forever, but he will give them over to the covenant curses they have brought upon themselves with their sin. In 2 Chronicles, we read that Manasseh is humbled near the end of his reign and tears down the altars and tries to make amends. But it is too little, too late for Judah.

6. **Think About It:** *The Davidic kingdom may have been flawed, but it had been established by God and had become, in some ways, a model for the heavenly kingdom, the Church. Several places in 1 and 2 Kings mention the office of a steward or vicar in charge of the king's palace and properties. Much like a prime minister is today, he was second only to the king in power and authority and acted with the king's authority in his absence.*

a. *Read about the steward in* **Isaiah 22:15-24,** *and record what you learn?*

The steward is a permanent position of authority in the palace. If one is cast out for any reason, the job does not end; another is put in his place. Isaiah says the steward will be a "father" to the house of Judah. He is the person who carries the keys of the house, a symbol of dynastic authority. What the steward says, goes.

b. *Now read* **CCC 552–553.** *What continuity do you see between this Old Testament office and the office of the papacy?*

The significance of the steward to the office of the papacy lies in Jesus' words to Peter when he gives him the keys to the kingdom. Jesus sets Peter in the office of "prime minister" and gives him dynastic authority to rule the Church in his absence. And in giving him the keys, he is giving him something that will be passed on. This stewardship does not end with Peter the apostle.

The *Catechism* says that the power of the keys, or "the power to 'bind and loose,' connotes the authority to absolve sins, to pronounce doctrinal judgments, and to make disciplinary decisions in the Church. Jesus entrusts this authority to the Church through the ministry of the apostles (cf. Matthew 18:18) and in particular, through the ministry of Peter, the only one to whom he specifically entrusts the keys of the kingdom" (CCC 553).

Prophets Sent to the Southern Kingdom

7. *Isaiah is perhaps the greatest Old Testament prophet. He is quoted more often in the New Testament than any book except Psalms. His book is given pride of place in Scripture, appearing first in the section devoted to the prophets. Isaiah lived in Jerusalem and wrote primarily to the Southern Kingdom. Read* **Isaiah 5–6.**

    a. *What does Isaiah say is going on in Judah that gives God concern?*

    The worship of other gods bears bad fruit in Judah. Isaiah 5 reads like a litany of what happens when people flout God's commands. The rich get richer to the neglect of the poor. Self-indulgence and drunken revels fill their days and push out thoughts of God, whom they cease to value. They continue in sin while calling on God to prove himself. People confuse good and evil, light and darkness. They acquit the guilty and deny justice to the innocent.

    b. *How will God deal with the sins of the Southern Kingdom? (Read also* **2 Kings 20:16-18,** *in which Isaiah tells King Hezekiah this directly.)*

    Woe will come to all of them until the land is utterly forsaken. Isaiah speaks of ruin and desolation, of exile and death. To Hezekiah, he says the people will be carried into captivity in Babylon. Yet, there is hope. God does not forget those he loves. A remnant of the people, a "stump," will remain, out of which the nation will grow again. (**Facilitators:** The word "stump," which is used in the RSV-CE, does not appear in all translations.)

8. *Micah is another prophet sent by God around the time of Isaiah. He prophesies during the reigns of Jotham, Ahaz, and Hezekiah (find them on your* Bible Timeline *Chart) and speaks to the conditions prior to Hezekiah's reforms. Up until now, we have been reading a lot about what God's people are not supposed to do. Read* **Micah 6:1-8.** *What does God want from them more than burnt offerings?*

    God requires of his covenant people that they walk humbly with him, acting justly and loving mercy.

D. Application

Facilitators: If time allows, have group members share their responses to the following application questions.

Are there voices in this world that hold out the enticements of life, love, or goodness apart from God? What are they? Do you hear any echoes of Sennacherib's offer to Hezekiah or the Serpent's questions to Eve? Hear the words for what they are. What can you learn from Hezekiah's example to help you fight their allure?

E. Wrap-Up

1. Remember the Divided Kingdom by its color, black, which represents this dark time in Israel's history.

2. Answers will vary. One possible reply: In the Divided Kingdom, Israel split into two. The North established a counterfeit religion, and the kingdom ended after two centuries of instability and corruption. The South lasted nearly 350 years, most of these under good kings, primarily because God upheld the Davidic throne. But both kingdoms ended in apostasy and destruction.

Close with the Responsive Prayer found on the inside front cover of this Study Set Workbook. Pray through the Divided Kingdom period.

After the small-group discussion, watch Jeff Cavins' video presentation on *Session 14 – Divided Kingdom: Part 2.*

Facilitators: Read these recommended responses to the questions ahead of time to help you prepare to lead the small-group discussion.

Participants: Reinforce what you have learned by reviewing these recommended responses after the small-group discussion and before you go on to the next session.

A. Establish the Context

Facilitators: Take a moment to review what was learned in the previous session and to establish the context for the Exile. If you like, use the following question to encourage discussion:

- *How could a people so blessed by God fall away so quickly? Did you hear any warnings that might apply to you today?*

B. Read the Story

Facilitators: If there is time, have someone read each passage aloud before it is discussed.

C. Take a Deeper Look

Israel (the North) Goes into Exile Under Assyria: 722 BC (2 Kings 17)

1. *Read **2 Kings 17**. What reasons are given for Israel's exile to Assyria?*

    The immediate reason for Israel's exile is that King Hoshea has stopped paying tribute to Assyria. Hoshea is imprisoned, Samaria captured, and the Israelites deported. But as the author of 2 Kings points out, this is not just a random occurrence. It represents divine judgment on Israel for breaking the covenant. They have left God for other gods, broken his commands, and ignored his prophets. Seeking to be like other nations, "they went after false idols, and became false" themselves (verse 15). They have gone so far as to worship the stars and Baal and to sacrifice their children in the fire; they practice divination and sorcery and have sold themselves to do evil.

    Worshiping the stars and other gods and practices like divination and sorcery reveal a profound lack of appreciation of who God is and his relationship with creation and humanity. It shows disregard for the lessons the nation of Israel has been taught since its infancy. One who recognizes God as the Creator of the universe cannot possibly worship the created stars. One who realizes that God exposed the emptiness and impotence of the Egyptian gods at the Exodus cannot possibly bow down to any but the LORD. And one who seeks knowledge and guidance from divination and sorcery has clearly decided to go his or her own way. In all of these sins, God's people are not just saying, "Come on, God, there's room for all kinds of belief here." They are explicitly rejecting him and his covenant.

2. *The king of Assyria (probably Sargon II) sends people from five other captured nations to repopulate Samaria after he exiles the Jews. Even though he sends a Jewish priest back to teach the people how to worship God, what is the result of repopulating the land in this way?*

When Sargon resettles Samaria with people from five other nations, they bring all their various religions with them. When God sends lions among them and people are killed, Sargon sends one of the Northern priests back to teach the people how to worship God. Still, they make their own gods and worship God in the way that the North had done: as one god among many, in their own separate ways, with their own people as priests.

Judah's Failure to Proclaim Liberty

3. *The prophet Jeremiah is sent by God toward the end of the Southern Kingdom to announce the imminent approach of judgment. Read* **Jeremiah 34,** *which is a final warning to Judah under King Zedekiah. What reason does Jeremiah give for the impending judgment?*

   Jeremiah berates Israel because, after freeing their slaves according to their covenant promise, they change their minds and take them back into captivity. Because they will not proclaim liberty for their countrymen, God will proclaim a different kind of "liberty" for them: liberty "to the sword, to pestilence, and to famine." Not only that, "the men who transgressed my covenant and did not keep the terms of the covenant which they made before me, I will make like the calf which they cut in two and passed between its parts"—God will give them up to their enemies. They have failed to learn the lessons of the Exodus, so they will learn them again through exile.

4. a. **New Testament Connection:** *Jesus tells a parable about a man who is unwilling to forgive the debt of another man. Read* **Matthew 18:21-35.** *What is Jesus teaching Peter with this parable, and how does it relate to the concept of Jubilee and the reason for exile?*

   This parable illustrates the mercy that God, who has freed us from the shackles of sin and has forgiven us all, expects to characterize his kingdom on earth. Jesus is taking the idea of Jubilee and breathing new life into it. This is what the Jubilee and the release of slaves every seven years is all about: extending God's mercy to others.

   In the parable, the king forgives the servant his great debt, but the servant is unwilling to waive even a minor debt someone else owes him. When the king hears of it, he turns him over to the torturers until he has paid back his own debt. This is analogous to what we have just learned about the reason for Judah's exile.

   b. *Read* **CCC 2838–2845.** *What does this add to your understanding of the importance of forgiveness in light of this lesson of the Jubilee and the Exile?*

   Answers will vary. Encourage discussion of anything that has been learned. You might bring out the message of CCC 2840: God's "mercy cannot penetrate our hearts as long as we have not forgiven those who have trespassed against us. Love, like the Body of Christ, is indivisible; we cannot love the God we cannot see if we do not love the brother or sister we do see (cf. John 4:20)." This is what Judah experiences. Their unwillingness to release their brethren from debt and slavery renders them unable to receive God's mercy. Not until they go through exile and confess, will they be open again to receiving God's grace.

   Optional: You might ask if anyone is holding someone in bondage because of a lack of forgiveness. According to this session, what will be the result if they continue? It is not necessary to discuss individual situations, but it should be clear to all that when we fail to forgive others, God will not forgive us (Matthew 6:15).

Judah (the South) Is Exiled to Babylon – 587 BC (2 Kings 24–25)

5. *The first deportation: Read **Daniel 1–7**. Daniel is one of the bright young men taken to Babylon after Nebuchadnezzar's initial foray into Judah. The book of Daniel, which is part historical narrative and part apocalyptic literature, is an important supplemental book of this time period.*

   a. *In Chapter 2, Daniel's vision of the five kingdoms gives us a road map for the rest of the story. Re-read Nebuchadnezzar's dream and the interpretation God gives to Daniel. What is the dream, and how does Daniel describe the kingdom that will one day be set up by God?*

   Nebuchadnezzar dreams of a huge statue with a head of gold, chest and arms of silver, belly and thighs of bronze, legs of iron, and feet of iron and clay. These represent four successive empires of decreasing power, traditionally identified as Babylon, Persia, Greece, and Rome. A rock smashes the feet; the statue crumbles while the rock becomes a huge mountain that fills the earth.

   The rock represents a fifth and final kingdom, the kingdom of God. It is a kingdom that will never be crushed or destroyed, a kingdom that will bring all other kingdoms to an end but will itself endure forever.

   b. ***Daniel 7:1-14** relates a dream Daniel has during the reign of Nebuchadnezzar's son and successor, Belshazzar. Describe the "Son of Man" and his kingdom that the dream foretells (verses 13-14).*

   The "Son of Man" comes with the clouds and enters the presence of God, who gives him glory and an everlasting dominion over a kingdom that will never pass away. This is a reference to the Messiah, who will one day rule the whole earth forever.

   c. *Now read **Mark 14:60-65**. Why do you think Jesus' words prompt such a drastic reaction from the high priest?*

   By borrowing language from Daniel's prophecy, Jesus identifies himself with the "Son of Man" who is led into God's presence and given authority and everlasting dominion, with authority second only to God. That Jesus would claim this for himself is seen as shocking blasphemy.

6. *The second deportation: Ezekiel is exiled to Babylon in the second deportation. As both a priest and a prophet, Ezekiel is called by God to minister to the exiles who are cut off from both the Land and the Temple. Read **Ezekiel 34**.*

   a. *On whom does Ezekiel lay the weight of blame in this chapter?*

   Ezekiel lays the weight of blame on Israel's "shepherds" or leaders. Whether kings or officials or prophets or priests, God is angry with all who have failed the people. Ezekiel rebukes them for caring for their own interests at the expense of those in their care. Rather than healing and caring for them properly, the shepherds are harsh and allow the people to become prey to their enemies.

   b. *What promise of consolation does Ezekiel offer?*

   God's promise of consolation through Ezekiel is beautiful. He himself will search out the lost sheep. He will rescue and take care of them, bringing them back to pasture in their own country. He will heal and strengthen those who need it—but those who have grown sleek and strong on the backs of the others, he will destroy. Then God will put one shepherd over them, a king from the line of his "servant David," and the LORD will be their God. They will lie down in peace and dwell in safety, showered with blessings from God.

7. *The third deportation: Read the account of Zedekiah's defeat in **2 Kings 25:5-7**.*

   a. *How does the way in which he is carried off reflect the state of the people's hearts and spirits?*

After seeing his sons—heirs to the throne of David—killed before his eyes, Zedekiah is bound and taken off blind and in shackles into exile in Babylon. His state perfectly mirrors that of the people: blinded to truth by years of idol worship, shackled by sin, all hope snuffed out before them.

b. *Find Babylon on the "Abraham's Journey" map on page 26. Think back through the history you have learned so far. What else has happened here? Is there anything notable or ironic about where God's people are taken into captivity?*

The people of Judah are making the long trek back to Babylon, fourteen hundred years after God called Abram to leave a city in that region and make the journey to a land God promised to give him. Abram could see but did not know where God was leading him. He was strong in faith and moving forward in God's promise. Zedekiah and Judah know where they are going, although they are blind: right back where they started.

8. *Read **Jeremiah 31 and 33**. What good news does he announce in these chapters? (Recall that "Ephraim" is sometimes used to refer to the Northern Kingdom.)*

Jeremiah announces that a remnant will return to Israel and find rest. In his great love, God will restore and rebuild, cleanse and heal. Their weeping will be turned to shouts of joy. Best of all, God will make a new covenant with his people, "not like the covenant which I made with their fathers when I took them by the hand to bring them out of the land of Egypt, my covenant which they broke, though I was their husband, says the LORD. But this is the covenant which I will make with the house of Israel after those days, says the LORD: I will put my law within them, and I will write it upon their hearts; and I will be their God, and they shall be my people" (Jeremiah 31:32-33). They will all be forgiven, and all will know God.

Jeremiah also says in Chapter 33 that a "righteous branch" will sprout from the line of David. It may look now as though the royal line has ended, and God's promise of an everlasting throne may seem to have come to nothing, but it will be restored. For "David shall never lack a man to sit on the throne of the house of Israel" (verse 17). The promise is as certain as God's covenant with the fixed laws of nature. God will have compassion.

D. Application

Facilitators: If time allows, have group members share their responses to the following application questions.

Have you ever heard anyone condemn the Catholic Church because it holds itself up to be true? "Tolerance" in America has degenerated into condemnation of any religion that does not give others equal weight. How do you handle charges of "intolerance"? Is there anything in the pressures Israel and Judah faced during the Divided Kingdom or in the messages of the prophets that can help you stand strong?

E. Wrap-Up

1. Remember the Exile by the color baby blue: Judah "singing the blues" in "Baby-lon."

2. Answers will vary. One possible reply: Israel was exiled for breaking the covenant with God—first the Northern Kingdom in 722 BC and then the Southern Kingdom in 587 BC. They were punished for their sin, but God promised to bring them back to himself and their land.

Close with the Responsive Prayer found on the inside front cover of this Study Set Workbook. Pray through the Exile period.

After the small-group discussion, watch Jeff Cavins' video presentation on *Session 15 – Exile*.

Facilitators: Read these recommended responses to the questions ahead of time to help you prepare to lead the small-group discussion.

Participants: Reinforce what you have learned by reviewing these recommended responses after the small-group discussion and before you go on to the next session.

A. Establish the Context

Facilitators: Take a moment to review what was learned in the previous session and to establish the context for the Return. If you like, use the following question to encourage discussion:

- *What have you learned about the spiritual conditions that "exile" can represent?*

B. Read the Story

Facilitators: If there is time, have someone read each passage aloud before it is discussed.

C. Take a Deeper Look

The Return Foretold

1. *The events recorded in Ezra were prophesied by Isaiah two centuries previously during the time of the Divided Kingdom. Read **Isaiah 44:24-28 and 45:1-6, 13.** Who does Isaiah mention by name, and what does he say will be this man's role in the restoration?*

    Isaiah prophesied that God, desiring Judah to be restored, would raise up a king named Cyrus to subdue other nations and would summon him to rebuild Jerusalem and the Temple and set the exiles free. It is curious that God calls and anoints and moves this Gentile to do his work and calls him "my shepherd," although Cyrus "does not acknowledge" God.

The First Return (Ezra 1–6)

2. a. *Read **Ezra 1.** How is Isaiah's prophecy fulfilled?*

    God moves King Cyrus of Persia in the first year of his reign to release the exiles to return to build a new Temple in Jerusalem (Solomon's Temple was destroyed in 587 BC, when Judah fell to Babylon, and the Jerusalem walls were left in ruins).

    b. *Why might God have given his people such exact information so far in advance?*

    A prophecy this precise makes one stand up and notice. The Bible does not tell us God's reasons for announcing the rise of Cyrus and his role in freeing Israel, but we can surmise that for the generations sent into exile, it provides hope. The punishment will not last forever; there will be an end that includes returning to the land and seeing the restoration of what had been destroyed. For the generation that returns, it will be an affirmation of God's care as well as a reminder that they are not getting to go back simply because a new king has decided to look kindly on them. They are returning because God is faithful to his promises. This is a sign of God's care and providence, of his control over history. God is in charge, and he can and does use even Gentiles to effect his purposes. God is working on Israel's behalf.

    c.   *Ezra 1:1 mentions a prophecy by Jeremiah. Read **Jeremiah 29:10-14.** What is the prophecy?*

Jeremiah does not give the details that Isaiah does, but he prophesies that after seventy years of exile, God will bring Judah back from captivity. From the outset of their exile, he gives them the knowledge that God's plans are to prosper them and fulfill his promises, returning them to the land when they have returned to him in their hearts. Ezra is announcing that that time has finally come.

3.   **Think About It:** *Judah was exiled for failing to learn the lessons of the Exodus. Do you see any parallels between this return and the way the children of Israel left Egypt originally?*

Answers will vary. In both cases, the people are delivered from a state of bondage so they can go to the land God promised them and worship him. One of the first things God had them do after leaving Egypt was build the Tabernacle; this time they are going to build the Temple. And in both cases, they leave enriched with silver and gold and goods and livestock from the people in the country they leave behind. Both accounts begin with lists of the people involved. And before doing anything else, both groups build altars on which to sacrifice burnt offerings.

This is another Exodus, with similar lessons for the people. They are being given another start.

4.   a.   *Read **Ezra 3.** What is accomplished in the first return?*

After rebuilding the altar and sacrificing to God, those who return rebuild the Temple in Jerusalem and dedicate it with great joy. They are led by a man named Zerubbabel, who not incidentally is from the line of David (1 Chronicles 3:19).

    b.   *Read **Ezra 4–6.** What kind of opposition do they face, and how are they helped?*

When the people from Samaria ("the adversaries of Judah and Benjamin" mentioned in Ezra 4:1) are not permitted to help in building the Temple, they actively oppose the work. They hire people to frustrate the plans, and when Artaxerxes becomes king of Persia, they try to enlist his help. These people are rebuilding this "rebellious and wicked city," they write (see Ezra 4), "and if they finish they will stop paying tribute to you. Just look in the records and see why Jerusalem was destroyed in the first place," they say.

Judah's enemies are able to stop them for a time, but in the long term, the plan backfires. After questioning them about their work, a Persian official replies back to the king: Cyrus has not only sent them back to rebuild; he has returned the Temple treasure. King Darius, finding this to be true, instructs his governor not to interfere and also to pay their expenses and all that is needed for their sacrifices.

The Second Return (Ezra 7–10)

5.   *Read **Ezra 7.** A descendant of a high priestly line that goes back to the days of David and Solomon, Ezra returns with the next wave of exiles. He is also a scribe (or teacher of the Law of Moses) who has devoted himself to studying, observing, and teaching the Word of God.*

a.   *Why is Ezra sent back to Jerusalem, and what assistance is he given?*

King Artaxerxes sends Ezra along with other priests and Levites specifically to teach and enforce the Law of God and to offer the appropriate sacrifices to God. They also are to appoint ministers of justice in the land. They are to take with them silver and gold from the royal treasury, as well as offerings from Babylon and from any exiles who want to send offerings back to the Temple.

b.   *Read **Ezra 9:1–10:17**. What does Ezra find when he arrives, and what kind of reform does he find it necessary to make?*

Ezra arrives to find that, in spite of God's grace and mercy in allowing the people to return to the land and rebuild the Temple, they are continuing to do what had gotten them into trouble in the first place. Some of them, including some of the priests and officials, have disobeyed God's explicit command and have taken wives from among the neighboring peoples. Appalled, Ezra calls on God. He then calls on the people to confess to God and to separate from the people around them and from their foreign wives.

A physical return to the land is not enough. The people have to return to God with their hearts, cut their attachments to other gods, and follow him alone.

The Third Return (Nehemiah)

6.   *The book of Nehemiah tells about the third wave of return from captivity.*

a.   *Read **Nehemiah 2 and 4**. Why does Nehemiah return, and how does he fare?*

Nehemiah, hearing that those who have returned are in great trouble because the walls of Jerusalem have not been repaired, and they have been left vulnerable to their enemies, receives permission from Artaxerxes to return and rebuild the walls. He does so, despite continued opposition from the Samaritans.

b.   *Read **5:1-13**. What additional crisis does Nehemiah confront at this time?*

Nehemiah discovers that the people are falling back into the sins that got them sent into exile to begin with. There has been a famine, and some of the Jewish officials are charging heavy interest to their fellow Jews for food and supplies. The burden has become so great on them that many have been forced to sell themselves or their children into slavery to pay off their debt. Nehemiah is outraged that they would leave bondage in Babylon only to become slaves in their own country. He reproaches the officials—who agree to return land and interest.

c.   *After the walls are built and the people are settled in their towns, Ezra brings out the Book of the Law and reads it to the assembled people. There is great joy as they celebrate the weeklong Feast of Tabernacles. Following this, they confess their sins and worship God, remembering all he has done for them through the ages. Read **Nehemiah 9:32–10:29**. What else do they do?*

In their desire to turn back to God, and in their distress as they labored to satisfy foreign kings who have jurisdiction over them, the people enter into a covenant with God, "into a curse and an oath to walk in God's law which was given by Moses the servant of God, and to observe and do all the commandments of the LORD our LORD and his ordinances and his statutes" (Nehemiah 10:29).

Life in Babylon After the Exile

7. *The book of Esther fits between the first and second returns (between Zerubbabel and Ezra). Many of the Jews do not return to Israel. Esther gives us a window into the lives of those who choose to remain in Persia. Read the book of **Esther**. Interestingly, God is not mentioned in the original Hebrew text (although he is in the "Preliminaries," also called "Chapters A–F" or numbered as Chapters 10:4–16:24. These Greek additions were retained in the canonical Catholic Bible but were removed from Protestant Bibles.) Does God forsake the people left behind in exile, or is he faithful yet?*

> God may not be mentioned in the earlier version, but he certainly is mentioned in the later, Greek portions, which say explicitly what is assumed throughout the rest of the book. God is clearly watching over his people and is faithful to them even in exile. A line from Esther's uncle Mordecai reveals a deep faith: "For if you keep silence at such a time as this, relief and deliverance will rise for the Jews from another quarter, but you and your father's house will perish. And who knows whether you have not come to the kingdom for such a time as this?" (Esther 4:14). The very existence of the Jews is threatened by the king's edict, yet Esther is received with favor and is able to save them. This is a story not unlike those of Joseph and Moses, in which God raises one of his people to a position of prominence in another court so they will be able to save his people.
>
> The Jewish feast of Purim is in celebration of this victory.

D. Application

Facilitators: If time allows, have group members share their responses to the following application questions.

Have you ever had an experience where you strayed from the Lord, repented, and returned to him? This may be in a relationship or attitude. What rebuilding did you need to do?

E. Wrap-Up

1. Remember the Return by its color, yellow, which stands for Judah returning home to brighter days.

2. Answers will vary. One possible reply: During the Return, the exiles come home in three waves to rebuild the Temple and the Jerusalem walls, and they renew their covenant with God.

Close with the Responsive Prayer found on the inside front cover of this Study Set Workbook. Pray through the Return period.

After the small-group discussion, watch Jeff Cavins' video presentation on *Session 16 – Return*.

Facilitators: *Read these recommended responses to the questions ahead of time to help you prepare to lead the small-group discussion.*

Participants: *Reinforce what you have learned by reviewing these recommended responses after the small-group discussion and before you go on to the next session.*

A. Establish the Context

Facilitators: Take a moment to review what was learned in the previous session and to establish the context for the Maccabean Revolt. If you like, use the following question to encourage discussion:

- *God worked through an unlikely Savior to restore his children to the Promised Land. How has he worked through unlikely people in your life?*

B. Read the Story

Facilitators: If there is time, have someone read each passage aloud before it is discussed.

C. Take a Deeper Look

1. ***1 Maccabees 1*** *tells the story of Antiochus Epiphanes and his brutal suppression of the Jews and desecration of the Temple. This is not the first time Israel has faced serious opposition. How would you summarize the threat to Israel, and how the people respond to that threat?*

   The events of the last few time periods have graphically illustrated the spiritual and physical dangers to God's people of mixing with the neighboring populations. This is not because God does not love those other people, but because their polytheistic religion and customs are ultimately destructive to Israel's relationship with God. Almost from the time his people enter the land of Canaan, intermarriage is a serious problem and causes many to turn their hearts to other gods. God's laws are designed to help them live as God created them to live, free and in his image; by breaking those laws, they drift more and more into bondage.

   In the days leading up to the Maccabean revolt, a new threat arises. Certain Jews who do not follow God's laws begin enticing others to make alliances with the Gentiles as a way to better their political situation. This time it is not intermarriage that is the problem so much as enculturation: to fit in, some join in the cultural and intellectual activities of Gentiles (these center around the gymnasia—see 1 Maccabees 1:14) and become more and more secular. They even go so far as to cover or reverse the mark of circumcision—which is the permanent sign of their covenant relationship with God—and abandon the covenant.

   Soon, direct attacks are made. Antiochus Epiphanes strips the Temple and then destroys part of the city and builds a fortified tower to house his army. By the time he orders everyone to conform to Greek customs and religion, many of the Israelites go along with the new form of rule. Israel is divided into those who abandon the Law and join in the general sacrilege and those who love God's Law and are driven into hiding to escape death.

2.   *Read **1 Maccabees 2.***

    a.   *When Mattathias sees what has been done to Jerusalem, he moves with his sons to Modein. What threat do they face there?*

The king's officers organize pagan sacrifices in the town and try to get Mattathias to set an example for the other citizens by worshiping false gods. They flatter Mattathias, tell him "everyone else is doing it" down in Jerusalem, and try to bribe him with a high-ranking title and gifts.

    b.   *What are Mattathias and his sons able to do against this threat?*

Mattathias steadfastly refuses to forsake the covenant or God's commands. Rather than setting an example for the others to sin, he and his sons stand as remarkable models of faith and courage by resisting the command of the king and fighting back. On the altar, Mattathias kills a Jew who steps forward to offer pagan sacrifice and then kills the messenger of the king and tears down the altar. He flees to the mountains with his sons, calling other faithful Jews to join him. They are not afraid to die for God, nor are they afraid to fight against the Gentiles and even against their own countrymen to stand firm for God.

    c.   *How does Mattathias strengthen his sons before he dies?*

In verses 51-64, Mattathias reminds his sons of all the faithful "greats" who went before them: Abraham and Joseph, Joshua, David, Elijah, Daniel, and others—all men who hoped in God and stood faithful despite the odds. He knew his Scripture! "And so observe," he said, "… that none who put their trust in him will lack strength. … Be courageous and grow strong in the law, for by it you will gain honor" (verses 61 and 64). Mattathias appoints his son Simeon (also called Simon) to be as their father and Judas Maccabeus to command their army in his place. (It is from him and his brothers that 1 and 2 Maccabees get their name.)

3.   *How do you explain the victories of Judas Maccabeus and his family over far greater armies? What is their attitude and motivation? (See **1 Maccabees 3 and 4.**)*

The short answer is that God fights on their behalf. But consider also the following, which could serve as a model for a step-by-step plan for moving forward in adversity:

- They have the right attitude: "They gladly fought for Israel" (1 Maccabees 3:2). Remember that Ezra, encouraging the weeping Israelites after reading to them the Law, tells them not to be grieved, for "the joy of the Lord is your strength." Something of that spirit is maintained here. It is founded in the knowledge of God's sovereign love.

- That knowledge holds Judas and his brothers in good stead. They know God, they know what he has done for their fathers (1 Maccabees 4:8), and they trust him to be faithful to his covenant with them.

- They do not rely on their own strength. So confident are they that God himself will fight for them that they do not hesitate to go against the much larger armies that attack them. As Judas explains to those who are afraid, "It is easy for many to be overcome by a few; in the sight of heaven there is no difference between deliverance by many or by few; for victory in war does not depend upon the size of the army, but on strength that comes from heaven … He himself will crush them before us; so do not be afraid of them" (1 Maccabees 3:18, 19, 22).

- They ask for help. They fast. They consult the Scriptures. They cry aloud to heaven and step out in faith (end of Chapter 3), relying on God to fight for them. Early in Chapter 4, they cry out to

God in hopes that he will remember his covenant and deliver them. Judas' prayer in verses 30-33 is a beautiful example of faith-filled prayer.

- They have the right motive: not simply that they will beat the bad guys, but that "all the Gentiles will know that there is One who redeems and saves Israel" (1 Maccabees 4:11).

4. *After crushing their enemies, Judas and his brothers turn their attention toward home. Describe what they accomplish in 1 Maccabees 4:36-61, and why it is important.*

The Maccabees' first effort when the fighting is finished is not to rest but to restore God's Temple, which has been defiled, burned, overgrown, and abandoned. After crying out to God, they repair the sanctuary and purify it. They carry away the defiled stones and prepare new ones for the altar and create new vessels and furniture. When all this is complete, they light the lamps and burn incense. On the anniversary of the Temple's desecration, they offer sacrifices to God and rejoice in an eight-day-long celebration. The memory of this occasion is continued today in the Jewish Festival of Lights, or Hanukkah.

In addition to restoring the Temple, Judas Maccabeus and the others also build walls around Mount Zion and a garrison to protect it.

It is hard to overestimate the importance of the Temple and Jerusalem to the people of Judah. It was more than a symbol of their religion. The Jerusalem Temple was where God lived among them and where he made his throne. Jerusalem was the place where he caused his Name to dwell. It was a holy city, the seat of the everlasting throne of David. With the walls destroyed and the sanctuary burned and desecrated, it was as if there was no place for God in Jerusalem, no visible sign of his presence among his people. No wonder "all the people fell on their faces and worshiped and blessed heaven, who had prospered them" (1 Maccabees 4:55). Once again, there was a place for God in their midst.

5. *2 Maccabees is a supplemental book for this time period. While it contains some of the same history (the fifteen years covered in 1 Maccabees 1–7), it is more of a theological commentary on the time and was written to help build morale. Read 2 Maccabees 7.*

   a. *What enables these brothers and their mother to stand steadfast in the face of such cruelty?*

   Going Deeper (optional): Read **CCC 988–996**, especially **CCC 992.**

   These seven martyrs and their mother are steadfast in their faith in God, the Creator of heaven and earth and the source of all life and goodness. They firmly believe that God, who gave them life to begin with, will give it back to them in eternity. They also believe that God will judge all people in the end, and they would rather face the fleeting wrath of man than the eternal wrath of God.

   While God revealed the truth of the resurrection of the dead to his people only gradually, this belief has been part of the Faith since Christ rose from the dead (CCC 991–992).

   b. *The book of Sirach, which is used extensively today in the liturgy, was written during this period. Read Sirach 2, keeping in mind the types of trials God's people were apt to face at the time. What strength and encouragement does it offer them—or anyone whose faith is being tested?*

   Sirach 2 prepares God's people to expect trials but at the same time, to face them with complete trust and faith in God's faithfulness, compassion, and mercy. If you cling to God and trust him through your suffering, each trial will refine you and prove your worth the way gold is tested in fire. Lasting joy and mercy belong to those who fear God, who trust him, and who do not turn away in times of trial. The author encourages God's people to study the way God has dealt with his people from the beginning, and to see how faithful God has been to those who persevere in hope and call on him in time of need.

6. Read **2 Maccabees 12:38-46,** *which follows an account of some of the battles of Judas Maccabeus.*

   a. *What does Judas Maccabeus do on behalf of those who have died?*

   Finding tokens of pagan idols under the tunics of the dead men, Judas and the others turn to prayer. They make atonement for the sins of the dead soldiers and thus give witness to their belief in the resurrection of the dead, "for if he were not expecting that those who had fallen would rise again, it would have been superfluous and foolish to pray for the dead" (2 Maccabees 12:44).

   b. *Read* **CCC 957–958 and 1030–1032.** *What does the Catholic Church say about practice of offering prayers for the dead?*

   The Magisterium teaches that the Church is more than an assembly of believers on earth; it is the communion of all saints, whether they are still "pilgrims" on earth, are undergoing purification in purgatory, or are among the blessed in heaven. As Judas prayed for his men, Catholics pray for the dead to be loosed from their sins and purified before the final judgment.

7. *The Wisdom of Solomon was written well after the events of 1 Maccabees and fifty to one hundred years before Christ. Not surprisingly, it warns of the dangers to one's faith of living in a secular environment. The author may have had in mind the plight of such Israelites as the brothers of 2 Maccabees 7 when he wrote the beautiful words found in* **Wisdom 3:1-8.** *This passage is often used today in the Church's liturgy when martyrs are remembered. Read it, and meditate on God's loving care and our hope of everlasting life. What strikes you that you would like to remember?*

Facilitators: Read aloud Wisdom 3:1-9 and ask participants to share what they learned while meditating on this passage.

D. Application

Facilitators: If time allows, have group members share their responses to the following application questions.

Think for a moment of the pressures hellenization placed on devout Jews to stifle their faith. Do you see any parallel in the spirit of the world today? What influences in today's society threaten to desecrate your life or home, and how are you putting up a fight? Is there anything you can learn from these stories to strengthen you in your life?

E. Wrap-Up

1. Remember the Maccabean Revolt by its color, orange, for the oil lamps in the purified Temple.

2. Answers will vary. One possible reply: During the Maccabean Revolt, Mattathias and his descendants saved Israel from enforced secularization. The desecrated Temple was purified with what is now celebrated as the eight-day Feast of Lights, or Hanukkah.

Close with the Responsive Prayer found on the inside front cover of this Study Set Workbook. Pray through the Maccabean Revolt period.

After the small-group discussion, watch Jeff Cavins' video presentation on *Session 17* – Maccabean Revolt.

Facilitators: *Read these recommended responses to the questions ahead of time to help you prepare to lead the small-group discussion.*

Participants: *Reinforce what you have learned by reviewing these recommended responses after the small-group discussion and before you go on to the next session.*

A. Establish the Context

Facilitators: Take a moment to review what was learned in the previous session and to establish the context for the Messianic Fulfillment. If you like, use the following question to encourage discussion:

- *How has the example of Mattathias and his sons helped you this week?*

B. Read the Story

Facilitators: If there is time, have someone read each passage aloud before it is discussed.

C. Take a Deeper Look

1. *In Luke's Gospel, we finally meet the "woman and her seed" announced in Genesis 3:15. Is there anything in the account of the Annunciation (Luke 1:26-38) that makes you think that here, at last, is a "new Eve"—a woman who will do what Eve failed to do so many years before?*

   Eve failed to obey God's Word and became the cause of death, not just to herself, but to the whole world. In contrast, Mary listens to the Word of God and obeys. With her *fiat*, Mary does what Eve did not do. As St. Irenaeus of Lyons wrote, "And thus also it was that the knot of Eve's disobedience was loosed by the obedience of Mary. For what the virgin Eve had bound fast through unbelief, this did the Virgin Mary set free through faith."[1]

2. *Who is Jesus?*

   a. *Review the details of Jesus' early life found in* **Luke 1–2.** *What is his background? What kind of upbringing has he had? What is he like? Record everything you can find out about the boy born to save the world.*

   Jesus is Jewish and grows up in a devout Jewish home, first in Bethlehem and then in Nazareth. Joseph and Mary's devotion is evident—they have Jesus circumcised as required on the eighth day, make the customary sacrifices, and go to Jerusalem every year to celebrate the Passover. As any typical Jewish boy, he would have been taught both a trade and the *Torah*. Jesus amazes adults in the Temple when, at twelve years old, he speaks with great wisdom and understanding about the Scriptures. He is obedient to his parents and as the years pass, he "increased in wisdom and in stature, and in favor with God and man" (Luke 2:52); he "grew and became strong, filled with wisdom; and the favor of God was upon him" (Luke 2:40). A fitting beginning for one whose birth was announced by angels as one who would reign forever on the throne of David (see Luke 1:31-33).

---

[1] *Adversus haereses* [AD 180/199], bk. III, Chapter 22, no. 4.

b. *What do the following witnesses from Luke's Gospel tell us about who Jesus is and why he has come?*

God through the angel Gabriel (1:26-38) and with his own voice (3:21-22): Gabriel announces the astonishing fulfillment of what everyone has been waiting for. This is not just any child, but the Son of God. He will be given David's throne and will reign over the house of Jacob forever. During Jesus' ministry, God's voice from heaven twice proclaims Jesus to be his Son.

Simeon (2:25-35): Simeon reveals that Jesus will be not just a light for glory to Israel, but also something new: "a light for revelation to the Gentiles." He prophesies that Jesus will be "for the fall and rising of many in Israel, and for a sign that is spoken against."

John the Baptist (3:15-17): John the Baptist says Jesus is far greater than he, and that Jesus will baptize not just with water, but "with the Holy Spirit and with fire." He also speaks of Jesus as a judge: With his "winnowing fork," he will gather people into his kingdom like wheat into a granary, while he burns others like chaff with unquenchable fire.

Demons (4:33-34, 41 and 8:26-31): Even the demons recognize that Jesus is the Son of God, the Christ (Messiah), and they assume he has come to destroy them.

The centurion (7:1-9): The centurion, a Gentile, recognizes Jesus' power and authority to heal.

c. *What does Jesus say about himself? (For help with this question, see **Luke 4:16-21, 4:43, 5:24, 5:32, 6:5, and 9:22, 44, 48**.)*

There are many things people may have drawn from the reading. From the verses listed, they should have noted some of the following:

Jesus says he has been sent to preach the good news of the kingdom of God to the poor, to proclaim freedom and release to captives and the oppressed, and to give sight to the blind. At times, Jesus calls himself the "Son of Man," a reference to the figure in Daniel 7 to whom God gave an everlasting dominion and glory and kingdom. As the Son of Man, Jesus says he has authority to forgive sins and has come to call sinners to repentance. He also says he is "lord of the Sabbath," one of the signs of Israel's covenant relationship with God, and that whoever receives him, receives God. Surprisingly, Jesus also says that he must suffer, be rejected by the Jewish leaders, be killed, and then be raised again.

d. *How would you describe Jesus to someone who asked you about him?*

Answers will vary, whether they echo things said in Luke or are more personal. Encourage discussion.

3. ***Think About It:*** *After his baptism, Jesus is tempted by the devil in the desert (Luke 4). Read the story. Are there any similarities or contrasts between this and the Serpent's temptation of Adam and Eve in the Garden (see **Genesis 3**) or between this and the temptations Israel faced in the desert? (See **Exodus 17:1-7** and **Deuteronomy 6 and 8**.) Choose one of these parallel stories, and discuss how Jesus does what previous children of God failed to do and becomes both a "new Adam" and a "New Israel."*

Jesus, the "new Adam": Jesus is tempted directly by the devil: If you are hungry, feed yourself. Turn this stone into your bread. This echoes the Serpent's "Did God say you cannot eat that fruit?" The Second Adam, Jesus Christ, answers as they should have: "It is written, 'Man shall not live by bread alone'" (Luke 4:4). This comes from Deuteronomy 8:3, which ends "but … by everything that proceeds out of the mouth of the LORD." Adam and Eve chose to forget God's word and live by the forbidden fruit. Jesus chooses to go hungry rather than fail to follow his Father. Next, Satan offers to give Jesus authority and glory in exchange for worship, echoes of the Serpent's "you will be like God" if you obey me and eat. Both Adam and Eve and Jesus already have, from the hand of God, what Satan offers. Adam and Eve succumbbed to deception, but Jesus insists on following God's word and worshiping him only.

Finally, Satan challenges Jesus' status as the Son of God and asks him to prove it, just as he made Adam and Eve feel they were not "like God" and needed to disobey him in order to achieve that status. In every case, the solution as Jesus presents it is to stand on God's word.

Jesus, the "New Israel": All three verses Jesus quotes are from admonitions Israel received in the desert. Israel wandered for forty years "that [God] might humble you, testing you to know what was in your heart, whether you would keep his commandments, or not" (Deuteronomy 8:2). Jesus' forty-day temptation seems to be for a similar purpose. "Man does not live by bread alone" is what Israel was meant to learn by the gift of manna. Following their forty-year period of wandering, Moses left Israel with commands to follow if they were to prosper in the land God promised them (Deuteronomy 6). Worshiping and serving God alone was one of them (verse 13); not putting God to the test as they did at Massah was another. Israel had a hard time remembering and following these things. Jesus does not.

4. *In **Luke 4:16-30,** Jesus launches his public ministry by standing up in the synagogue and quoting a passage from Isaiah. Read what he says. What does he mean by, "Today this scripture has been fulfilled in your hearing"? (Review Session 15 for help with this question.)*

   "The acceptable year of the Lord" that Jesus says he has been anointed to proclaim is the Year of Jubilee (Session 15, pages 106-107)—the year that slaves are to be set free, debts canceled, and everyone returned to their ancestral property. Jesus is saying that not only has the long-awaited Jubilee year arrived, but *he* is the one anointed to proclaim and enact it.

5. ***Think About It:*** *Luke's "Sermon on the Plain" (6:17-45) parallels the Sermon on the Mount and the Beatitudes in Matthew 5–6. Both show Jesus as a "new Moses" giving God's law to his people. The original Law taught the freed slaves how to live as the free children of God. In Christ, people are free not just externally from slavery, but internally from sin. How does Jesus' teaching illuminate the inner reality and meaning of the Ten Commandments? (See **Exodus 20.**)*

   To the new nation of Israel, the Ten Commandments were a guidebook for living as God's children in freedom from slavery. When Jesus comes to free people from the slavery of sin, which that earlier freedom pointed to, he shines a light on the spiritual depths of the Ten Commandments. "You shall not kill," for example, sets a standard for negative behavior. Jesus takes it a step further by adding the positive and asking people to love their enemies. This is radical, given the kind of enemies they have! Do not fight and kill them; love and pray for them. "You shall not covet" sets another standard, and Jesus opens it up by asking people to give to all who ask without demanding repayment. The true meaning of the Ten Commandments can be summarized as, "Love God and love your neighbor." All of Jesus' teachings bear this out.

6. *Luke tells of Jesus feeding five thousand men with five loaves and two fish in **Luke 9:10-17.** Read that, and then read **John 6.** What added insight does John bring to the significance of this event? (See also **CCC 1384.**)*

   John points out that it is near Passover, the event which foreshadowed the perfect sacrifice of Christ that is made present to us in the Eucharist. When Jesus feeds the five thousand, he shows them something about himself. Immediately, they recognize him as someone who can feed them with miraculous bread—as Moses did in the desert. But Jesus points out that it is not Moses who provided bread, but God. And the true bread, which this multiplied bread and manna only point to, is he who comes down and "gives life to the world" (verses 32-33). Just as there seems to be no end to Jesus' provision of the loaves, his flesh will provide bread enough for the whole world. And that bread is much better, because it brings eternal life and not just a day's sustenance.

7. a. *The question, "Who is Jesus?" comes to the fore in Luke 8–9. Read the following verses, and record who asks the question, and why.*

    Luke 8:22-25: Jesus' disciples marvel and wonder, "Who is this?" when he calms a raging storm.

    Luke 9:7-9: King Herod, perplexed by reports of Jesus' miracles and hearing that one of the prophets (even John the Baptist, who he beheaded) must have been raised from the dead, wonders, "Who is this?"

    b. *Now read* **Luke 9:18-22,** *in which Jesus poses the same question twice. The second time, it is not a rhetorical question. Who answers, and what do they say?*

    When Jesus asks his disciples who the people say he is, their answers are the sort of thing Herod has been hearing: John the Baptist, or Elijah, or a prophet of old. But when he asks who his disciples say he is, Peter replies, "The Christ of God." ("Christ" is the Greek word for the Hebrew "Messiah"—Peter knows that Jesus is the Anointed One of God.)

    c. **Think About It:** *What event does Luke place between Herod's question in* **9:9** *and Peter's answer in* **9:20?** *What difference, if any, does this make in the way you read* **verses 18-22?**

    Answers will vary. It is interesting to reflect on the way Jesus makes himself known in the act of breaking bread, blessing it, and distributing it. In Luke 24, we will see this more explicitly as the disciples on the road to Emmaus discover that their hearts burn within them when Jesus explains the Scriptures, and that their eyes are opened to who he is when he takes bread, blesses and breaks it, and gives it to them. Other passages may come to mind; for example John 21:1-14, in which Jesus appears to his disciples by the Sea of Tiberias. When they bring their enormous load of fish to shore, and Jesus offers them breakfast, "none of the disciples dared ask him, 'Who are you?' They knew it was the Lord. Jesus came and took the bread and gave it to them, and so with the fish" (verses 12-13). Bread and fish once again—but this time, he already is known.

8. *Read* **Luke 9:28-35.** *What more is revealed here about who Jesus is?*

    Jesus appears in glory here on the Mount of Transfiguration. A voice from heaven proclaims, "This is my Son, my Chosen; listen to him!" (verse 35). For Peter, James, and John, there can be no more question of who Jesus is.

D. Application

Facilitators: If time allows, have group members share their responses to the following application questions.

Put yourself in the story: If you were living when Jesus came to earth, and he came through your town, what would you ask? Would your encounter with him be like any of those you read in Luke's Gospel? What would your dialogue with him be like?

Close with the Responsive Prayer found on the inside front cover of this Study Set Workbook. Pray through the Messianic Fulfillment period.

After the small-group discussion, watch Jeff Cavins' video presentation on *Session 18* – Messianic Fulfillment: Part 1.

Facilitators: Read these recommended responses to the questions ahead of time to help you prepare to lead the small-group discussion.

Participants: Reinforce what you have learned by reviewing these recommended responses after the small-group discussion and before you go on to the next session.

A. Review the Context

Facilitators: Take a moment to review the context and what was learned in the previous session. If you like, use the following question to encourage discussion:

- *Of all the names Jesus was given in the last session, which means the most to you? Why?*

B. Read the Story

Facilitators: If there is time, have someone read each passage aloud before it is discussed.

C. Take a Deeper Look

Jesus Trains His Disciples

1. *Jesus is always attracting followers, but they do not always stay with him as disciples. What does Jesus say it will cost his disciples to follow him? (See **Luke 9:57-62 and 14:25-34**.)*

    Following Jesus or any rabbi as a disciple in those days was a radical proposition. It meant leaving behind the security of home and family attachments, which must be secondary to one's commitment to God. It required single-hearted devotion. If you looked back, you were not fit for service. Jesus tells his disciples, "Whoever does not bear his own cross and come after me, cannot be my disciple" (Luke 14:27). To bear one's own cross here means total commitment, even to death. Count the cost, Jesus says, and make sure you can finish the journey. The cost is complete surrender.

2. *Read **Luke 11:1-13**, in which a disciple asks Jesus to teach them to pray.*

    a. *In light of Israel's history, do you find anything interesting in the fact that Jesus asks his disciples to begin their prayer, "Our Father"? (Read also **Galatians 3:26–4:7**.)*

    At the burning bush, God revealed his name: "I AM." "Yahweh." For centuries, he was known by that name and others: God of Abraham, Isaac, and Jacob; Creator; LORD; Redeemer; Provider. Not until Jesus came as Son, was God revealed to be Father (see CCC 2779ff). Even though he called Israel his "firstborn son," and although he freed them time and time again, they continued to sink back into slavery. By the time of the New Testament, it is clear that it is slavery to sin, more than human slavery, that holds the people in bondage and that separates them from God. But as St. Paul says in Galatians 4, "When the time had fully come, God sent forth his Son, born of woman, born under the law, to redeem those who were under the law, so that we might receive adoption as sons. And because you are sons, God has sent the Spirit of his Son into our hearts, crying, 'Abba! Father!' So through God you are no longer a slave but a son, and if a son then an heir" (verses 4-7).

The Lord's Prayer asks us to recognize this and act on it, directing our spirit-filled prayer to our Father in heaven.

b.   Read **CCC 2762–2766 and 2803–2806.** *How would you summarize what Jesus teaches about how we should pray?*

Answers will vary. Jesus teaches his disciples to approach God in confidence as a father, knowing that God *is* a good Father who answers prayers and gives good gifts to his children. In this model, prayer is a family conversation in which we are to speak to God as little children.

If the Beatitudes revealed the spirit behind the Law, the Lord's Prayer reveals the true spirit that should lie behind our prayer. It properly orders our hearts and desires and directs them toward God. Even the sequence of petitions in the prayer is instructive. Lest we be tempted to make our prayers "all about us," the first three petitions focus us in on God and his Name and kingdom. Only then do we turn inward, to ask for sustenance, spiritual healing, and freedom from temptation. In praying this way, "we are strengthened in faith, filled with hope, and set aflame by charity" (CCC 2806).

c.   *What attitude does Jesus urge his disciples to take in prayer, and why? (See **Luke 11:5-13.**)*

Jesus urges his disciples to be bold and persistent in prayer, because God—like any good father—will surely answer.

3.   *Knowing he will be leaving them, Jesus prepares for his absence by training his apostles to carry on after he is gone and by investing them with authority to rule in his place. By appointing twelve apostles to lead the twelve tribes of Israel, he reconstructs the kingdom around himself. Read the following passages, and note the kind of authority Jesus invests in the apostles (some passages are taken from other Gospels to round out the picture).*

a.   **Matthew 18:18-20 and CCC 553:** He gives them power to "bind and loose." As the *Catechism* explains, this power "connotes the authority to absolve sins, to pronounce doctrinal judgments, and to make disciplinary decisions in the Church. Jesus entrusted this authority to the Church through the ministry of the apostles and in particular through the ministry of Peter, the only one to whom he specifically entrusted the keys of the kingdom" (CCC 553).

b.   **John 20:21-23:** After breathing the new life of the Holy Spirit into his disciples, Jesus gives them a power that previously belonged only to God: the power to forgive sins or hold them unforgiven.

c.   **Luke 10:18-20** *(Think back to Genesis 3:15. How are the disciples sharing in Christ's mission?):* Jesus says something remarkable to the seventy disciples he sends out to proclaim the advent of the kingdom. "I saw Satan fall like lightning from heaven. Behold, I have given you authority to tread upon serpents and scorpions, and over all the power of the enemy; and nothing shall hurt you" (verses 18-19). Satan's power has been broken. And here, sons of Adam and Eve are given authority to tread on the heads of serpents, a picture in miniature of Christ giving the fatal blow to the head of the Serpent, the devil, as God had announced so many years before.

d.   **Matthew 16:13-20** *(This account gives more details of Peter's confession than Luke does in 9:20. What does Matthew add?):* After Simon names Jesus "Christ, the Son of the living God," Jesus gives Simon a new name, Peter—"rock"—and says he will build his Church on Peter. Along with his new name, Peter is given the keys to the kingdom and the power to bind and loose in a unique way. In the Davidic kingdom, the king invested authority to rule his kingdom under him in a steward (a type of "prime minister" or CEO), and after him, his successors. The keys were the badge of this office. Through Jesus' action here, we understand that the Church is Christ's kingdom, and that Jesus is giving Peter and his successors the job of ruling the Church on earth under him.

Jesus Proclaims the Kingdom

4. ***Think About It:*** *The kingdom of God is a frequent topic in Jesus' parables and teaching. Think about what you have learned regarding the kingdom of David and Israel's history since the Divided Kingdom. What kind of kingdom do you think people are expecting?*

> The kingdom God promised to Israel and founded on David and Solomon was an earthly kingdom that enjoyed an expanded rule over the surrounding nations. Since the exile, there has been little but humiliation and subservience to others. Many people expect the promised Messiah to return in earthly glory to physically defeat Rome and establish Jerusalem as the power it once was. Many also think the kingdom will be exclusively for the children of Israel.

5. *Read the following passages that deal with the kingdom of God (one is from Matthew's Gospel, which deals extensively with the kingdom):* ***Luke 13:22-30, 14:15-24, 17:20-21 and Matthew 25:31-46.***

   a. *Where is the kingdom?*

   > The kingdom of God is inside and not outside. It is spiritual and internal, not something physical that can be seen or touched.

   b. *Who is invited?*

   > All are invited—not just the "worthy" Jews, but the outcasts as well (see Luke 14:15-24).

   c. *Who will get in?*

   > Not everyone will get into the kingdom of God. In fact, many will try to enter and will not be able to. People will be turned away who assume they can get in because they went to church and heard God's teaching (an interpretation of Luke 13:26—Jesus seems to be speaking of people like the Pharisees who presume upon their birthright and their observance of the Law and try to bar the door against others), while other people from nations all over the world will come in and take their places. Among those who were initially invited (the Jews), some will delay or refuse to accept the invitation. They will be replaced by "the poor and maimed and blind and lame," and those on "the highways and hedges"—the unclean outcasts and the Gentiles—will take their place (Luke 14:21, 23).

   > In a marked contrast to any earthly kingdom, acceptance to God's kingdom in these parables is based on the individual's response to the invitation and not on any special rights of birth or position. In Matthew 25, we are told that the kingdom is reserved not for those who focus on avoiding doing wrong, but for those who actively do good: those who extend a loving and merciful heart and hands to the needy around them.

   d. *How does this image square with the one you described in your answer to question 4?*

   > The two kingdoms do not coincide. One is an exclusive, earthly power that crushes its enemies. The other is an inclusive, spiritual kingdom that loves and shows mercy to its enemies.

6. *Read the three parables Jesus tells in* ***Luke 15*** *and the event described in your answer to* ***Luke 19:1-10.***

   a. *What is their common message?*

   > The common message in these three stories can be found in Luke 19:10: "For the Son of man came to seek and to save the lost." Each of the stories has to do with celebrating over something lost which has been found and over sinners who repent. Lost people are important to God like lost things are to us. They are not to be snubbed or cast out or left for lost, rejected, despised. Their intrinsic worth is greater than that of any fortune or property.

b. *Jesus tells these particular stories in answer to the Pharisees' displeasure that he has received tax collectors and sinners and has eaten with them. The Pharisees themselves are fastidious in their avoidance and condemnation of anything "unclean" for fear of contamination. What different perspective do the stories provide? (Read **CCC 588–589** for help with this question.)*

The first two parables in Chapter 15 set the stage for the parable of the Prodigal Son. They seem to ask, "What is the proper response to make when something valuable is lost?" Now, what is the proper response to make when that something is found? You celebrate with rejoicing.

None of this would raise an eyebrow among the Pharisees, but the third parable is a stinging indictment of their holier-than-thou attitude. The lost thing that is so valuable to the father is a lost son. A prodigal who has insulted his father, gone into a self-imposed exile (any "far country" was exile to the Jews, for whom only the Promised Land was home), and squandered his inheritance, degrading himself with prostitutes and contact with Gentiles, finally working among pigs—the least of the unclean animals. The lost son is Israel (and also can be seen as the other nations—younger sons in a sense—that are separated from God). The Father—God—is holding out open arms to his repentant son, rejoicing even though he is a sinner. God is calling his prodigals home, and these Jewish leaders, like the older brother, are turning up their noses in anger. "Have mercy!" Jesus is saying. "Rejoice with the Father!" Enter into heaven's joy at welcoming home those who were lost.

Jesus Prepares His Disciples

7. *As Jesus and his disciples draw near Jerusalem, he prepares them to understand that his coming throne will not be in Jerusalem but in heaven. Read the parable he tells them in **Luke 19:11-27,** in which Jesus is the man of noble birth who leaves to become king. What does he expect of his disciples in his absence?*

Jesus' disciples are to be diligent and fearless in his absence and to take what he has given them and make good use of it. They are servants with a job to do.

8. *Read **Luke 18:31-34.** This is the third time Jesus has explained to his disciples that he must die and in what manner he will die. However obvious this may seem to us in hindsight, the disciples do not understand it. Why do you think that is?*

Answers will vary. The meaning of Jesus' suffering has been hidden from the disciples. They do not know of or understand the Resurrection. They have yet to receive the Holy Spirit. Not only that, they believe that Jesus will establish the kingdom. How can he do that if he is killed? That sounds too much like defeat or as if God is not behind Jesus. And how could the long-awaited Messiah be missed by the religious leaders and killed like a criminal? There are too many questions. None of it makes sense, and they are afraid to ask more.

D. Application

Facilitators: If time allows, have group members share their responses to the following application question.

In Jesus' parable of the Prodigal Son (Luke 15:11-32), the younger son sets off for a distant country and squanders his wealth. This is a picture of Israel in exile, squandering its inheritance. Re-read the parable, and put yourself in the position of that son. Describe the inheritance you have in Christ (things like the richness of the Eucharist, for example, or Mary as your Mother). Is there any sense in which you are squandering your inheritance?

Close with the Responsive Prayer found on the inside front cover of this Study Set Workbook. Pray through the Messianic Fulfillment period.

After the small-group discussion, watch Jeff Cavins' video presentation on *Session 19* – Messianic Fulfillment: Part 2.

THE BIBLE
TIMELINE
The Story of Salvation

Facilitators: *Read these recommended responses to the questions ahead of time to help you prepare to lead the small-group discussion.*

Participants: *Reinforce what you have learned by reviewing these recommended responses after the small-group discussion and before you go on to the next session.*

A. Review the Context

Facilitators: Take a moment to review the context and what was learned in the previous session. If you like, use the following question to encourage discussion:

- *What does it mean to you that you can approach God as Father?*

B. Read the Story

Facilitators: If there is time, have someone read each passage aloud before it is discussed.

C. Take a Deeper Look

The Approach to Jerusalem

1. *Jesus' approach to Jerusalem is made along a road that goes down from the Mount of Olives and then up to Jerusalem. Read **Luke 19:28-44**. Jesus rides on a donkey just as the first son of David, Solomon, rode a donkey to his coronation years before (see **1 Kings 1:33**). "Blessed is the king who comes in the name of the Lord!" (Luke 19:38) the people shout in praise—a quote from Psalm 118, which is a psalm of praise written in celebration of a Davidic king's victory over his enemies. Jesus is approaching Jerusalem in triumph as the Son of David, heir to the throne. Why, then, does he weep as he approaches the city?*

   Jesus weeps because in spite of the fact that Israel's savior and king is approaching Jerusalem, he knows that many will not recognize him and that the day is coming when Jerusalem will be destroyed. Just two chapters later, in Luke 21, he will prophesy the city's destruction within a generation. This will, in fact, happen: In AD 70, the Temple and many of the Jews will be destroyed in the Jewish revolt against Rome.

The Last Supper

2. ***Luke 22:7-20** tells of the Last Supper—the final meal Jesus has with his disciples. It is a Passover meal. Read **Exodus 12**, and find the Passover in the Egypt and Exodus period on your* Timeline Chart.

   a. *What is the Passover, and why is it still celebrated more than thirteen hundred years later? (**Optional:** Read **Isaiah 52**.)*

   The Passover commemorates Israel's great Exodus from Egypt and freedom from slavery and is the defining event in their history. It is named for the night God "passed over" Israel's firstborn when he slew all the firstborn sons of Egypt, and it celebrates the birth of a new and free nation. It is such an important event that God changed Israel's calendar year to start with its memorial—making it a kind of New Year's Day and Independence Day rolled into one. More than a simple remembrance, however, the Passover brings God's mighty work of deliverance into the present for those who celebrate it. At its institution, God commanded that it be celebrated annually and described in detail how it should be carried out. The prophet Isaiah said that one day there would be a greater exodus (Isaiah 52), and so the celebration came to include a looking forward in hope amidst pagan occupation and exile to another exodus and return to their homeland.

b.   Read **1 Corinthians 5:7; 1 Peter 1:18-20;** *and* **Revelation 5:6-14.** *How does Jesus fulfill the Passover? (For help with this question, read also* **CCC 613–614 and 1340.***)*

In the Passover, it was the blood of the lambs spread on the doorposts that saved the sons of Israel. Jesus Christ is the Passover Lamb those lambs merely pointed to. The Passover, which saved Israel from Egypt, finds its fulfillment in Christ's Passover, which saves men from sin. As the *Catechism* says: "By celebrating the Last Supper with his apostles in the course of the Passover meal, Jesus gave the Jewish Passover its definitive meaning. Jesus' passing over to his father by his death and Resurrection, the new Passover, is anticipated in the Supper and celebrated in the Eucharist, which fulfills the Jewish Passover and anticipates the final Passover of the Church in the glory of the kingdom" **(CCC 1340).**

The Lamb of God, which has been anticipated since Abraham offered his only son, Isaac, on the altar, believing that God would provide the lamb (Genesis 22:8), has come.

3.   Read **Luke 22:31-34 , 54-62.** *Peter, "the rock," appears to have failed in spite of Jesus' prayer. Now read* **John 21:1-19,** *which deals with an event that occurs after Jesus' resurrection.*

a.   *In Luke 22, does it seem to bother Jesus that Peter will deny him? What kind of man has Jesus chosen to be the foundation of his Church?*

No, Peter's denial does not seem to "bother" Jesus or make him regret choosing him as the "rock" on which the Church will be built. He knows Satan will press and tempt Peter. Jesus has not chosen a man who is perfect (because no one is perfect!) but one who loves him, who acts on Jesus' word even when it does not make sense, who is ready to die for him (Luke 22:33). Jesus knows Peter's heart and uses him in spite of his weakness.

b.   *What does this say to you about the failures in your own life and God's ultimate plan for you?*

Answers will vary. God knows our weaknesses. Jesus intercedes for us. He uses ordinary men and women to effect his plans. Failure does not disqualify us, as long as our hearts keep turning to God in repentance.

The Passion

4.   **Think About It:** *Christ's passion begins in a garden on the Mount of Olives in an olive grove called Gethsemane. Read* **Luke 22:39-46,** *paying particular attention to Jesus' words.*

a.   *Describe the struggle Jesus is going through.*

Jesus is facing an intense internal struggle between his desire to do his Father's will and the temptation to avoid suffering.

b.   *In what sense is Jesus' struggle here similar to that faced by Adam and Eve in the Garden of Eden? (See* **Genesis 3.***)*

Adam and Eve, like Jesus, were tempted not to do the will of the Father. It is likely that the aspect of the Serpent (which is elsewhere translated "great dragon"—see Revelation 12) was frightening and that its words caused them to struggle with the fear of suffering as well.

   c.   What does Jesus do that our first parents failed to do?

Jesus, the "last Adam," does several things the first Adam failed to do. Perhaps most importantly, he cries out to the Father. He defends his bride and willingly suffers and lays down his life for her. He does the will of the Father. He trusts God.

5.   *How does God fulfill the curse on Satan that he made in Genesis 3:15—"I will put enmity between you and the woman, and between your seed and her seed; he shall bruise your head, and you shall bruise his heel"—and deliver his children from Satan's power? (Read also* **Hebrews 2:14-18.**)

God himself becomes a man, taking on human nature so that he can die. It seems strange that he would succumb to Satan so far as to be killed as a common criminal, but what looks like failure ends up being only a "bruise." By entering into death and rising again, Jesus deals Satan a deathblow and makes his greatest weapon against humankind—death—the pathway to eternal life with God.

6.   **Think About It:** *If all Jesus has to do is die, couldn't it be in some easier way? Why does Jesus have to suffer? Read* **Isaiah 53** *and* **Galatians 3:13.** *(Hint: How does Jesus' death on the Cross solve these two problems: (1) the curse on Adam and (2) Israel's broken covenant with God?)*

The Messiah redeems, not in spite of his suffering, but precisely because of it. As the prophet Isaiah wrote, "He was wounded for our transgressions; he was bruised for our iniquities" (Isaiah 53:5). It is Jesus' suffering and nothing else that heals us from sin. On the Cross, Jesus becomes the ultimate sin offering.

In his suffering, Christ takes upon himself the curse of Adam: the toil; the thorns and thistles (in his crown of thorns); the sweat of his face (in the blood he sweats in Gethsemane, bathing the cursed ground); and the curse of death. We saw in Genesis how Adam and Eve were to learn to love through fruitful suffering—and Jesus takes this upon himself in the extreme. By pouring himself out even to death, he saves. He takes on our deathly curse and offers us his life.

In his suffering, Christ also takes upon himself the covenant curses of Israel. Moses clearly spelled out Israel's covenant obligations and the resultant blessings and curses for keeping or breaking them. They agreed and sealed that covenant in blood. Israel is guilty of rebellion and deserves the covenant curses. The only way the curses can be canceled is for one or the other of the parties to die—and God loves his children so much that he, in a mysterious way, dies himself.

7.   *Even with the penalty paid for sin, a problem remains for humanity: the broken nature, the loss of grace, and the tendency to sin (concupiscence) that all inherit from Adam. Jesus' mission is not complete without his resurrection. Read* **Romans 6:1-14.** *(**Optional:** Read **CCC 1213–1216 and 1227–1228.**)*

   a.   When we unite ourselves to Christ in baptism, what happens to our old nature?

Our old nature dies—it is buried in the water of baptism as though with Christ in the tomb—and we rise with him in new life, no longer enslaved to sin but free from its power. Death no longer has dominion over us, but we are alive to God in Christ and able to yield ourselves to God as "instruments of righteousness," instead of remaining enslaved to sin and its passions.

   b.   Of what does the Resurrection assure us? (See also **Romans 6:5.**)

Christ's resurrection assures us that we can trust the Father! His promise stands sure: "For if we have been united with him in a death like his, we shall certainly be united with him in a resurrection like his" (Romans 6:5).

8. *How does Jesus make sure the good news of his death and resurrection will spread beyond Jerusalem? (See Luke 24:36-53.)*

Jesus does several things to make sure the good news of his death and resurrection and our release from sin will spread beyond Jerusalem. First, he "[opens] their minds to understand the Scriptures" (Luke 24:45), so they will know what is written about Christ in Scripture and the reason for his death and resurrection. Then, he commissions the disciples to preach the gospel of which they are witnesses to all nations. He tells them of "the promise of my Father," the Holy Spirit, and asks them to wait until they have received the Spirit's empowering strength before leaving the city. Finally, he blesses them.

There is, at last, a way out of exile.

D. Application

Facilitators: If time allows, have group members share their responses to the following application questions.

From the beginning of this study, we have seen how person after person faced a test: "Can you trust God?" Based on what you know now, can you trust the Father? Why? On what do you base that trust?

E. Wrap-Up

1. Remember the Messianic Fulfillment by its color, gold: the gift of the Magi to the Christ child.
2. Answers will vary. One possible reply: In the period of Messianic Fulfillment, Jesus Christ comes to fulfill the promises of the Old Covenant, releasing people from sin and death and establishing a New Covenant with God in his blood.

Close with the Responsive Prayer found on the inside front cover of this Study Set Workbook. Pray through the Messianic Fulfillment period.

After the small-group discussion, watch Jeff Cavins' video presentation on *Session 20 – Messianic Fulfillment: Part 3.*

Facilitators: Read these recommended responses to the questions ahead of time to help you prepare to lead the small-group discussion.

Participants: Reinforce what you have learned by reviewing these recommended responses after the small-group discussion and before you go on to the next session.

A. Establish the Context

Facilitators: Take a moment to review what was learned in the previous session and to establish the context for The Church. If you like, use the following question to encourage discussion:

- *What spoke to you as you focused on the Passion in light of the story of salvation as a whole?*

B. Read the Story

Facilitators: If there is time, have someone read each passage aloud before it is discussed.

C. Take a Deeper Look

Pentecost and the Holy Spirit (Acts 1:1–2:42)

1. *Jesus appears to his apostles over a period of forty days following his resurrection. Along with **Acts 1:1-8,** read **Matthew 28:16-20; Mark 16:14-18; Luke 24:13-49;** and **John 20:19-23 and 21:15-19.** Based on the things Jesus says to the apostles, what seems to be his chief purpose or desire during this time before his ascension?*

   Jesus seems to appear to his disciples specifically to prepare them to continue the work of the kingdom in his absence. He encourages them; he works to establish them in their faith and open their hearts to the meaning of the Scriptures and the purpose of his suffering, death, and resurrection; he gives them his peace and special power to forgive sins; and he commissions them to bring his message of forgiveness to the world and make disciples of all nations. He also charges them to stay in Jerusalem until they receive the "promise of God"—the Holy Spirit and God's power.

2. *Read **Acts 2:1-42,** which describes the outpouring of the Holy Spirit at Pentecost.*

   a. *Compare and contrast this to **Genesis 11:1-9.** What parallels do you find between the two events, and what is their significance? (See also **CCC 761.**)*

   The situation in the world in the first century AD was a result of the confusion of language caused at Babel: People were scattered across the earth, and each spoke his or her own language. In Genesis 11, the people of one language gathered to settle and make a name for themselves; in Acts 2, "devout men of all nations" and languages gather to worship the name of God. And the dispersal that occurred in Babel is reversed: Each hears in his own language what God has accomplished through Jesus Christ, and three thousand souls are drawn into the Church. As the *Catechism* says, "The gathering together of the Church is, as it were, God's reaction to the chaos provoked by sin. This reunification is achieved secretly in the heart of all peoples" (CCC 761).

b.   *Read **CCC 767–768**. Why does God send the Holy Spirit?*

According to CCC 767, God sends the Holy Spirit so "that he might continually sanctify the Church" (*Lumen Gentium* 4; cf. John 17:4). The power of the Holy Spirit makes the Church visible and enables the spread of the gospel. The Holy Spirit also empowers members of the Church to carry out its mission through various gifts to proclaim and establish the kingdom of God.

The Early Christian Community (Acts 2:42–8:4)

3.   *Describe the early Christian community based on **Acts 2:42-47 and 4:32-34.***

Acts describes the early Christian community as being devoted to learning from the apostles, to fellowship, to the breaking of bread, and to prayer. They hold all possessions in common, worship together in the Temple, and give gladly and generously so that no one is in need. They live in unity and testify to the resurrection with power. "And great grace was upon them all" (Acts 4:33).

4.   *Read **CCC 765 and 771**.*

a.   *What do you learn in these paragraphs about the visible Church?*

Jesus, in choosing twelve apostles, reconstructs, as it were, the twelve tribes of Israel in his kingdom. He establishes the apostles (placing Peter at their head) as foundation stones of the Church. This foundation will remain until the fulfillment of the kingdom at the end of time. The visible community of the Church on earth is established and sustained by Christ, and through it, "he communicates truth and grace to all men" (CCC 771).

b.   *What "seeds," or early indications of this visible structure, can you see in the reading for this session, even at the very beginnings of the Church? (Take note especially of **Acts 1:12-26 and 6:1-7**.)*

When Judas betrays Jesus and then takes his own life, the first order of business is to replace him and maintain the foundation of the Twelve. It is Peter who stands up as head of the group and initiates the process, defining the qualifications for apostleship. As the Church grows, the structure grows organically based on this foundation. In the reading for this session, deacons are added to take over particular tasks (Acts 6). Later chapters in Acts show the position of "elder," and Paul's letters to the churches established as missionary activity spread show that bishops are appointed as well.

5.   *Read **Acts 6:1-7** together with **1 Timothy 3:8-13**. Why are deacons needed, and what kind of people are they supposed to be? (The Greek word used to describe the responsibility of "the Seven," which means "server" or "one who waits on," is the same verb from which the word "deacon" comes.)*

Deacons are initially needed to relieve the apostles of overseeing the daily distribution of food free them to focus on prayer and ministering with the Word. Seven men of good reputation who are full of the Spirit and wisdom are chosen and commissioned. Paul later instructs Timothy as to the kind of men who should be tested and made deacons in local churches: not just anyone, but serious, good men and women who are temperate and faithful—not slanderers—and who "hold the mystery of the faith with a clear conscience" (1 Timothy 3:9). They also must be monogamous and good managers of their own households.

6. One deacon, a man named Stephen, *"full of grace and power, [does] great wonders and signs among the people"* (Acts 6:8). *Nonetheless, he soon attracts opposition from among various groups of people. Read* **Acts 6:8–7:60.**

    a. *What charge is made against Stephen?*

    Stephen is charged with speaking against the law and announcing the destruction of the Temple.

    b. *How does Stephen answer his accusers?*

    Stephen answers his accusers by telling the story of God's call and care of Israel from the time of Abraham and ending with an account of the building of the Temple. He then reinterprets the old story, showing from Scripture that even though God directed the building of the Tabernacle and allowed the building of the Temple, he does not dwell in man-made houses, but is above them. In telling them this, Stephen exposes his accusers for what they are: stiff-necked unbelievers who resist the Holy Spirit, ignore the words of the prophets, and fail to keep the Law.

7. *Notice the role that the "young man named Saul" plays in Stephen's martyrdom.*

    a. *What effect does Stephen's witness and death have on Saul? (See* **Acts 8:1-3.**)

    Stephen's witness and death sets Saul and others off on a rampage of persecution against the Church.

    b. *Why might Saul react this way instead of like the "devout men" of 8:2 who "buried Stephen, and made great lamentation over him"?*

    As a Pharisee, Saul may have been better educated in the Scriptures than the other men, but clearly his mind has not been opened to the true meaning of the Scriptures as they speak of Christ.

8. **Think About It:** *In the days after Jesus' death, his disciples are fearful, sad, and hiding from the authorities. The picture painted of them later in* **Acts 1–8** *is remarkably different. Find examples of the way the disciples face opposition and suffering. How do you account for the change?*

    The disciples become bold and fearless after Pentecost. They speak openly and boldly about the Lord to the people and the religious leaders and continue worshiping at the Temple and healing and doing other miracles by Christ's power. Through them, Christ's ministry is multiplied. When they are arrested, beaten, threatened, and ordered to stop preaching, they refuse. Even threats of death fail to deter them. Instead of stopping, they preach without ceasing. Instead of cringing and hiding, they pray for boldness and power. Instead of bowing to the authorities, they insist on following God before men. Instead of despairing when beaten, they rejoice at being counted worthy to suffer for Christ's name.

    Most startling is the example of Stephen, who boldly proclaims the truth of Christ to his death, following Jesus' example even in his last words: "Lord Jesus, receive my spirit," and, "Lord, do not hold this sin against them" (Acts 7:59, 60).

    Only the presence of the Holy Spirit can account for the new boldness in Christ's disciples as they go out to bear witness to him.

D. Application

Facilitators: If time allows, have group members share their responses to the following application questions.

Stephen is the first New Testament example of someone who looks at Jesus' actions and his resurrection and faces death without fear. Are there things in our world or society that cause you fear? Is your faith challenged at work or by your neighbors? Can you find anything in these chapters to strengthen you so you can proclaim the truth without fear?

Close with the Responsive Prayer found on the inside front cover of this Study Set Workbook. Pray through The Church period (the entire prayer).

After the small-group discussion, watch Jeff Cavins' video presentation on *Session 21* – The Church: Part 1.

Facilitators: Read these recommended responses to the questions ahead of time to help you prepare to lead the small-group discussion.

Participants: Reinforce what you have learned by reviewing these recommended responses after the small-group discussion and before you go on to the next session.

A. Review the Context

Facilitators: Take a moment to review the context and what was learned in the previous session. If you like, use the following question to encourage discussion:

- *What did you learn in the previous session about the Holy Spirit?*

B. Read the Story

Facilitators: If there is time, have someone read each passage aloud before it is discussed.

C. Take a Deeper Look

The Gospel Begins to Spread (Acts 8:5-40)

1. *Philip, like Stephen, is one of the seven deacons appointed in Acts 6. He is one of the believers scattered throughout Judea and Samaria by the persecution that follows Stephen's death. Describe his witness and ministry as recorded in Acts 8.*

   Philip goes about preaching the Word, healing, and casting out demons in Samaria and all the way to Caesarea. Many are baptized. That his ministry to Gentiles as well as to Jews is inspired by God is evident in the story of the time God sends Philip to meet an Ethiopian eunuch. Directed and empowered by the Holy Spirit, Philip explains to him the Scripture and baptizes the man before being taken miraculously from the scene.

Saul's Conversion (Acts 9)

2. *Acts 9 reintroduces us to the young man Saul, who stood by and assented to Stephen's death.*

   a. *Why is he on the road to Damascus, and what happens to him there?*

   Saul is "breathing threats and murder against the disciples of the Lord" (Acts 9:1) and planning to take into custody any Christians he should find. On the way he is confronted by a vision: a strong light and the Lord's voice asking, "Saul, Saul, why do you persecute me?" (verse 4). Temporarily blinded by this confrontation with the risen Christ, Saul nonetheless comes to recognize Jesus as Messiah and Son of God because of it. In this way, God himself converts a strong enemy of the early Church and commissions him to carry his name to both Jews and Gentiles.

   b. *Why is temporary blindness a particularly apt result of this experience?*